DISCARD

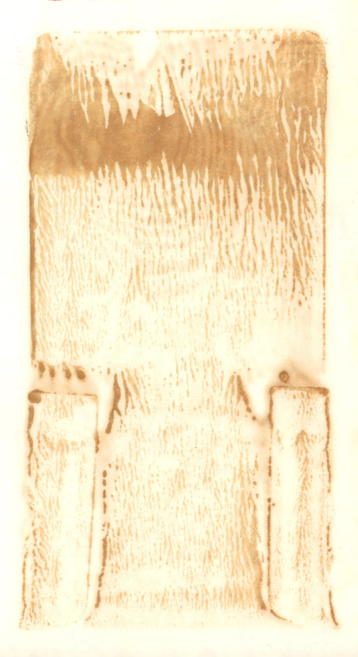

USING ELECTRICITY
on the FARM

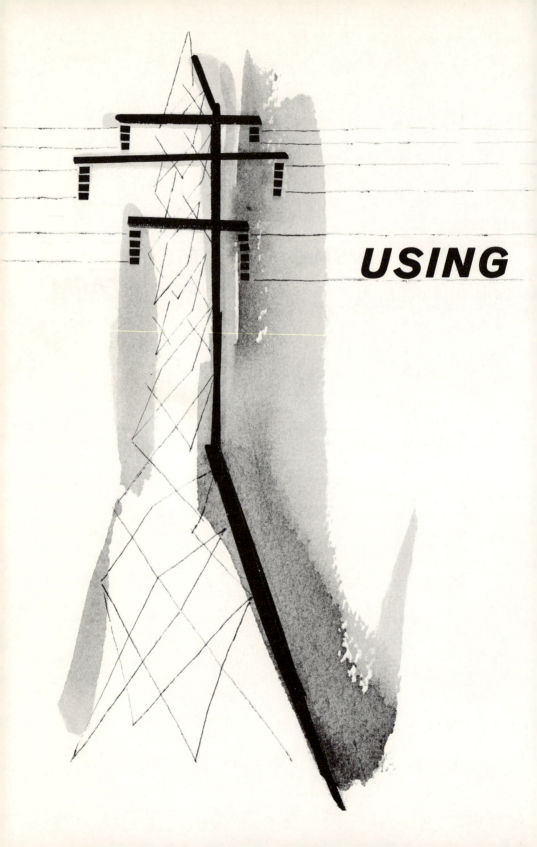

USING

PRENTICE-HALL, INC. • *Englewood Cliffs, N. J.*

ELECTRICITY
on the FARM

By

J. Roland Hamilton

Professor and Head, Department of
Agricultural Education, East Texas State College.
Associate Member American Society of
Agricultural Engineers.

USING ELECTRICITY on the FARM

BY
J. ROLAND HAMILTON

© **1959 by PRENTICE-HALL, INC.**
Englewood Cliffs, N. J.

Library of Congress Catalog Card No. 59-13382

Printed in the U.S.A.
93962

Preface

Using Electricity On The Farm is a simplified reference and how-to-do-it guide for agriculture students, club workers, and farm people. It is built largely around practical ideas for using electricity to improve the farm, with instructions on how to plan and do each major job. The abundance of illustrations and simplified examples in the book make it easy to read and understand.

The text consists of six problem-units dealing with the following phases of farm electricity: (1) opportunities in using electricity to improve the farm; (2) common everyday principles of electricity for the farm; (3) farmstead wiring; (4) electric motors for the farm; (5) water pumps and lighting for the farm; and (6) electric farming equipment.

1. In presenting *opportunities* for using electricity to improve the farm, actual stories of "electrified" farming throughout the country are cited. At the same time, however, the economic side is stressed by discussing factors involved in both cost of and returns from electric equipment.

2. In discussing *basic electricity*, only those laws and principles that are necessary in using electricity on the farm are included. For example, voltage, amperage, and wattage are dealt with to the extent that they affect and control wire size, safety, economy, and quality of electric service. Each major principle is clearly illustrated and explained.

3. *Farmstead wiring* is given strong emphasis because it appears to be the number one problem in farm electrification. This section starts with the exterior wiring system and shows by illustrations and simplified examples how to plan and wire the service entrances, feeder circuits, and other parts of the distribution system. Most of the wiring skills needed in farmstead wiring are presented in the form of drawings and instructions.

4. The section on *electric motors* presents instructions and illustrations on how to choose the right motor for a given farm job, how to gear it up so as to get the most from it, and how to identify and correct common motor troubles.

5. The problem-unit on *water systems* and *lighting* is built largely around practical examples and illustrations showing how to provide good light and an adequate water system for the farmstead.

6. The final problem-unit is devoted to the selection and care of *electric equipment for farm production*. This unit stresses important things to watch for in selecting electric appliances for livestock, dairy, and poultry production; for automatic feed handling; for crop drying; and for farm-shop power tools.

Some practical projects are suggested at the end of each problem-unit, and questions are listed at the end of each chapter to encourage more thorough reading. Also, "Additional Readings" are listed at the end of each chapter to help solve problems that are not fully covered in this book.

Over 200 individuals and organizations contributed subject materials and illustrations that helped to make this book possible. The names of these persons and firms are listed in footnotes and on pages 387-389. I therefore take this means of expressing my deep gratitude to all of you who assisted me. Special thanks to the following people who were kind enough to review the manuscript: Stanley S. Richardson, Professor, Agricultural Education, Utah State University; L. B. Swaney, Department of Vocational Agriculture, Clinton (Missouri) High School; Bob E. Taylor, State Supervisor Agricultural Education, Phoenix, Arizona; Curtis R. Weston, Instructor, Agricultural Education and Agricultural Engineering, University of Missouri; Walter E. Jeske, Vo-Ag Instructor, Waverly (Iowa) Community Schools; Wilbur R. Bryant, Canton (South Dakota) High School.

J. Roland Hamilton

Contents

PROBLEM-UNIT

USING ELECTRICITY
on the FARM

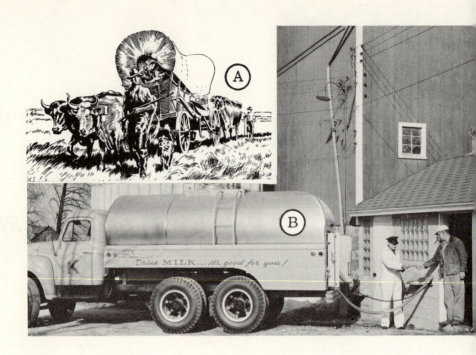

Fig. 1. During the 150 years from pioneer days in *A* to bulk-tank milk handling in *B*, more progress in farming was made than during the preceding 4,000 years.

PROBLEM-UNIT |

How to Use
Electricity to Improve the Farm

The whole world recognizes the American farmer as top man in his profession. Undoubtedly he deserves this high honor. Within the short span of one hundred years, farm progress in the United States has surpassed all farm achievements of the previous four thousand years.

The American farmer's ability to out-produce other farmers of the world was a major factor in the winning of the two world wars. This same ability, along with the famous American ingenuity, has brought to this country the highest standard of living ever achieved by any nation.

In view of the past centuries of famine and drudgery on the farm, how has the farmer accomplished so much in such a short period? The answer can be summarized as follows: The American farmer has applied *scientific methods and mechanical power to the farm*. The use of electricity in farming, while still in its infancy, is an important part of the American farm-power story. This book is intended to help you discover and take advantage of the many benefits that you can acquire from wise use of the power lines that run past your farm.

CHAPTER 1

Discovering and Using Opportunities in Farm Electrification

In a recent poll, * leading farmers throughout the United States gave first rank to mechanical power as a contributor to farm progress. Table 1 shows how 1,235 farmers voted on the question "What development has made the greatest contribution to fifty years of agricultural progress?" Notice that both items at the top of the list—"improved farm machinery" and "farm electrification" —belong in the farm-power area. These two power items together received almost two-thirds of the total votes cast for first place. There were less than two percentage points of difference between first and second rank.

TABLE 1

The Most Valuable Contribution to 50 Years of Agricultural Progress, Ranked According to Per Cent of Votes Cast **

Placing	Development	Per Cent Giving First Rank
1	Improved Farm Machinery	32.4
2	Farm Electrification	30.8
3	Improved Soil and Water Conservation	20.7
4	Better Livestock Breeding	6.5
5	Better Varieties of Crops	5.1
6	New and Improved Fertilizers	2.5
7	New Pest Control Products	2.0

* Lloyd E. Partain, *Personal Report on National Farm Study*. Philadelphia, The Curtis Publishing Company (no date).
** Based on 1,235 farmers' votes.

Fig. 2. In less than a century the handling of grain on the farm has progressed from the hand-powered grain thresher in A to the operator setting dials for automatic feed grinding and mixing in B. In C, cured grain pours into storage.

Although the importance of the other five items on the list is not questioned, mechanical power has played the leading part in reducing human labor in farming. This point is verified by the following facts: In 1830, when nearly all farm work was done by man and beast, almost 80 per cent of the total labor force in this country worked on the farm. At the present time, less than 12 per cent of the nation's workers are engaged in farm work; mechanical power does the rest. What has happened to the "extra" workers who used to do farm work? They are manning the factories and doing other jobs that have helped to bring this country its high standard of living.

Fig. 3. Handling silage and manure by electric power in A and B releases man labor for other work.

3

How Adequately Are Farmers Using Their Opportunities in Electrification?

When a farm is connected to receive electricity from a central-station power line, it is classified as being "electrified." This does not imply that the farm is electrified adequately. Indeed, the present use of electricity in farming is lagging far behind the opportunities that are available. This fact is obvious when you drive around the countryside and observe that many farms are using electricity for home lighting only. Others have farm home lighting plus a small water system and nothing else. Are these farm people taking full advantage of their opportunities for a better way of life?

Electricity Is Available to a Majority of Farms in the United States. Table 2 shows that electricity has come to almost all American farms. The amazing thing about this movement is that it has taken place with such unbelievable speed. A study of Table 2 will show this.

There is no point in showing the number or per cent of electrified farms before 1920, since in that year only 1.6 per cent were connected. But the real roots of rural electrification in the United States can be traced to Edison's first workable incandescent light

Fig. 4. Thomas Edison, in *B*, started farm electrification by inventing incandescent lamps such as those used for lighting the farm market in *A*.

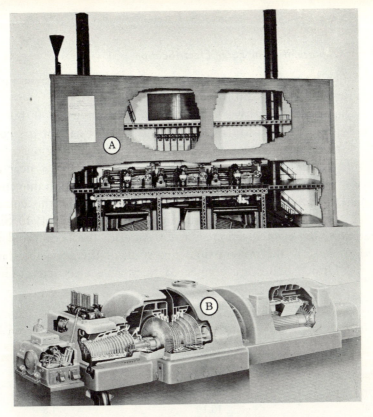

Fig. 5. Edison's Pearl Street dynamo (*A*) used about 10 pounds of coal in producing 1 kilowatthour of electricity. A modern steam turbine (*B*) produces 1 kilowatthour with less than 1 pound of coal.

TABLE 2

Total Farms in the United States, and Number and Per Cent
Electrified, by 5-Year Intervals*

Year	Total Farms	Electrified Farms	Per Cent Electrified
1920	6,448,343	103,000	1.6
1925	6,371,640	204,800	3.2
1930	6,288,648	596,000	9.5
1935	6,821,350	743,952	10.9
1940	6,096,799	1,853,249	34.0
1945	5,859,169	2,679,184	45.8
1950	5,382,134	4,154,359	77.2
1955	4,792,393	4,468,043	93.4
(1959)**			95.0

* Taken from U.S. Census.
** USDA estimate.

bulb (1879), followed by the opening of his Pearl Street power plant in 1882. That plant is shown in Fig. 5.

Some electricity was used in farming prior to 1900, but this was confined mostly to irrigation in the western part of the country. Gradually, however, a few farms in scattered sections of the United States began to tie onto community power lines near city stations; then from 1920 to 1925 the farm electrification movement gained momentum. By 1935 about one farm in ten in this country was electrified, and this figure jumped to 34 per cent by 1940. Since that time, the electrification of rural America has been rapid and widespread. At the present time almost all of the accessible farms in the United States are connected to receive electricity. The 5

TABLE 3

Total Farm Employment and Horsepower Per Farm Worker on U.S. Farms, by 10-Year Intervals*

Year	Total Farm Employment (Millions)**	Horsepower Per Worker
1870	8.0	1.6
1880	10.1	1.8
1890	11.7	2.2
1900	12.8	2.2
1910	13.6	2.2
1920	13.4	5.3
1930	12.5	12.7
1940	11.0	20.0
1950	9.3	37.0
1955	8.2	45.0
(1959)***	8.0	50.0+

* Data covering the period 1870 through 1930 were taken from USDA Miscellaneous Publication 157. Data for the period 1940 through 1955 are estimates of the USDA Agricultural Research Service.
** *USDA 1957 Agricultural Outlook Charts*, p. 71.
*** USDA estimate.

per cent not electrified either are voluntarily so or cannot conveniently be reached by a power line.

How Can You Use Electricity to Improve Your Farm?

The increase in mechanical power on the farm is shown in Table 3. Electric power is included in these figures. You will notice that the horsepower per farm worker was 12.7 in 1930, but has since increased to more than 50. What does this mean in terms of manpower? For practical purposes one man is considered equal to a ¼-hp motor. Using this figure, it is easy to estimate the power available to the average farm worker today, as follows: 1 horsepower = 4 men; therefore, 50 horsepower = 50 × 4 men = 200 men. This means that the average farm worker has the working power of 200 men at his disposal.

No doubt this vast amount of power on the farm will force you, if you farm, to do most of your work with mechanical power. Many cost studies in doing farm work with electric power have shown that a grown man can earn only 3 to 5 cents per hour in competition with an electric motor and machine. For example, while pumping water by hand pump you can earn only 5 cents per 1,000 gallons in competition with an electric pump!

How to Find and Use Your Opportunities in Electrification. In order to use your opportunities in electrification, you must find out *what they are* and then decide *what to do*. The first step in finding opportunities is to make a survey of the conditions of the electrical system on your home farm. Table 4 is a suggested form for making this study. The form is simple and can be copied onto a sheet of note paper in a few minutes' time. Study the examples listed in Table 4 before attempting to complete your own form. Then take the form home and fill in the two left-hand columns. Do not fill in the two right-hand columns until you have had time to give thorough study to your needs. Some of the items that should be listed in these columns on the right are covered in detail further on in the book. Moreover, you may need to obtain advice and instruction on some of these items before completing your form.

Fig. 6. From power plants such as the one shown here comes a part of the 50 or more horsepower (average) available per farm worker in the United States.

TABLE 4

Survey of Present Uses and Future Needs for Electricity on the Farm

Present*		Future	
Major Farm Use	Description (Number, size, etc.)	Major Farm Use	Description (Number, size, etc.)
Examples			
1. Service entrance	1 main service, 60 amp	1. Service entrance	1 main, 200-amp, and 4 individual service entrances, 100-amp, 100-amp, 60-amp, 60-amp
2. Farmstead lighting	1 yardpole lamp, 200w	2. Farmstead lighting	2 yardpole lamps, 200w and 300w each
3. Farmstead water system	¼-hp motor, 120-gph pump, 2 faucets	3. Farmstead water system	¾-hp motor, 500-gph pump, 5 faucets
4. Feed handling (grain)	none	4. Feed handling (grain)	5-hp motor, crimper-mixer with feed dispenser and portable elevator
5. Feed handling (silage)	none	5. Feed handling (silage)	3-hp unloader and 1½-hp dispenser
6. Dairy	conventional ½-hp milker, pail type	6. Dairy	1½-hp pipeline milker
7.			
8.			
9.			

* Make your own form and complete the left-hand columns at home; then complete the right-hand columns as a school project.

8

Study Your Needs for the Use of Electricity in Farming. One interesting way to find out whether you need to increase your use of electricity is to keep records of man labor spent in various farm jobs for one month. Then use these data to estimate the annual man labor required in the various chores. Convert these figures to dollars and cents. Next, obtain estimates of the cost of electric equipment, installation, and cost of electricity to do some of these farm jobs. Figure about 12 years of useful life for an electric machine, and refer to Chapter 2 for instructions on how to estimate cost of electricity. You should then be in a position to say whether or not it would pay you to electrify a given job or perhaps to increase the size of some of your equipment.

Decide What Electrical Projects You Should Undertake. Throughout this book you will find instructions on how to do many things in farm electrification. These range from the simple repairing of an electric cord to the wiring of a house. As you turn through the book you may decide to wire a farm building or to construct and install a yard light. You might construct a portable electric motor project or install an automatic feed-handling system. In fact, your opportunities for using electricity as a means of improving your farm are almost unlimited.

Investigate National Awards Programs. Before you complete your plan for electrical work it may pay you to investigate the national awards programs. The National FFA Foundation sponsors a national awards program in farm electrification, and the Westinghouse Educational Foundation sponsors a similar program for 4-H Club workers. By entering one of these programs you may win state or national recognition for your electrical work in addition to considerable prize money. You will still have your electrical projects whether or not you win any prizes. Moreover, as a result of your project work you may become interested in the electrical field and make a career of it.

What Farming Operations Should Be Electrified?

From a modest beginning as a source of light for the farm home, electricity has now been used in more than four hundred ways on the farm. Although more than 75 per cent of these uses have been in the farm home, the use of electricity in farm production, processing, and storage is increasing greatly.

Authorities in the farm-power field are predicting an era of push-button, electric, automatic farming in the years ahead. Whether or not you can have such a farm will depend upon many factors, but the size of your operations will have the greatest influence on whether you can electrify. For example, it is uneconomical to own and operate a $2,000 combine milker for a herd of 10 cows, or to buy a $2,500 automatic feeding system for a 25-steer feeder project. The conclusion is clear: if you expect to have an electrified farm, your operations must be large enough to justify the cost of the equipment and the cost of its operation.

On the other hand, rural people throughout the United States have improved their farms—both large and small—with the help of electrical projects. One good example of this is shown in Fig. 7. The homemade elevator in this scene was built at a total cost of about $120, including $25 for the ¼-hp motor. On the basis of 12 years' useful life, depreciation is charged at $10 per year. Assuming 20 days of use each year, the daily charge for depreciation is 50 cents. Since repairs are negligible and are made at home, no charge is included for them.

Fig. 7. This homemade elevator, powered by ¼-hp motor, is constructed of metal parts so as to last many years without repairs.

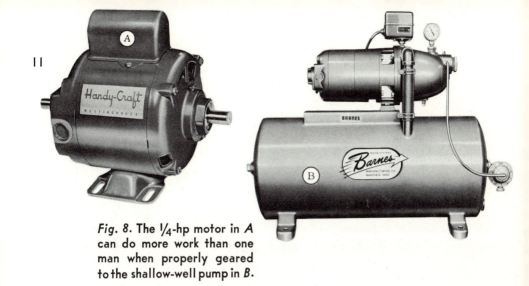

Fig. 8. The ¼-hp motor in *A* can do more work than one man when properly geared to the shallow-well pump in *B*.

The cost of electricity for operating the motor for 8 hours is figured as follows: A ¼-hp motor draws about 300 watts; therefore:

$$300w \times 8 \text{ hr} = 2{,}400 \text{ watthours}$$

$$\frac{2{,}400 \text{ watthours (wh)}}{1{,}000} = 2.4 \text{ kilowatthours (kwh)}$$

(See Chapter 2 for instructions on how to compute the cost of electricity.) At 3 cents per kwh the cost of 2.4 kwh is 7.2 cents ($3 \times 2.4 = 7.2$).

The total daily cost of owning and operating the elevator in Fig. 7 is $50 + 7.2 = 57.2$ cents.

The point of the example is this: In many feed-handling jobs, this elevator has been used to replace a hired man valued at $5 to $8 per day. Don't you think this kind of project is a paying proposition, even for a small farm?

Amount of Electrified Farming on United States Farms. Some knowledge of what other farmers are doing in electrification should help you to decide whether or not to electrify your own farm. Records of the use of electricity on several hundred farms in ten major type-of-farming areas are available for this purpose. The USDA recently completed a study* of the amount and cost of electrification on randomly selected farms throughout the United States—some large and some small.

* Joe F. Davis, *Use of Electricity on Farms, A Summary Report of Ten Area Studies*, USDA Agriculture Information Bulletin No. 161 (Washington, D.C., Government Printing Office, 1956), p. 6.

The average annual electric bills ranged from $36.17 for the small farms to $157.52 for the large farms. The price of electricity averaged from 1.54 cents to 4 cents per kwh, depending on the amount used. (NOTE: These "average" farms are not representative of the heaviest users of electricity; for example, on some irrigated farms the monthly electric bill runs to $150 or more.)

The heaviest users of electricity in the study were the dairy and poultry producers, followed by grain-livestock farms. The lightest users were the small farms, where there was little or no opportunity to put electricity to work outside the farm home.

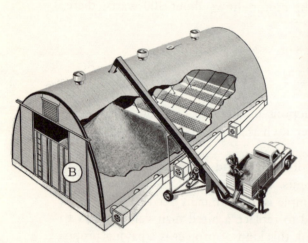

Fig. 9. (A) The old method of handling grain depended on horse and man labor. (B) The modern method takes advantage of low-cost electricity in handling, drying, and storing.

A study of the electric bills revealed that the use of electricity has been increasing by 21 per cent per year on certain types of farms. Much of this increase is going into farm production, processing, and storage.

The investment in electric equipment on these farms varied widely. Dairy, poultry, and livestock farms topped the list with an investment figure of $8,900. For example, on a well-equipped dairy farm in Wisconsin, $3,200 went for household equipment; $5,700 covered the cost of a combine milker, a gutter cleaner, a silo unloader, a bulk-milk tank, a water heater, barn ventilators, shop equipment, and miscellaneous items. An additional $1,500 to $2,500 was spent for farmstead wiring. This layout is considered adequate for a modern electrified 30-cow dairy operated by one man.

The study also brought out the fact that farmers generally do not acquire a modern electrified farm in one or two years. They grow into this status by buying their electric equipment a piece or two at a time. They even wire their farmstead by stages.

The amount of electrified farming carried out by farmers, according to this study, was controlled largely by farm economics. You, too, must consider these factors in deciding whether or not to electrify your farm. Some of the most important ones follow.

How the Money Question Relates to Electrification. When you are making a decision on whether to buy a major piece of electric equipment, the money question will have three important aspects: (1) cost and returns based largely on increased production; (2) market demands and better prices; and (3) insurance against risk.

Cost and Returns. This is the most important consideration. for most farmers. Unless you are financially able to indulge in luxury, a piece of farm equipment must be justified on the basis of money returns. Of course, returns may take several different forms, as you shall presently see. The following examples will illustrate this point:

One Alabama farmer operates a laying-hen unit of 12,000 birds without hired help. He is able to do this with the help of electric equipment that cost about $2,000. This includes electric

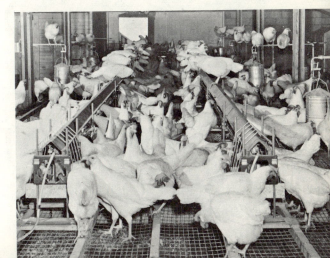

Fig. 10. Electric automatic feeders, waterers, night lighting, and ventilation equipment are required in modern egg production on this Ohio farm.

14

Fig. 11. Electric automatic equipment has greatly reduced labor and risk in broiler production: (A) hover brooding; (B) heat-lamp brooding.

feeders, waterers, and egg handling machines. His investment in this modern equipment has made it possible for him to triple the size of his flock in comparison with that possible with hand methods.

Another farmer, in Indiana, handles 32,000 broilers per turn (four turns per year) without outside help. His automatic feed grinding and dispensing machinery and other electric equipment have helped to reduce labor requirements to two-fifths of a minute per bird. The cost of the mill, bins, and installation was about $500, and the cost of operation of the mill was approximately $21 per

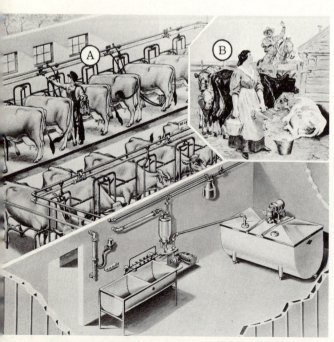

Fig. 12. The early settlers in *B* never thought of milking cows with electric energy as the dairyman in *A* is doing. Electricity also takes care of feeding, watering, washing milk lines, storing and cooling milk, and lighting in this modern dairy.

turn of birds. He saved $1,353 on feed costs during the first turn of broilers. This operation is based in large measure upon electric equipment.

Experiments have shown that a dairyman can handle about 50 per cent more cows with the same effort after installing a pipeline (combine) milker. The cost of this machine, including the in-place cleaning equipment, is about $1,800 to $2,000 for a two-unit outfit. Further reductions in labor, which would make possible further increases in herd size, can be effected by the addition of a silo unloader, a barn cleaner, a cow trainer, an automatic waterer, and other miscellaneous dairy equipment.

There are, of course, hundreds of additional opportunities for putting electric equipment to work in farm production. The hard economic fact here is that a certain volume of production is necessary in order to justify the cost of the equipment.

Market Considerations. Market demands may force you to comply with certain trends or else give up that type of farming. For example, in some areas there is little or no market for milk in cans; it can be sold only in bulk form. This trend could force you

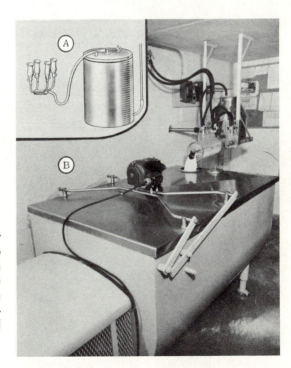

Fig. 13. The combine milker releasing milk directly into a bulk-tank cooler in *B* is a great improvement over the 1878 model milker in *A*. The modern system reduces labor, improves sanitation, and eliminates milk cans.

to purchase a bulk-milk tank whether or not it is favorable to do so. A bulk tank large enough to take care of a 30-cow dairy costs from $2,000 to $2,500. Better prices for bulk milk, along with other savings, should pay for this tank in three to five years.

Farmers are finding that the better-quality farm products resulting from the proper processing and storing of them bring better prices sufficient to justify the cost of the equipment. For example, the increase in market value of eggs, as reported by numerous poultrymen, pays for the equipment used in cleaning, grading, and storing in one to three years; that is, if the volume is adequate.

Fig. 14. An egg cooler normally will pay for itself in 1 to 3 years, depending upon volume to be handled, from increased prices for better quality eggs.

Fig. 15. An electric fan (A) blowing air through a wire duct (B) can take the risk out of storing green hay. (C) Forage crops were plowed by oxen and harvested by hand methods 150 years ago.

Fig. 16. The heat lamp and wiring for this pig brooder cost less than $10 and save an average of 1 to 3 more pigs per litter.

Again, it is clear that larger operators have the advantage in electrifying their farms.

Insurance Against Risk. For an investment of $1,000 to $1,200 in drying equipment, you can take the worry and risk out of storing grain, hay, and seed. The cost of electricity would be about $1 to $1.50 per ton for hay; and total cost, including depreciation, repairs, and so on would be about $3.50 per ton. Other gains would include better market prices, better selection of harvesting period, and less loss of crops in the field.

Other electric equipment for insurance against risk includes brooders for pigs, lambs, and other young animals; heater cable and heaters for the water system; burglar alarms; egg coolers; various storages for other farm products; and similar items. A well-lighted farmstead may easily pay for itself by preventing accidents.

Whether or not you should buy hay or grain dryers or other expensive electrical equipment will depend upon the size of your farming operations. You cannot afford to invest $1,000 in hay- or grain-drying equipment for just a few tons of hay or a few bushels of grain.

How the Labor Problem Relates to Farm Electrification. In this day of expensive and often undependable labor, farmers who use hired workers are gearing up every possible operation to electric power. This makes sense when you realize how little it costs to operate an electric motor. By referring to Table 8 you will see that one Michigan farmer milked 20 cows an average of twice a day for a whole year at a cost of $8.02 for electricity. Another farmer in New York recently invested less than $2,500 in a barn cleaner and feed-handling equipment that allowed him to release his $180-a-month hired hand.

Fig. 17. This barn cleaner takes the backache out of manure handling and reduces labor.

The trend toward part-time farming in this country has been made possible, in large measure, by the use of electric and sometimes automatic equipment. A farmer can handle the milking chore for 30 cows in 1 to 1½ hours if his barn is fully electrified. A large poultry operation can be carried on, along with a full-time off-the-farm job, if the houses are equipped with the proper electric appliances.

Electric, automatic feed-handling equipment can be purchased now that will enable one man to handle the feeding chore for 500 to 1,000 head of beef cattle; or 2,000 to 5,000 head of sheep; or up to 12,000 laying hens. A part-time operation of fewer head could be handled with smaller equipment.

Statistics show that the trend in farming is toward *larger operations* and *less human labor*. Electric equipment for stationary farm jobs holds out real opportunities for you in the coming age of automation.

How Personal Matters Relate to Electrification. Prevailing standards in your community will influence your decision on whether or not to buy certain equipment. For example, if "everybody" has a television set, you are likely to get one even if you must buy it on the installment plan. This community pressure, no

Fig. 18. (A) The farmer in this milking parlor can milk 30 cows per hour. (B) A self-cleaning bulk-tank cooler further reduces labor in the modern dairy.

doubt, influences many farmers to purchase things that could hardly be justified on a monetary basis.

Farmers, like everyone else, surround themselves with as many comforts and conveniences as they can afford. Thus, appliance sales have now reached a total of more than a billion dollars a year in the United States. Included in this are food freezers, refrigerators, ranges, air conditioners, radios, vacuum cleaners, television sets, electric blankets, toasters, and many other appliances.

Another factor that influences farmers to purchase electric equipment, or indeed any kind of equipment, is that of personal prestige and respect in the community. Studies have shown that farmers place a high value on the esteem of their neighbors.

Some appliances are bought and justified on the basis of the family's health. A home-size pasteurizer is an example of this.

Personal considerations, as you have seen, certainly enter into all decisions on buying major equipment for the farm or farm home. Your financial backing will be the limiting factor here.

Conclusion on Whether or Not to Purchase Electric Appliances. The preceding discussion makes it clear that the decision on whether or not to electrify your farm or any part of it is not an easy one. It will be necessary to take account of the total cost of a machine, but it will be equally important to consider the use of

Fig. 19. An Indiana farmer setting dials for proportioning, mixing, and grinding 1,200 pounds of feed per hour for his 32,000 broiler operation. The machine cuts itself off at the proper time.

Fig. 20. A combination feed mill, mixer, and auger controlled by a time clock greatly reduces the labor required to feed 2,500 head of sheep.

Fig. 21. Over 50% of all farmhomes in the United States now have television sets.

this machine in expanding farm operations, improving market value, reducing risk, and improving the labor situation on the farm. And finally, your personal tastes and ambitions will certainly influence your decisions. It has been shown that the addition of one key piece of equipment often sets off a "chain reaction" that ends only with re-equipping a whole farm operation.

Considering the almost unlimited opportunities in farm electrification, no doubt you will decide to live and farm electrically in the years ahead. The limitations in electrification rest mostly with you. The possibilities for a better way of farm life through electrification have not been fully determined at this time. Indeed, many of the known benefits have not been tried out by a majority of American farmers.

Fig. 22. A combination refrigerator-food freezer contributes to the economic welfare and health of the family.

Summary

The electrification of rural America stands as one of the milestones in fifty years of agricultural progress. Approximately 95 per cent of the farms in the U.S. are now connected to receive electricity. Electricity, together with other sources of power, now provides the average farm worker with the equivalent working power of 200 to 400 men. This is about four to eight times the total power available per worker in 1930.

The first step in using your opportunities in electrification is to make a study of the need to expand the use of electricity on the farm. This process requires the making of a survey of all parts of the present electrical system, including all pieces of electrical equipment. Also, jobs now done by hand should be studied to determine whether or not it would be economical to electrify them. Several national awards programs in farm electrification are available to farm boys and girls in every state.

When properly applied, a ¼-hp motor will do as much work as a grown man. This motor, geared up to a homemade elevator at a combined cost of about $120, can be used to replace a hired man in handling feed-stuff or grain. The cost of electricity, at 3 cents per kwh, is less than 8 cents for 8 hours of operation. Depreciation on the motor and elevator is about 50 cents per day of operation.

Electricity has been used in more than four hundred ways on the farmstead. Many of these uses are economical for small farms, but the greatest advantages in using electricity to do farm work lie with larger farms. This fact is especially true in farm production, processing, and storage.

A recent USDA study showed that investment in electric equipment for a modern 30-cow dairy, a farm shop, household appliances, a water system, and the like runs as high as $8,900. Equipment for choring and other farming operations accounted for $5,700 of this amount, while household appliances cost $3,200. Farmstead wiring cost between $1,500 and $2,500. Getting a farm of this kind electrified usually requires a period of years.

Opportunities in electrification are influenced or controlled by the cost balanced against possible returns. The purchase of an electric appliance is often justified on the basis of increased production from larger herds, flocks, and other operations; better market prices; and insurance against risk.

The labor situation on a farm may dictate the addition of electric appliances. The replacement of hired help or the release of a farmer's time to do other work may justify the cost of a new piece of electric equipment.

Personal values often influence farmers to buy new appliances: Comfort, convenience, health, and personal prestige are taken into account along with economics in deciding whether to buy a new appliance.

There is no practical limit to a farmer's opportunities in electrification except in his own mind.

Suggested Projects for Problem-Unit One

Do you want to take advantage of low-cost electricity to reduce labor, increase production, and make other farm improvements? If so, study the National Electrical Awards Program to see whether you might qualify for awards while carrying out some electrical projects. There are two awards programs in electrification that are national in scope, yet operate at the state and local levels:

1. The National FFA Foundation sponsors an electrical awards program for FFA boys. This program provides several $200 Regional Awards and a $250 National Award. You may win one of these prizes. Moreover, electrical organizations give additional awards at the state and local levels. Thus your chances of winning prize money are much greater if you live in an area where one of the contests is in operation.

2. The other national program is the 4-H Electric Awards Program, sponsored by the Westinghouse Educational Foundation. The Rural Electrification Administration and numerous power suppliers throughout the United States assist in this 4-H work. Each year six college scholarships are awarded to national winners; also, state winners receive a trip to the 4-H Club Congress in Chicago each year. Numerous awards are given to district and local winners.

Winning Projects. In Fig. 23 you will see one of the recent national winners in the FFA Foundation Awards Program. This Alabama Future Farmer is shown with his vocational agriculture teacher adjusting a home-made saw—one of the projects he used in winning a national award.

Fig. 23. An Alabama FFA boy and his agriculture teacher adjusting the guide of a homemade table saw which is part of a collection of electrical projects that won the National FFA award recently.

Fig. 24 shows a 4-H Club winner from Colorado. This young lady used discarded parts to build the water-cooled fan shown in the photo. She has done house wiring and other electrical project work that brought her national recognition and over $500 in prize money.

Other Projects. Perhaps the first and most important project to start would be to make a study of jobs on your farm that should be electrified. Simply list the jobs now being done by hand, or not being done at all, then check those that you would like to electrify.

Fig. 24. A 4-H Club girl from Colorado beside the water-cooled fan she constructed from junk materials.

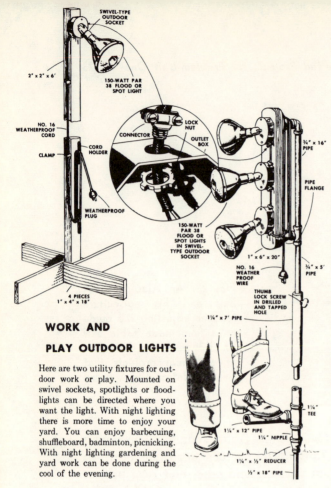

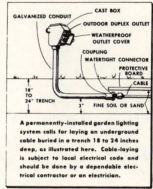

A permanently-installed garden lighting system calls for laying an underground cable buried in a trench 18 to 24 inches deep, as illustrated here. Cable-laying is subject to local electrical code and should be done by a dependable electrical contractor or an electrician.

WORK AND

PLAY OUTDOOR LIGHTS

Here are two utility fixtures for outdoor work or play. Mounted on swivel sockets, spotlights or floodlights can be directed where you want the light. With night lighting there is more time to enjoy your yard. You can enjoy barbecuing, shuffleboard, badminton, picnicking. With night lighting gardening and yard work can be done during the cool of the evening.

Fig. 25. The portable yard lights shown here can be constructed in a few hours at very little cost.

This might include a feeding system for livestock, automatic watering for stock, yard lights for the farmstead, farm shop improvement, or hundreds of other things. Refer to Table 4 for suggestions regarding a form to use in making your survey.

Questions

1. Do you think that farmers were correct in placing rural electrification and improved farm machinery at the top of the list of greatest contributions to fifty years of agricultural progress? Why?

2. In what ways has mechanical power affected the farm labor situation? The total economy of the country?

3. How can you use a farm survey in planning for future farm electrification?

4. What advantages does a large farm have over small farms in using electricity for farm production?

5. In what ways can an electric appliance contribute to farm income? To personal prestige in the community?

Additional Readings

Davis, Joe F., *Use of Electricity on Farms*. Agricultural Information Bulletin No. 161. Washington, D.C., U.S. Department of Agriculture, 1956.

McColly, H. F., and Martin, J. W., *Introduction to Agricultural Engineering*. New York, McGraw-Hill, 1955.

Runkle, Karl H., *What Is Electrification Doing for Agriculture?* Schenectady, New York, General Electric Co., 1955.

U.S. Department of Agriculture, Rural Electrification Administration, *How Electric Farming Can Help Your Business*. REA Bulletin 140-1. Washington, D.C. (no date).

————, *Profits from Electrified Farms*. REA Bulletin No. 140-6. Washington, D.C., 1955.

U.S. Department of Commerce, *Statistical Abstract of the United States*. Washington, D.C., 1956.

Fig. 26. Improper wiring and lack of lightning protection are two major causes of farm fires. This costly fire could have been prevented.

PROBLEM-UNIT ❚❚

How to Apply the Common Laws of Electricity

If you violate the laws of society you may be fined or imprisoned, but if you violate the laws of electricity, you may pay with your life or with the loss of your home. Failure to observe the common laws of electricity has resulted in tremendous losses of property and human life in the United States during the past twenty-five years, to say nothing of the impairment of electric service.

Your future all-electric farm and home are not likely to materialize unless you learn how to apply a few basic principles of electricity in planning and using your future electrical system. To this end you should learn all that you can about the nature of electricity and about safe and correct practices in using it. In so doing, you will provide a better way of life for yourself and your family.

CHAPTER 2

The Nature of Electricity —What It Is and How to Measure It

In one sense, electricity "flows" through a conductor. And though the flow of an electric current is not quite the same as water flowing through a pipe, it does have many similar characteristics. In fact, the flowing of electricity is most easily understood when compared to a pressurized water system. By studying this comparison, you should be able to understand the ordinary principles of electricity.

The first thing to understand about electricity is its basic form. You may assume that *electricity is one form of energy*. Heat, light, and motion are the forms that you know best. The progress of the civilized world has been closely associated with man's knowledge of and skill in harnessing forms of energy to do useful work. In order to be of value to people, electricity must first be converted to heat, light, or motive power. As you will see later, the process can be reversed so that heat or motion *may produce* electricity.

Because of its peculiar nature and the difficulty of controlling and studying it, electricity was not harnessed for human use until long after heat, light, and motion were serving mankind. For example, primitive man could light a fire and enjoy the benefits of heat energy; he could use a lever to develop motive power. These simple uses of energy, however, did not require an understanding of them.

Electricity is more complex. It was not brought under control until man acquired a reasonable understanding of it. In contrast

Fig. 27. (A) This early model feed mill depended on hand power for operation. (B) On a modern farm electricity handles the entire feeding operation at the push of a button.

with electricity, solids and liquids are easier to understand because they have weight, color, odor, length, width, and other tangible qualities. Despite these difficulties, however, the scientist has now produced a reasonable and workable explanation of electricity.

How Can the Movement of Electron Particles Produce an Electric Current?

The explanation of electricity grows out of the nature of matter and its innermost parts. All matter is composed of minute particles called *molecules*. A molecule is too small to be seen by even the highest-power microscope. Yet the scientist has been able to prove that a piece of metal, for example, is not "solid" but consists, rather, of countless billions of particles (molecules).

As small as the molecule is, however, it is composed of even smaller particles called *atoms*. The nature of electricity is explained by the structure of atoms.

Protons and Electrons in the Atom. By referring to Fig. 28, you can see the scientist's concept of an atom. Notice that the

Fig. 28. A diagram of the theoretical arrangement of electrons in an atom. The lone electron in the outer ring can be displaced by a generator or a battery.

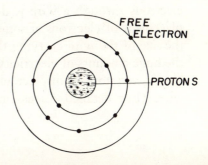

FREE ELECTRON

PROTONS

center, or nucleus, is made up of separate particles called *protons.* Each proton carries a *positive charge.*

Notice also that the number of particles arranged in rings about the nucleus is equal to the number of protons in the nucleus. These are called *electrons*, and each carries a *negative charge.* The scientist knows that positive and negative charges *attract* each other and believes that the atom is held together by the attraction between the protons and electrons.

By referring again to Fig. 28, you will see that the outer ring contains only one electron, which is referred to as being "free" because certain forces can *displace* it. When this happens, the protons will outnumber the electrons, then a free electron in an adjoining atom will move over and occupy the vacant spot. The displacement of billions of free electrons and the resulting movement of other billions of free electrons along a piece of wire is an *electric current.* This movement is accompanied by the production of energy—energy that can be converted into heat, light, or motion.

In order to understand how electricity flows you must visualize a piece of wire as being made up of countless billions of atoms lying so close together that they form what appears to be a solid substance. Every atom in a piece of copper wire is exactly alike so that the displacement of free electrons at one point in the wire will cause a movement of electrons throughout the entire length of the wire. The flowing of electrons cannot be continuous, though, unless the wire is connected in a continuous *circuit;* that is, the ends of the wire must be joined together. (See simple circuit in Fig. 29.) So you see why electricity is defined as energy, not as a substance; it is a movement of electrons.

Not all substances have a free electron in their atomic structure. Such substances will not *conduct* an electric current; for example, rubber, glass, plastics, and similar materials. These *nonconductors* are used as a cover for metallic conductors and are referred to as *insulators* or insulation material.

How Free Electrons Are Set in Motion. The rate of flow of electrons through a wire is determined, first, by the rate of displacement of electrons at some point in the wire; and, second, by the size of the wire carrying the current. Power suppliers produce the huge amounts of electricity required in modern living by using large generators to displace electrons at one point in a circuit of wire. (For detailed discussion of generators, see page 51.) The resulting imbalance of electron pressure between two (or more) wires causes electrons to flow. They will move from the high-pressure ("hot") wire to the low-pressure ("ground") wire. In short, the electrical pressure on the "high" lines serving your farm is greater on one wire than on the other. This difference in pressure is referred to as *voltage*. (See further discussion of voltage on page 32.)

Electrons can be set in motion also by batteries in which acid solutions act on unlike metallic plates which are connected to a circuit of wire. Batteries do not generate sufficient electrical pressure to supply electricity for high lines in a community; generators are used for this.

An understanding of the electron theory of electricity, as discussed in the preceding topic, should enable you to make safer and more economical applications of the laws of electricity when you plan your future electrical system. You should remember the electron theory as you study voltage, amperage, and the like in the remainder of this book.

How Does an Electric Circuit Resemble a Water System?

In Fig. 29, a point by point comparison of the corresponding principles of electric circuits and water systems is shown.

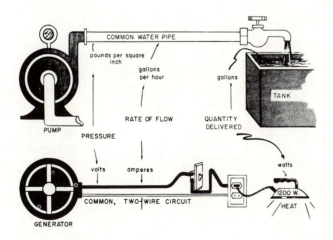

Fig. 29. The "flowing" of electricity closely resembles a water system.

Notice that the circuit consists of one black (hot) wire and one white (neutral or ground) wire. When the circuit is closed, electricity flows through the black wire, from the source (generator) at 115 volts pressure, to the iron. Then it flows, at very low voltage, through the white wire back to the source. A switch installed in the black wire (never in the neutral) provides a means of breaking the circuit and thus stopping the current. So that electricity may be available at all times, the generator must operate continuously; this kind of electricity cannot be stored.

In the water system shown in Fig. 29, water is supplied at 40 pounds pressure per square inch. It is this pressure that causes the water to flow. The faucet corresponds to the switch in the electric circuit. A pump and pressure tank maintain the proper pressure while the water is flowing.

How Voltage Corresponds to Pressure in a Water System. Just as the pressure in a water system causes the water to flow, so voltage causes an electric current to flow; more simply stated, *voltage is electrical pressure.* The electrical pressure required to operate most household appliances is 115 volts; a range, a water heater, or a large motor, however, requires 230 volts. Some motors operate on 440 volts.

All conductor wires offer some resistance to the flow of electricity. Consequently, power lines that span hundreds of miles must carry a high voltage, which, on rural lines, may be as much as 12,000 volts. High voltage must then be reduced to a usable and safe voltage at your farm, probably to 115 or 230 volts. This is accomplished by the use of a transformer, which is usually placed

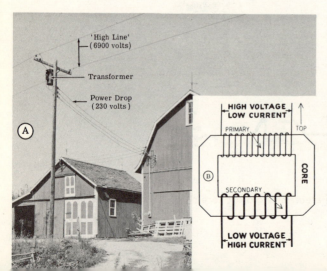

Fig. 30. (A) The "high" line coming into a farm carries 6,900 volts to the transformer at the top of the yardpole. The transformer reduces voltage to 230 volts for a three-wire circuit; 115 volts for a two-wire circuit. (B) Diagram shows how voltage is reduced by using a greater number of turns of wire in the primary winding (at top).

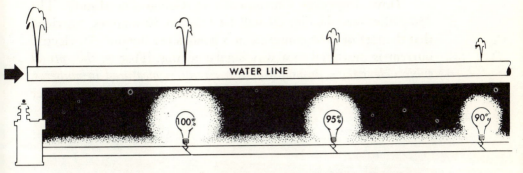

Fig. 31. Electricity, like water pressure, loses some of its pressure (voltage) as it flows along a circuit. To avoid too much drop in voltage, use the correct wire size.

near the service drop that connects to your meter. Fig. 30 shows a cutaway section of an ordinary farm-type transformer.

What Is Voltage Drop? When an electric current flows through a conductor, it loses pressure because of the resistance in the conductor. The resulting loss is called *voltage drop*. The diagram in Fig. 31 compares loss of voltage in an electric circuit with loss of pressure in a water pipe. Just as friction in the water pipe "absorbs" some of the pressure, so resistance in the wire "robs" the current of some voltage. The results are similar: less water delivered at the far end of the pipe; less electric power delivered at the far end of the circuit.

To ignore the law of voltage drop is to invite trouble. For example, you could assume that it would be more economical to use No. 14 wire for a 300-foot circuit to your 1,150w brooder because this would cost $4 less than No. 12 wire. (NOTE: No. 12 wire is larger than No. 14.) That is exactly the mistake that is being made by farmers all across the country. The No. 14 wire is too small for a 300-foot run. The voltage at the farthest end would be too low to operate a 1,150w brooder. Small wire offers more resistance to the flow of electricity than does a larger wire.

Resistance causes heat to be generated in the wires, and you pay for it in wasted electricity when you pay your electric bill. Moreover, the low-voltage current supplied to the brooder may result in damage to the heating mechanism. Finally, the faulty operation of the brooder could result in the loss of chicks or pigs.

How Amperage Corresponds to Gallons-Per-Minute. The 250-gallon tank in Fig. 29 will be filled in 50 minutes, provided that the rate of flow continues at 5 gallons per minute. An electric current is measured in a way similar to this. That is, *the rate at which electricity flows through a circuit is measured in amperes.* This is about the same principle as gallons-per-minute in the water system.

Fig. 32. This combination meter is used to measure the exact voltage and amperage flowing in a circuit or an electric motor.

In both illustrations the pressure is the main factor that affects the rate of flow. However, there are three other things that tend to restrict or reduce the rate of flow in a water pipe as well as in an electric circuit. These are: (1) long runs of pipe or wire; (2) poor condition of pipe or wire; and (3) small pipe or wire.

To illustrate this important point, assume that the rate of flow of water is 5 gallons per minute for a 50-foot length of ¾-inch pipe. What happens if a ½-inch pipe is substituted, while the other factors remain the same? The rate of flow is reduced, of course, and reduced more than one half. If the pipe (or the wire) is lengthened, a further reduction in the rate of flow results. If the inside walls of the pipe become rusted (or if a wire is damaged) there is a still further reduction.

When you begin to plan your own electric circuits, remember the important principle that amperage depends not only on voltage but on *wire size, length of circuit,* and *condition of wire.*

The 1,200w iron in Fig. 29 draws at the rate of approximately 10.4 amperes. This is found as follows:

$$\frac{1,200 \text{ watts}}{115 \text{ volts}} = 10.4 \text{ amperes}$$

If the wiring for the iron is too small, however, the voltage may drop to 100 volts or less. At 100 volts the current flows at approximately 8 amperes and the wattage output is as follows: 100 volts $\times$ 8 amperes $=$ 800 watts, a loss of 400 watts. This lost wattage is paid for, yet does no work. At the same time, the low-voltage current may damage the circuit wiring as well as the heating coils of the iron.

Amperage, then, is referred to as the *rate at which a current flows* and, when multiplied by voltage, equals the output of electric power—watts or horsepower.

How Electric Power Is Measured in Watts as Well as Horsepower. Power is the measure of the *rate of doing work.* This is easily computed for an electric motor, because its output is in the form of mechanical power. When the output of power is in the form of heat or light, however, it is more convenient to measure power in terms of the *watt.*

Referring again to Fig. 29, you can see that a certain amount of power is required to force the water to flow at the rate of 5 gpm (gallons per minute). More power would be required to pump water at a faster rate—10 gpm, for example. The exact amount of power required in the setup in Fig. 29 is determined by rate of flow (5 gpm), vertical lift, and amount of friction in the water lines. (Refer to Chapter 11 for details on figuring pump motor size.)

Similarly, a certain amount of electric power (in the form of heat) is being developed in the iron in Fig. 29 and is expressed as watts—1,200 watts in this instance. It is a simple step to convert watts to horsepower or horsepower to watts by using the formula:

746 watts = 1 horsepower. The 1,200w iron is equivalent to the following in terms of horsepower:

$$\frac{1,200 \text{ watts}}{746 \text{ watts}} = 1.6 \text{ horsepower}$$

Of course, it is customary to refer to a 1,200w iron rather than a 1.6 horsepower iron.

A further word of explanation on motor power is necessary. A 1-hp motor actually draws more than 746 watts. The reason is that some power is lost in heat, vibration, wind resistance, and friction. The actual *draft* of electricity by a 1-hp motor is from 1,200 to 1,400 watts (and may run higher) although it puts out only 746 watts of power. Larger motors, however, are more efficient; for example, some 5-hp motors draw as little as 4,500 watts, or 900 watts per horsepower; whereas a ½-hp motor draws 700 to 800 watts. Therefore it is more economical to use one 1-hp motor than to use two ½-hp motors wherever it is possible to do so.

For solving most ordinary power problems on the farm, the following relationships should be remembered:

1. Watts   = volts × amperes

2. Volts   = $\dfrac{\text{watts}}{\text{amperes}}$

3. Amperes = $\dfrac{\text{watts}}{\text{volts}}$

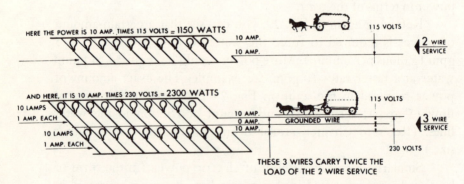

HERE THE POWER IS 10 AMP. TIMES 115 VOLTS = 1150 WATTS

10 AMP.

10 AMP.

115 VOLTS

2 WIRE SERVICE

AND HERE, IT IS 10 AMP. TIMES 230 VOLTS = 2300 WATTS

10 LAMPS 1 AMP. EACH

10 LAMPS 1 AMP. EACH

10 AMP.

0 AMP.   GROUNDED WIRE

10 AMP.

115 VOLTS

3 WIRE SERVICE

230 VOLTS

THESE 3 WIRES CARRY TWICE THE LOAD OF THE 2 WIRE SERVICE

Fig. 33. A two-wire service at 10 amperes and 115 volts will develop 1 hp. By adding 1 "hot" wire the resulting three-wire service will develop twice as much power as the two-wire circuit.

How Is the Cost of Electricity Determined?

The average selling price of electricity now is less than one-fifth what it was in 1882. Great improvements in the manufacture and distribution of electricity have made this reduction possible. For less than 10 cents today, you can purchase enough electric energy to operate a ¼-hp motor for 8 hours; and, in many farming operations, you can thus replace a grown man.

Electricity is measured by the kilowatthour, but the price usually varies in accordance with the amount used during one month.

How to Figure Kilowatthours of Use. You have already seen that the watt is the measure of electric power. One watt, however, is too small to use in calculations, so the *kilowatt* (1,000 watts) is used in figuring electric bills. That is, ten 100w lamps = 10 × 100 watts, or 1,000 watts. If you used these 10 lamps continuously for one hour, you would use *1 kwh of electricity* (1,000 watts used for one hour = 1 kwh).

To estimate the amount of electricity used by an appliance in one month, do the following:

1. Determine the wattage rating of the appliance. (See label.)
2. Estimate the total number of hours used during the month.
3. Multiply wattage rating by the total number of hours.
4. Divide by 1,000.

EXAMPLE ONE:

1. A range oven is rated at 3,000 watts.
2. By checking the time on several different days it is found that the oven is used one-half hour per day, or a total of 15 hours during one month.
3. Then, 3,000 watts × 15 hours = 45,000 watthours.
4. 45,000 ÷ 1,000 = 45 kwh.

Assuming an average price of 3 cents per kwh, the cost of operating the oven for one month would be 45 × 3 cents = $1.35.

EXAMPLE TWO: In order to estimate the cost of using an electric motor, it is necessary to convert horsepower to watts before you can apply the four-step formula in the preceding example. The data in Table 5 can be used as a quick means of making this conversion.

TABLE 5

Electric Motor
Size in Horsepower and Wattage Equivalents

Horsepower	Watts*
1	1,200-1,400
¾	900-1,000
½	600- 800
⅓	400- 500
¼	300- 400
⅙	200- 250
⅛	150- 175

* Wattage data shown are not exact. Use only for estimating loads. See motor nameplate to find exact rating.

Assume that you operate a ½-hp grain elevator as follows: First day, 6 hours; second day, 5 hours; third day, 8 hours; fourth day, 4 hours. How much electricity will be used?

ANSWER: Apply the four steps as outlined in Example One.

1. 600 watts (½-hp motor)
2. 23 hours used (6 + 5 + 8 + 4)
3. 23 × 600 = 13,800 watthours
4. 13,800 ÷ 1,000 = 13.8 kwh

Assuming 3 cents per kwh, the cost of operation would be 41.4 cents.

Fig. 34. This ¼-hp motor will use about 300 whr of electricity under normal load. It will use up to 400 whr when fully loaded.

Fig 35. The typical watthour meter measures the amount of electricity used.

In computing electric bills, power companies use actual meter readings. The preceding examples were for estimating purposes only.

How Electric Rates Vary. Power companies usually charge more for the first 25 to 50 kwh. The next block of 50 or so, and each succeeding block, may cost you less per kwh. This is what the power supplier calls a "sliding scale." The company's expenses on power lines, poles, and transformers continue whether you use any electricity or not. Therefore, it is only fair that every customer pay a minimum monthly charge; you use the electrical

TABLE 6

General Rural Rate in a Southern State

Kwh Used			Price	Cost of This Bracket	Total Cost
First bracket	first	50	4 cents	$2.00	$ 2.00
Second bracket	next	50	3	1.50	3.50
Third bracket	next	100	2	2.00	5.50
Fourth bracket	next	200	1	2.00	7.50
Fifth bracket	next	1,000	.4	4.00	11.50*

* The 1,400 kwh covered by the five brackets would cost $11.50, as shown by the figure in the last column. This would average .8 cents per kwh for the first 1,400 used. (This is a more favorable rate than the average throughout the country.)

equipment whether or not you use any electricity. This minimum charge usually covers the first 25 to 50 kwh.

Table 6 shows the rate charged by one electric cooperative in a southern state. The total cost by brackets is also figured for the first 1,400 kwh. (NOTE: The price of the first 50 kwh is 4 cents each, or a total of $2. The last bracket of 1,000 kwh (at .4 cents) costs only $4. This gives a spread of ten to one between the price in the first bracket and that in the last bracket.)

You should study your power rates and decide whether you are using a sufficient amount of electricity to get into the more favorable price brackets. In view of the low cost of electric energy, it may be to your advantage to put more electricity to work on your farm.

The Way to Read a Meter. Fig. 36 shows a meter face as of March 1 and April 1. The first reading—2,822—is the total of all the electricity that has been measured by that meter up to March 1. In other words, the meter simply adds the March consumption to this total and the difference is the number of kilowatthours used during that month.

Therefore, it is necessary to take readings on the first and last days of the month (if the electric bill is paid monthly) in order

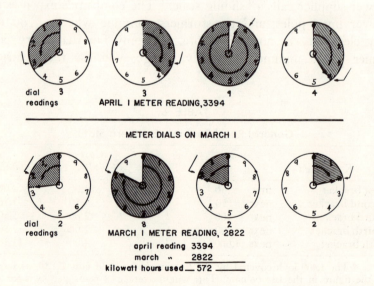

Fig. 36. Meter readings taken one month apart.

to determine the amount used. Then it is a simple matter of subtracting the first reading from the last.

Referring to the meter faces in Fig. 36, locate the four dials. Beginning on the left and reading to the right, each dial contributes one digit to the meter reading. For April 1, the reading is 3-3-9-4, and for March 1, it is 2-8-2-2.

Notice that the pointers on two of the dials (1 and 3) turn to the left while the other two (2 and 4) turn to the right. A number is counted only when the dial is at or fully past that number. Check this by looking at the dial next on your right.

How to Figure the Monthly Bill. After you have learned to read the meter, you may want to figure your monthly bill. Using the readings on the first and last days of the month, subtract the smaller amount from the larger and the result will be the total amount used.

TABLE 7
Typical Electric Bill

Meter reading April 1		3,394
Meter reading March 1		2,822
Kwh used		572
		Amt. to Pay
First bracket	first 50 kwh at 4¢	$2.00
Second bracket	next 50 kwh at 3¢	1.50
Third bracket	next 100 kwh at 2¢	2.00
Fourth bracket	next 200 kwh at 1¢	2.00
Fifth bracket	next 172* kwh at .4¢	.69
		$8.19**

* This is the amount in excess of the first 400 kwh and is paid for in the fifth bracket at .4 cents each.

** The average cost of 572 kwh would be $8.19 ÷ 572 = 1.4 cents.

You can now use the bracket system shown in Table 7 to figure your bill. On the basis of the readings previously mentioned, the amount is 572 kwh. This covers the first four brackets (400 kwh) and leaves 172 kwh to fall into the fifth bracket. The last column on the right shows the cost of each bracket. The present bill includes 172 kwh in the fifth bracket at .4 cents each, or 69 cents. Therefore, the total monthly bill is $8.19, which averages 1.4 cents per kwh.

Remember, though, that the per-kwh cost would be 4 cents if less than 50 kwh were used, and you would, of course, pay $2 whether you use any electricity or not.

The power company may allow a discount for prompt payment. In a year's time the discount may come to a considerable amount. If your service is discontinued, it is customary for the company to charge a re-connection fee. If you are beginning a new electric service you are likely to be charged a deposit on your meter.

Special Rates and Demand Charges. The rural service rate used in the preceding example may not apply for irrigation equipment or other heavy installations. When power companies have to install extra-heavy service equipment, they may require a *demand charge*, regardless of the amount of electricity used. This charge is similar to a rental charge to take care of the extra expense of improvement on property. You should find out about demand charges before planning electric irrigation or other heavy service.

Special rates, sometimes referred to as *off-peak* rates, may be available in your area for use in heating water. Check with your power supplier about this also. If such a rate is available, you can save a considerable amount on your electric bill in a year's time.

Fig. 37. A demand charge may be required by the power supplier to serve a large irrigation pump motor like the one in this installation.

TABLE 8

Amount and Cost of Electricity for Various Uses During One Year
at the Ray Lott Farm*

Farm or Farm Home Use	Kwh Used During 1 Year	Annual Cost @ 2 Cents	Work Done
Barn & Milkhouse Lights, Radio, Clippers	1,341	$26.82	Radio & lights for barn, silo, & milkhouse
Gutter Cleaner	120	2.40	Manure removed for 38 head of livestock
Milking Machine	401	8.02	Used twice a day—average 20 cows
Ventilators in Barn	741	14.82	Improves condition of stable
Milk Cooler	2,727	54.54	Cooled approximately 24,-000 lb of milk
Milk Cooler, Pump	184	3.68	Circulates spray in milk cooler
Uskon Heating Panels	771	15.42	Maintains milkhouse temperature above 38°
Implement Shed and Bull Barn Stock Tank De-icer	572	11.44	Lights
Farm Shop	94	1.88	Lights, welder, power tools
Chicken House	2,357	47.14	5 hr of light each day—poultry water warmers
Ultraviolet Lighting in Chicken House	261	5.22	Improves condition of air; dimmer for night lighting
Range	1,179	23.58	Meals and baking—4 people
Refrigerator	429	8.58	10 cubic foot size
Deep Freezer	812	16.24	18 cubic foot size
Oil Burner & Circulating Water Pump	388	7.76	Heating system in house
Water System Pump, House & Yard Lights, Radio, Washer, Iron & Small Appliances, Water Heater (off peak)	1,296	25.92	Flat rate $4.69 for 90-gallon tank
Total Amount and Cost of Electricity for One Year	13,673	$273.46	

* Cooperative demonstration project conducted by Ingham County Agricultural Agent, Agricultural Engineering Department, Cooperative Extension Service, Michigan State University; and the Detroit Edison Company, 1952. (The Lott Farm is located at Mason, Mich.)

Summary

There are a few everyday principles of electricity which you must understand if you are to enjoy its full benefits. For example, you should know about wire size and its effect on voltage drop; grounding and its effect on safety; two-wire versus three-wire service and its effect on economy and quality of electrical service. As you electrify your farm and your farm home in the years ahead, an understanding and use of the common principles of electricity will reward you with a safer farmstead, with many financial gains, and with greater comfort for you and your family.

An electric current is the movement of "free" electrons within the atomic structure of metals and other conductors. These free electrons are loosely held and can therefore be set in motion by chemical action. Another way to set electrons in motion is to move a loop of copper wire through or across a magnetic field. A generator operates on this principle.

In both chemical and magnetic generation, electrical pressure is built up when free electrons are displaced (drawn off) at one point in a circuit of wire. This is similar to creating a vacuum at one point in a pipe line, causing air or water to rush in to fill it.

Electrical pressure is called *voltage* and may be compared to pressure in a water system. The rate at which a current flows is referred to as *amperage* and is often compared to gallons-per-minute.

The measure of electric power is the *watt* and is found by multiplying volts by amperes; for example, a 1-ampere light bulb operating on 115 volts would use electricity at the rate of 115 watt-hours (1 ampere × 115 volts = 115 watts). It would be entirely correct to say that this light bulb is developing *115 watts of electric power*. To convert watts to horsepower, figure 746 watts = 1 hp. Of course, a 1-hp motor actually uses more than 746 watts, because of power losses caused by friction, vibration, and wind resistance. Normally about 1,200 to 1,400 watts are drawn from the line by a 1-hp motor, yet it delivers only 746 watts of power.

Electricity is paid for by the *kilowatt hour*. One kilowatt hour is 1,000 watts times one hour; ten 100w light bulbs burning for one hour is 1,000 watthours or 1 kwh. Divide watthours by 1,000 to obtain kilowatthours. A watthour meter automatically makes these calculations as electricity is used.

While the average price of electricity for the country is about 3 cents per kwh, rates vary from one part of the country to another. Moreover, power suppliers usually have a "sliding scale" on electric rates; that is, the first 1 to 50 kwh cost more than the next 50, and so on. Because of this, large consumers pay less per kwh than do those who use small amounts. Some power suppliers allow off-peak use of electricity at reduced rates, usually for heating water. Another rate is called a demand charge. This applies where the power supplier is required to install extra-heavy transformers and wiring.

Questions

1. What is meant by a "loosely" held electron? In what way does it relate to the flowing of an electric current? Can a current flow through your body?
2. How can you show that voltage corresponds to pressure in a water system?
3. In what way does the size of wire affect voltage? Amperage? Wattage?
4. How can it be shown that amperage corresponds to gallons-per-minute in a water system?
5. What is meant by a demand charge? An off-peak rate? A sliding scale?

Additional Readings

Henderson, G. E., *Computing the Cost of Electrical Service.* Southern Association of Agricultural Engineering and Vocational Agriculture. Athens, Georgia, University of Georgia, 1950.

———, *Electrical Terms: Their Meaning and Use.* Southern Association of Agricultural Engineering and Vocational Agriculture. Athens, Georgia, University of Georgia, 1958.

Richter, H. P., *Practical Electrical Wiring, 3d ed.* New York, McGraw-Hill, 1947.

Texas Education Agency, *Farm Electrification.* Austin, Texas, 1954.

CHAPTER 3

*H*ow Electricity Is Produced and Transmitted to the Farm

Even though electrification is recognized as a real milestone of progress in the United States, it has created some serious farm problems throughout the nation. Electrification of farms and farm homes has developed so rapidly that many farmers, although living in all-electric homes and doing most of their farm chores electrically, do not yet understand the principles of transmission. This has resulted in much dangerous wiring on the nation's farms, and has caused loss of life and property in every section of the country each year since rural electrification began on a large scale.

In addition, dangerous wiring is causing damage to electric equipment throughout the country. This is holding back farm progress. The many opportunities in farm and farm home electrification depend upon your understanding of the principles of transmission of electrical energy. In order to understand these principles, you must have a reasonable knowledge of how electricity is produced.

How Can Static Electricity Cause Lightning?

Although static electricity is similar in many ways to ordinary electricity, it does not flow in the manner of alternating or direct current. The static charge is considered an elementary form of electricity, however. While static electricity has little or no practical value, its presence in all substances has provided the scientist with a ready means of studying the nature of electricity.

Fig. 38. A flash of lightning is a giant spark jumping across an air gap between a cloud and some object on the earth.

One of the first things the scientist noticed about electricity was that there are two kinds—positive and negative. By rubbing a glass rod with a piece of silk cloth, you can cause the glass to pick up one kind of charge while the silk will take on the opposite charge. If you continue to stroke the rod with the piece of cloth for a few minutes, the two will cling together. This demonstrates a common law of electricity: *Unlike charges attract each other; like charges repel each other.* This principle is at work when your hair sticks to the comb on a cool, dry morning, or when you get a "shock" in your auto after sliding across a plastic seat cover while wearing woolen clothes. Aside from its value as a scientific area of study, static electricity will concern you most in the form of lightning.

Benjamin Franklin proved that lightning is the result of static charges. A flash of lightning is a giant electric spark that results

Fig. 39. Lightning set this house afire. Proper lightning rods could have prevented the fire.

from an extreme static buildup. In some way, a cloud gains or loses electrons, thus building up an excessive charge of positive or negative electricity. At the same time, another cloud (or some other object) becomes charged with the opposite kind of electricity. As the charging process continues, a point is reached at which the difference in electrical balance between the two clouds causes a giant electric spark to jump across the gap separating them. Sometimes opposite charges occur between a cloud and some object on the earth—a building, perhaps. When this happens, the spark may actually strike the building and set it afire. The proper grounding of a building with lightning rods gathers the electrical charge and conducts it into the earth, where it becomes harmless. The lightning neutralizes the difference in electrical pressure for the time being, but the same forces may begin to build up electrical charges again so that the process will be repeated.

How Can a Storage Battery Produce Electricity?

Less than one hundred years ago the main supply of the world's electricity came from storage batteries. This was before the discovery of the induced current. Electricity produced by a

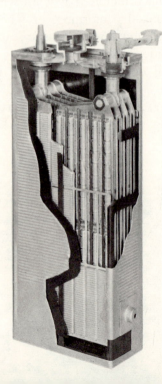

Fig. 40. In 1916, this type of battery was widely used as a source of electricity. Power plants and community high lines have largely replaced it.

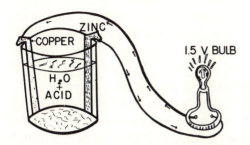

Fig. 41. The principle involved in this simple electric cell is the same principle that makes a modern storage battery operate.

battery is called *direct current*, because it flows in one direction—in a straight line.

An electric current can be started by the displacement of electrons in the inner structure of copper or other conductor metals if there is a complete circuit of wire. Fig. 41 shows an electric cell that can do this. This simple cell consists of a glass beaker containing a solution of water and sulfuric acid, a copper plate, a zinc plate, a piece of insulated wire, and a small lamp. The acid solution attacks the metals and displaces electrons in the atomic structure. One of the metals, however, is broken down more rapidly than the other. This process produces an unbalanced condition of electrons and therefore causes them to move through the wire circuit. Electrons move from the negative (zinc) plate, through the wire and lamp, back to the positive (copper) plate, and then through the acid solution back to the zinc plate. This movement is an electric current.

Fig. 42. Cutaway of a storage battery for a modern auto or tractor.

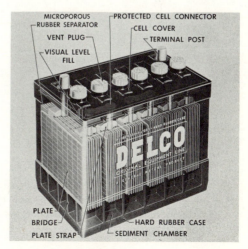

Electricity continues to flow until the acid has broken down the metal plates. In a tractor or automobile battery, a generator takes over and recharges the plates as the acid breaks them down. The electric current from the generator has the power to stimulate chemical action in the battery and thus rebuild these plates. This is why a battery may last for several months or even years.

Although batteries have many uses on the farm, they are not satisfactory for operating a modern electrical system. The limited voltage and direct current from a storage battery can be transmitted only two or three miles. The alternating current (a-c) which serves your farm comes from a generating plant which may be located five hundred or more miles away. Fig. 42 shows a cutaway section of a storage battery that is suitable for use with a tractor.

How Can a Generator Produce Electricity?

About two thousand years ago a Greek tribe, the Magnesites, found some pieces of ore which had the power to attract other particles of metal. This power of attraction was later named "magnetism" in honor of the Greeks who discovered the original ore.

Little value was placed on magnetism for centuries after its discovery, although early scientists believed there was a relationship

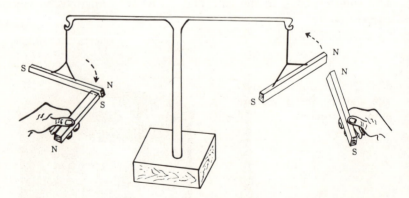

Fig. 43. If a bar magnet is suspended freely in the air, the N-pole of another bar magnet will repel (push) the N-pole of the suspended magnet and will attract the S-pole of the suspended bar. Electric motors and generators make use of this principle in their operation.

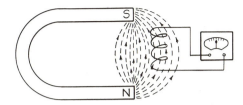

Fig. 44. An electric current is induced (generated) when a coil of wire is thrust through magnetic lines of force between the N- and S-poles of a magnet.

between electricity and magnetism. This was due to the similarity between the two; *both* electricity and magnetism have north and south poles. These poles, or centers, are referred to as *positive* and *negative.*

In 1819, Hans Christian Oersted, a Danish scientist, proved that there is a basic relation between magnetism and electricity. His discovery paved the way for Michael Faraday to produce an electric current from magnetism. This happened in 1831. Faraday's experiment consisted of a magnet with north and south poles opposite each other, and a means by which he could thrust a coil of wire back and forth between the two poles. In the experiment, each time the coil passed between the two magnetic poles a small charge of electricity was generated. This process is referred to as *inducing a current*, and the electrical flow so produced is called *induced current*. Fig. 44 shows how this may be done. It is possible to reverse this process and produce magnetism from an electric current. This latter principle is employed in electric motors, transformers, and electric arc welders.

How a Generator Produces A-C Electricity. Commercial generators, usually called *alternators*, produce most of the world's supply of electricity. A modern power plant gives the appearance of being extremely complicated; however, it produces electricity by the simple principle of induction, first demonstrated by Faraday.

By studying the series of diagrams in Fig. 45, you will see how electrical pressure (voltage) is induced in a loop of wire. This loop represents the coils of wire in the rotating part of an alternator or generator.

The magnet, with its north and south poles, represents the stator, or stationary part of the alternator. Notice the magnetic field of force (flux) which is shown by the dotted lines. This field is produced by the attraction between the north and south poles of the magnet.

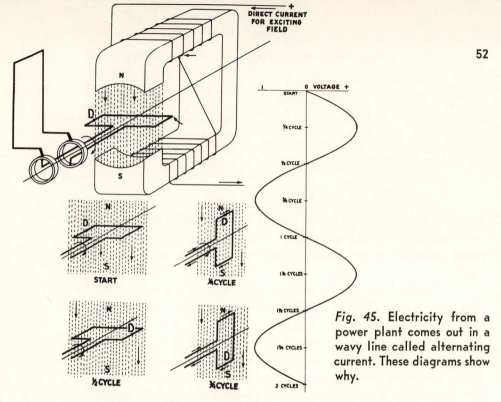

Fig. 45. Electricity from a power plant comes out in a wavy line called alternating current. These diagrams show why.

Remember that Faraday's experiment showed that a loop of wire will have an electrical charge induced in it when it cuts through the lines of force in a magnetic field, such as you see represented by the dotted lines in Fig. 45.

After locating point "D" on the wire loop in Fig. 45, observe what happens while the loop is making one complete revolution through the magnetic field. At the starting position the voltage is zero, but as the loop begins to turn, it cuts through some of the magnetic lines of force. This induces a voltage in the wire (*positive*), and it builds up to a peak, which is reached at the ¼-cycle position. When the loop has reached the ½-cycle position, the voltage has come back to zero. Why is this so? At this point the loop is not cutting across any magnetic lines. Study the position of point "D" again and you will see that the movement at the ½-cycle position is not *across* the magnetic lines but is *with* the direction of these lines.

As the loop starts into the third ¼-cycle a rather strange thing happens. Notice that point "D" is again cutting through some of the magnetic lines but in the opposite direction from that in the first ¼-cycle. The voltage rises again, similar to its action in the first part of the cycle, but this time it is *negative*. This is shown by the up-and-down voltage line crossing first to the positive, then to the negative side of the zero line. Study the voltage line at the right in Fig. 45 to see how this works. The peak of the negative charge is reached at the ¾-cycle position; that is, when the wire is cutting directly across the magnetic lines again. This is exactly like the positive charge as it occurred at the ¼-cycle position except that at this point the voltage is negative.

Finally, the voltage begins to fall as point "D" enters the last ¼-cycle; by the time the loop reaches the starting position again, the voltage has dropped to zero.

Thus one complete revolution of the loop (point "D") constitutes one cycle. By studying the wavy current line in Fig. 45, you will see that each cycle contains one positive peak and one negative peak, starting at zero voltage and finally coming back to zero.

A modern alternator has many more loops (coils) and more magnetic fields than are shown in the diagram in Fig. 45. As a matter of fact, most commercial alternators are constructed so as to produce 60-cycle current. This means that the current reaches 60 positive peaks and 60 negative peaks per second. Also, the voltage in 60-cycle current is zero 120 times per second, but the change is so rapid that you cannot detect the zero voltage in a light bulb.

Electricity produced by a generator (alternator) is referred to as *alternating current* because it is negative half the time and positive the other half. Fig. 46 shows a modern electric power plant

Fig. 46. The a-c electricity which operates the portable grinder at right is coming from the generating station at left which is almost 500 miles away. To cause current to flow across this great distance, the voltage must be several thousand volts when leaving the station.

where a-c electricity is produced and sent out under several thousand volts pressure. The rotor in one of these huge alternators is over 25 feet in diameter. It contains heavy masses of inductance coils, which require great power to rotate. Steam or water power is used to turn most of the alternators that make commercial electricity in the United States.

How Alternating Current Differs from Direct Current. In the preceding explanation, you observed that alternating current flows in a wavy line; that is, first to a positive peak in voltage, then to a negative peak. Direct current does not act this way at all. It flows in a straight line. At a voltage equal to a given a-c voltage, direct current flows in a straight line at the peak of the a-c line, either positive or negative. That is, the voltage in d-c current does not rise and fall as it does in a-c current.

How Can Electric Energy Be Converted into Heat, Light, and Motive Power?

Practically all of the electricity used on the farm and in the farm home is first converted into heat, light, or motive power.

How Electricity May Be Converted Into Heat Energy. When an electric current flows through a conductor it meets with some resistance in that conductor. This resistance, in a-c, a principle called impedance, produces heat in the conductor. For a given size of conductor, a greater flow of current produces more heat; for a given flow of current, a smaller conductor produces more heat.

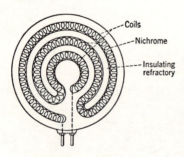

Coils

Nichrome

Insulating
refractory

Fig. 47. The heater at right contains coils similar to the one at left. Current causes the coils to become red hot.

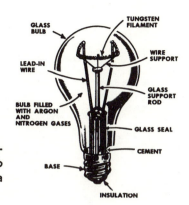

Fig. 48. The tungsten filament inside this light bulb becomes white hot when a current is flowing.

In getting heat from electricity, these principles are applied by using a coil of small wire through which a current is made to flow. The use of a coil of wire provides more surface for heating. The wattage rating of a heating element is determined by the size and length of the wire that forms the coil and by the voltage-amperage rating of its current. The size and kind of wire in the element must be such that it will have a reasonable life span.

How Electricity May Be Converted Into Light. Observe the diagram of the incandescent light bulb in Fig. 48. Incandescent light is produced in much the same manner as is heat, with one exception. A filament in the bulb, corresponding to a heater coil, carries an electric current in a space devoid of air. The space inside the bulb contains other gases, however, and in the presence of these gases the filament, which is made of a special metal, glows with a white heat and gives off light.

How Electricity May Be Converted Into Motive Power. By examining the cutaway section of a farm motor in Fig. 49, you will notice that it is similar to a generator. In fact, the two are very nearly identical in construction and operation. Both have two basic parts: (1) a stationary winding called a stator; and (2) a rotating part called a rotor or armature.

Generators and motors both operate on the principle of magnetic induction. You have already seen how this principle works with a generator. You will now see how magnetic induction can be used to make an electric motor run.

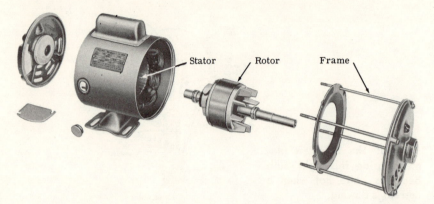

Fig. 49. The two basic parts of an electric motor are (1) the stator and (2) the rotor. Magnetic force operates in both parts, causing the rotor to turn.

The Rotor and Stator Constitute a Spinning Magnet. You are acquainted with the principle that an electric current flowing through a coil of wire creates a magnetic field about the coil. When a conductor (loop or coil of wire) cuts through a magnetic field, an electric current is induced in the conductor. This principle is involved in the turning of an electric motor. The stationary part of a motor (stator) contains several coils of insulated wire, and, when an electric current flows through them, a magnetic field is created about the coils. The rotor, which also contains metal conductors, turns inside this magnetic field. What makes it turn? The rotor is actually an electromagnet, getting its magnetism from the electric current that flows through it. Since the rotor has magnetism, it has *north* and *south* poles. The stator, too, has *north* and *south* poles.

You have previously studied the principle of like poles repelling each other and unlike poles attracting each other. Here is what happens when the current starts to flow through a motor.

Assume that a particular point on the rotor, marked "D," is a north pole. This pole will be "pushed" by another north pole in the stator if the relative position of the two is just right. This pushing force causes the rotor to turn, but, except for a special arrangement, it would go no farther than the next south pole in the stator. Just at the right instant, the north pole "D" is reversed, by a special mechanism in the motor, and becomes a south pole. The result is that the south pole in the stator gives the newly created south pole "D" another "push" and the rotor goes on its way.

The rotor in a farm motor spins around inside its case at approximately 1,725 or 3,450 rpm, the speed being determined by the construction of the motor. Its poles are constantly changing at just the right instant to receive the maximum "push and pull" forces. Thus, a motor can be constructed to run at a given speed and to develop a given horsepower. The number and size of the windings determine speed and power.

How Can Electricity Be Transmitted from the Power Plant to Your Farm?

You are already familiar with a simple two-wire electric circuit. As illustrated in Fig. 30, the two-wire "high" line, which may carry 6,900 volts, is similar to a simple two-wire circuit. That is, it has one "hot" and one neutral wire. The high voltage is on the hot line, and the current flows through this line to an appliance and then back through the neutral wire to the generating plant. The neutral is sometimes called the "ground" because it is connected to a ground rod at the meter pole or at the point of entry of each building.

The two-wire "high" line in Fig. 30 will supply single-phase current (usually 60 cycles) at 115 *or* 230 volts. If you need 230

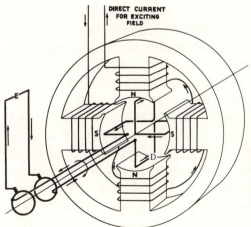

Fig. 50. When a current is flowing through the windings, push-pull forces between the stator and rotor poles go to work, and the rotor becomes a spinning magnet.

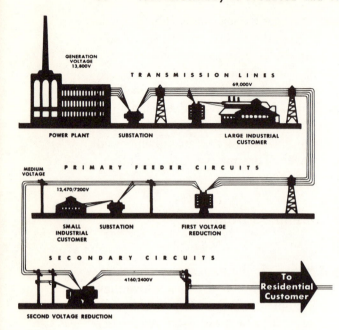

Fig. 51. The high-voltage electricity produced in the power plant at upper left passes through several reduction stations before reaching the farm.

volts, you must have two hot wires and one neutral wire leading in from the transformer. One hot wire and one neutral wire from the transformer will furnish only 115 volts.

In some sections of the country, three-phase current is supplied by high lines having three hot wires and one neutral wire. Increasing single-phase to three-phase current is similar to increasing the number of cylinders of an automobile from four to twelve. In single-phase, 60-cycle current, you get 120 "pushes" per second, but three-phase current produces 360 "pushes" per second. This provides smoother running and quicker starting of electric motors. Moreover the first cost of a three-phase motor is less than the same size in a single-phase type. Unfortunately, three-phase current is not available at the present time in most rural areas because of the expense involved in line construction.

Since rural high lines usually carry 6,900 volts or more and are therefore extremely dangerous, it is necessary for the wires to be of sufficient strength and quality to make them safe in every respect. In addition, the high lines must be large enough to allow an adequate amount of electricity to flow through them. High-grade insulators are required on the power poles to provide further safety.

How Can You Ground and Polarize
Your Electrical System?

Although the voltage at your meter will usually test 115 volts for a two-wire service or 230 volts for a three-wire service, this may build up to several thousand volts for a few seconds, because of lightning or other unusual conditions. *Grounding*, the method used to protect life and property against this hazard, refers to the neutral wire being permanently connected to the earth. When excess electrical pressure is present in the wiring, it may then pass into the earth through the ground wire.

Two methods of grounding are practiced: (1) in the city, the neutral wire is connected to the city water pipes by means of a copper ground wire and special clamps made for this purpose; (2) on the farm, it is customary to establish a permanent ground by driving a ½-inch or larger rod (non-rusting type) into the earth to

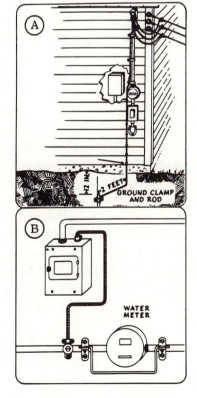

Fig. 52. In *A*, the electrical system is grounded by means of a ground wire connecting a neutral wire to a ground rod; the wire is fastened to the rod by means of a special ground clamp. In *B*, the system is grounded to the city water pipes. Note the special clamp for fastening the ground wire to the water pipe and also the jumper wire around the water meter.

a sufficient depth to assure a moist connection. (See Fig. 52.) (For detailed instructions on installing a ground wire, see page 185.)

In addition to grounding the service entrance at each building, all electric motors larger than ½-hp should have an individual and separate ground. This can be done by attaching a ground wire from the frame of the motor to the exterior ground rod or to city water pipes. Additional grounding assures protection against "shorted" motors. Make certain that the connections are made properly. An exterior attachment should be made with a standard ground clamp.

How to Polarize Your Wiring. Since one wire in each two-wire circuit in your buildings will be hot, it is important that you be able to tell which is hot and which is neutral. This is done by using black insulation for the hot wire and white for the neutral. When a circuit is wired into the main switch, the white wire should always be connected to a silver-colored terminal, which is usually located in the center section of the switch. This word of caution is in order: in actual practice, colors sometimes get crossed. Therefore, the only *safe policy* is to *disconnect the main switch* and not depend on code colors when working on electrical wires.

If two hot wires are required for a circuit, one is generally black and the other red. Green is used mostly for a second neutral wire for portable machines.

It is dangerous to get these colors mixed, as this could result in installing a switch or fuse in the neutral wire. If this happens, an open switch or blown fuse in the neutral wire would have the effect of destroying the ground. The white (or gray) wire must run an uninterrupted course from the main switch to every outlet in the circuit. If a white wire must be cut, as is required at a junction box, it must be spliced together again inside the box in accordance with the National Electrical Code.

Switches must always be installed in the hot line. (NOTE: In a few types of connections to three- and four-way switches, the white wire is allowed to function as a hot line. When this is done, the *white wire* must be painted *black* at the switch box to show that it is hot. Use rubber paint for this, not oil paint.)

In damp locations, the operation of portable electric tools can be a dangerous practice. This will be true if the ground wire inside the motor becomes shorted. Electrocution can result if the current runs through your body and into the damp floor. A special adapter

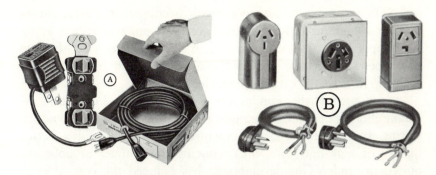

Fig. 53. The equipment in *A* provides three-wire service for 115-volt portable machines. The adapter at left plugs into the receptacle at center and the clip connects to the cover-plate screw. The three-prong plug on the cord (right) then plugs into the adapter, while the other end receives the three-prong plug-in of the machine. The plug-ins and receptacles in *B* are for 230-volt appliances. The plug-in automatically polarizes the circuit since it will fit in only one position.

plug-in can be used as a means of providing a third wire in the normal two-wire circuit. (See Fig. 53.) This extra wire is a safety measure to protect you if one of the wires in the motor becomes shorted while you are using the machine. The use of a three-prong plug-in is called *polarizing* the motor. Plug-ins for 230-volt appliances are equipped with blades which permit them to be inserted in only one position; that is, the two hot leads from the line are connected to the two hot leads in the appliance. (See Fig. 53-B.)

What Should You Know About Transmission Materials and Equipment?

A conductor wire must have proper conducting quality and must be properly insulated. For certain uses, wiring must have special protection in the form of a metal casement or a waterproof covering. Fig. 54 shows details of construction in a good grade of electric wire.

Fig. 54. Service entrance cable (SE) is constructed so as to provide for the safety and long life of the wire.

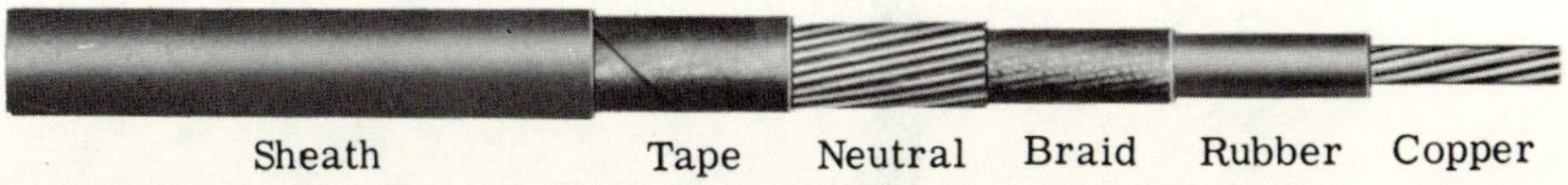

Sheath   Tape   Neutral   Braid   Rubber   Copper

The most widely used conductor is copper; however, aluminum or aluminum-alloy wire has become popular in recent years. Aluminum will conduct electricity at about 85 per cent the rate of copper for the same size wire, so aluminum wire must be larger than copper wire for carrying equal loads.

It is essential that conductors be rust-proof and corrosion resistant and have sufficient strength to withstand both wind and ice storms. In recent years, manufacturers have produced a better quality of high-line wire, thus reducing the number of poles required per mile. This development has reduced the cost of construction of rural high lines.

Insulation Materials. Electricity will not pass through rubber, plastic, and similar material. Therefore, such covering is used on electric wires to insulate them and make them safe, to prevent fires, and to reduce voltage loss.

Some plastic-coated wire is weatherproof and rot resistant and therefore may be buried directly in the ground. Although this type of wire is more expensive than other types, it is widely used for certain purposes. Rubber is commonly used on wiring inside a building where people are likely to come in close contact with it. If the wire is to be handled frequently, as is necessary with exten-

Fig. 55. The plastic-covered wire at right (Type UF) is ideal for underground wiring. It can be buried directly in the ground for wiring a post lantern.

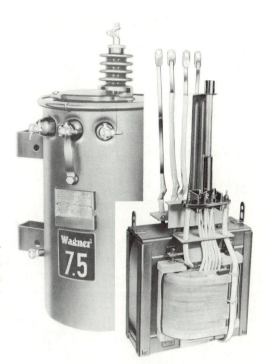

Fig. 56. The iron pot at left steps voltage down for safe use at the farm. At right is an inside view of the pot at left.

sion cords, rubber covering is recommended because of its durability.

Non-metallic sheathed cable for dry locations inside buildings has a weather-resistant covering used as insulation. This type of wiring has a coal-tar-coated, fibrous covering that is tough and will last many years if not otherwise damaged. The insulation may rot, however, in extremely wet and corrosive conditions. (For further discussion on wiring materials, see Chapter 7.)

How Does a Transformer Work?

The purpose of the high-line transformer was mentioned in Chapter 2, although its operation was not discussed. It is important to know a few basic things about this part of your electrical system since it controls the entire service.

The "iron pot" located on the power pole near your farm is rather simple in construction. Actually, it consists of two windings called (1) a primary and (2) a secondary. The *primary* receives the current from the line and passes it on to the *secondary* through the mysterious process referred to as magnetic induction. That is,

the current passes from the primary to the secondary without bene-
fit of a metal connection of any kind. Here is how the transformer
works:

Earlier in the book, the relationship between magnetism and
electricity was discussed. One thing mentioned was that a magnetic
field is formed around a wire carrying an electric current. Therefore a much greater magnetic field is formed about a *coil* of wire
carrying a current, since each wire adds its magnetic force to the
total field.

Now if the primary winding (coil) is energized and a secondary coil is placed within the magnetic field around the primary,
a current will flow in the secondary, even though there is no metal
connection between the two windings. Therefore, the current flowing from the transformer to your meter is an "induced" current;

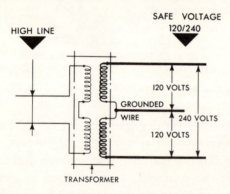

Fig. 57. The ratio and wire
size of the coil at left, in
comparison with the coil at
right, determines the voltage
and amperage of the current
in the wires leading to the
meter (three heavy lines at
right).

that is, it jumps across the space between the primary and the
secondary through the medium of magnetic force. The iron core in
the transformer is used to increase the magnetic force, not to conduct a current from one coil to the other.

If the size of wire and number of turns in both windings are
equal, the induced current will be approximately the same. If, however, the ratio is varied, the induced current will vary accordingly.
For example, if the number of turns in the secondary is one-tenth
the number in the primary, the voltage induced in the secondary
will be one-tenth that coming into the primary. The size of the wire
in the secondary in comparison to that in the primary determines
the amperage of the induced current.

Assuming that the voltage on the high line at your farm is 6,900, the ratio of the windings in your transformer is probably 30 to 1, reducing the voltage to 230. This is a matter of simple arithmetic; that is, 6,900 ÷ 30 = 230. The 6,900 volts pressure going into the transformer is stepped down to 230. Ordinarily a three-wire power drop—the wires from the power pole into the farm—splits the 230 volts into two 115-volt circuits. One hot and one neutral wire make a 115-volt circuit. Only one neutral is needed for the two hot wires, and this hookup is usually referred to as 230-volt service.

Three-phase service is different. Generally, three hot wires and one neutral are provided in a three-phase service and either two or three transformers are used. The advantage of three-phase service is that you can use larger motors that cost less to purchase than equal-sized single-phase motors.

The amount of electricity required at your farm determines the size of the transformer. The five-kilovolt size is most often used for a farm. A modern electrified farm may require a seven-and-one-half- or ten-kilovolt size.

Another farm use of a transformer is the farm arc welder. This machine takes 37.5 amperes at 230 volts from the high line and converts this to 180 amperes at 25 to 40 volts. This transformer produces an arc that is hot enough to weld steel.

In the Problem-Unit on farmstead wiring, you can find additional information on other transmission equipment needed in the distribution system of the farmstead.

Fig. 58. A farm arc welder uses a step-down transformer to convert 230-volt current to low voltage-high amperage.

Summary

Static electricity exists in all substances but is especially noticeable when unlike substances are rubbed together. The unlike charges generated cause the two to cling together, whereas like charges repel each other. Lightning is the result of a static charge jumping across an air gap between a cloud and a building or other object.

A storage battery generates direct-current electricity; that is, a current that flows in a straight line. The current from a battery is the result of chemical (acid) action on unlike electrodes. The acid action creates an imbalance between the electrodes, thus causing electrons to flow from one electrode to the other.

It is necessary for the electrodes to be restored while in use; otherwise they soon disintegrate altogether and the battery is then of no further use. A generator is used for the restoring process.

A generator is rather simple in construction and operation. It has a rotor (armature) that turns inside a magnetic field created by stator coils. As the rotor turns, an electric current is induced in its coils. This current is then sent out to the battery, where it causes a reverse chemical action that restores the electrodes.

Commercial electricity is produced by giant generators called alternators. These alternators produce a current at several thousand volts pressure. The current, however, is not direct but flows, rather, in a wavy line, first positive, then negative. This type of electric service is called alternating current.

The high voltage on a rural electric high line must be reduced to a safe level for farm use. Transformers are used for reducing the current, usually to 115 to 230 volts. This reduction is accomplished by the use of two windings called the primary and secondary. A high-voltage current flowing through the primary induces a lower voltage in the secondary winding. The farm arc welder operates on a similar principle.

Inside the farm home or other farm building, it is necessary to have a system whereby a hot wire can be distinguished from a neutral or ground wire. This is done by using black and red for the hot side of a circuit and white for the neutral.

For heavy electrical loads, three wires carrying 230 volts are sometimes used. Good insulation and good quality wire are necessary in making the electrical service safe and economical.

Questions

1. Why is a generator necessary in maintaining a storage battery?
2. How could you show by simple demonstration that a magnetic field can produce electricity?
3. What principle is involved in causing the rotor in an electric motor to turn? What determines its top speed?
4. Why must a neutral wire never be fused? Never interrupted by a switch?
5. Why is a transformer sometimes called a "step down" or "step up" transformer?

Additional Readings

Henderson, G. E., *Electrical Terms: Their Meaning and Use.* Southern Association of Agricultural Engineering and Vocational Agriculture. Athens, Georgia, University of Georgia, 1958.

Richter, Herbert P., *Practical Electricity and House Wiring.* Wilmette, Illinois, Fredrick J. Drake & Co., 1952.

Wright, Forrest B., *Electricity in the Home and on the Farm,* 3rd ed. New York, John Wiley & Sons, 1950.

CHAPTER 4

How to Comply with Safety Rules

Reports given out by the National Safety Council indicate that electricity has a killing power about forty times greater than other farm hazards. Whereas only one in two hundred ordinary farm accidents is fatal, one in each five injuries from electric shock ends in death. The total number killed by electricity each year shows that people apparently do not realize how dangerous it is. In one recent year 1,056 persons in the United States lost their lives in electrical accidents, and this rate is approximately the average for any given year. From 3 to 4 per cent of all accidental deaths in the United States can be traced to electricity.

In addition to personal injuries and deaths, electricity starts fires that destroy over $80 million worth of property in this country each year. An additional $17 million worth of appliances are destroyed or damaged beyond use every year by faulty wiring and other electrical hazards. Electric machinery also causes thousands

Fig. 59. An engineer checks current on an electric fence. Too much voltage in this wire could be fatal.

Fig. 60. Portable electric tools may be fatal, especially when the operator is standing on damp concrete or on the ground. Use a three-wire cord and adapter to reduce the chance of shock from a shorted circuit inside the machine.

of non-fatal accidents such as loss of eyesight, permanent crippling, loss of hands or fingers, and many others.

What Are the Common Causes of Electrical Accidents?

It is possible to avoid most of the accidents, both to persons and to property, resulting from electricity. In fact, studies show that the two most common causes are inexcusable. These are (1) *carelessness* and (2) *misuse*. The proof of this can be found in hazardous wiring, overloaded circuits, improper fuses, abuse of appliances, and many other unsafe practices in the handling of electricity on farms and in farm homes. These abuses can and do result in deaths, fires, and unsatisfactory electrical service.

As farm electrification increases, it will be more important than ever to use safe practices. Even in doing simple wiring jobs, it is essential that you understand the common principles of electricity and use reasonable skill in doing the job. Remember that a faulty circuit can result in a death or a costly fire. Even the simple job of putting in a fuse can be dangerous unless it is done properly. When you operate a portable power tool, you may be taking a chance unless the tool is protected by the right kind of wiring and plug-in arrangement.

How Much Electricity Is Necessary to Kill a Person?

Only a very small amount of electricity is necessary to kill a person. The current or amount of electricity is the thing that kills, not the voltage, although voltage is involved. Less than ¼ ampere will stop the heart of the average man. This is the amount of current flowing in a 25w lamp at 115 volts.

Fig. 61. A boy holding a metal socket and a 25w bulb could be killed if the socket becomes shorted. The current flowing through a 25w bulb (115 volts) is sufficient to kill a grown man.

The amperage in a current flowing in a 100w lamp will be fatal if your body is in good contact with the ground or with any conductor that is in contact with the ground. Because of this hazard, it is extremely dangerous to stand on wet ground or pavement and touch an electric circuit.

It is the purpose of the safety suggestions in this chapter to help reduce the common hazards of electric energy and to develop skill and judgment in using electricity.

If some of the rules discussed here seem trivial, remember that violations of simple precautions have caused the greatest number of deaths and the most property damage. You are likely to be more alert to the obvious dangers than to the simpler ones. For example, you would be more apt to use a penny to replace a blown fuse than

Fig. 62. The ordinary 15-ampere plug fuse is intended to protect life and property. Do not destroy this protection by using a penny underneath.

to take hold of a broken power line. Yet the penny represents just as great a danger, since this might result in a fire that could take the lives of your entire family.

Your all-electric farm and farm home will make it necessary for you to handle electricity and electric equipment almost constantly. You should learn now to avoid the hazards that could result in tragedy for you and your family.

What Practices Should You Follow to Avoid Electrical Hazards?

To prevent injury caused by ignorant or careless use of electricity, keep the following safety hints in mind:

1. The first rule of safety with electricity is to become *safety conscious*. Only one hot wire is necessary for a current to flow through your body. Remember that electricity is present in certain hot wires of electric circuits all the time unless the main switch is off or the main fuses are out. Your body can complete a circuit between a hot wire and the earth.

2. Always respect the danger of electricity in any form and never take chances with it.

Fig. 63. The repairman working on the convenience outlet (*B*) would be inviting suicide without first cutting off the main service switch (*A*). The arrow indicates the proper direction for this.

Fig. 64. The large fan motor in this hay-drying installation has an individual ground in addition to a magnetic switch for overload protection.

3. Avoid working on hot wires or appliances that are connected to a source of electricity; disconnect the appliance; open the main switch; pull out main fuses; and take all other measures to make your work safe.

4. Give your heart a break! It has been found that some people cannot stand even slight electric shock; it stops their hearts.

5. Before operating a large permanently mounted electric motor, be certain that it has an individual ground.

6. Before operating a portable electric machine, such as a portable saw, be certain that the circuit is properly grounded to the frame of the machine. Polarized plug-ins are available to make it easy to connect an extra ground wire to portable electric machines. The cost is reasonable and could save your life.

7. Avoid probing into a convenience outlet with a screwdriver or similar object.

8. Avoid touching electric wires, switches, drop cords, or appliances while standing in water. Switches and other electrical devices should not be installed within reach of the bath tub or shower. Wet shoes or wet concrete floors may prove equally hazardous. If it is necessary to use a portable electric tool while standing on damp

concrete, first place a dry board on the floor. Good rubber gloves will make the use of portable electric machines safer where the working area is damp.

9. Before cutting an electric wire, make certain that it is disconnected from the power source.

10. Assume that all electric wires are hot until proven otherwise.

11. Avoid touching or holding an electric fence. People as well as farm animals have been killed in this way.

12. Demonstrate your good judgment by refusing to take part in any horseplay with electricity. Never cause another person to be shocked; practical jokes with electricity have ended in serious injury to others.

13. Although a farm arc welder operates on low voltage, faulty wiring in the machine could cause you to receive the full

Fig. 65. Although the maximum voltage of the farm welder in *B* is 65, it is possible for the machine to become short circuited and cause the death of the person in *A*.

Fig. 66. The dangling electric wires left from a fire (caused by lightning) are still hot. Keep away from wires that have come down in a storm or fire.

load from the line—230 volts at 37.5 amperes. This amount of electricity would almost certainly be fatal if you were standing on damp ground. Check your welder periodically to make certain that connections are tight and not corroded. Blow out dust with a low-pressure air hose. This will help to prevent short circuits in the welder.

14. Avoid touching broken wires that are dangling from a power line, since this would be virtual suicide.

Fig. 67. The child got out but the house burned. Faulty wiring was blamed.

What Measures Should You Take to Protect
Your Property from Electrical Hazards?

Except for losses of farm animals and farm buildings due to lightning, the bulk of property loss from electricity is caused by fires. Of the major causes of electrical fires, faulty wiring is the main culprit. This may be due to mechanical damage, overheating, or using wire that is too small for a given electrical load. Enclosed wires often become shorted by improper installation or by corrosion resulting from poor splicing. "Cheap," poor-grade wire in the original job nearly always causes trouble in the end.

In addition, faulty electric appliances take their toll in fire damage. The wiring in an electric appliance may simply wear out and the insulation becomes hard and cracked from age and use,

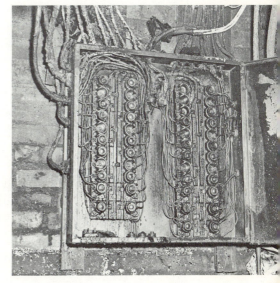

Fig. 68. Overloaded circuits, heavily fused, built up enough heat to start a fire.

especially if the wire is exposed to heat and moisture. Switches may be dangerous when used after they begin to show signs of failure.

Electric services on the farm have expanded so much in recent years that the wiring system is often overloaded. Fig. 68 shows an overloaded main switch box. This switch became so hot it started a fire. Check your wiring system to determine whether too many appliances are connected to a single circuit.

The only answer to overloaded electric wires is to add new circuits at the main switch, but this may require a new entrance switch. The old one may be too small with all circuit positions already taken. The lesson to be learned from an overloaded electrical system is that good planning should be done before it is installed. A well-planned system is less expensive and is less of a fire hazard in the long run.

Other property losses can be accounted for in the loss of efficiency, through low voltage and poor contacts, of the electric current to do farm work. Electric appliances wear out too soon when the voltage is below normal. In short, if your electrical system is not up to standard, you pay for electricity that does no work, and your electric appliances wear out before they should.

Fig. 69. A Texas farmer examines a 200-ampere main-switch. Adequate wiring is the first principle of safety.

Some of the common rules that can make farm property safer are:

1. In all phases of the farm and home wiring, follow the National Electrical Code.

2. Check the present electrical load on all circuits before adding other devices to it. Do not overload. For example, the

Fig. 70. Before resetting a breaker be sure to correct the cause of tripping.

load on No. 12 wire should not exceed 2,300 watts. If more than this amount is being used, the fuse should blow. (1) toaster, 700w + iron, 1,200w + lamp, 100w = 2,000 watts. This is a safe load. But, (2) toaster, 700w + iron, 1,200w + percolator, 600w = 2,500 watts. This circuit is over-loaded for No. 12 wire. The fuse should blow if it is of proper (20-ampere) size.

3. Keep the proper size fuses in your fuse panel. Never use a penny as a substitute. This practice causes fires.

4. Check the cause of a circuit breaker tripping or a fuse blowing. The purpose of a fuse is to provide protection from overloads. A penny or oversize fuse destroys the safety feature provided by the fuse system.

Fig. 71. (A) A Fustat is said to be tamper-proof because it cannot be exchanged for a larger size. (B) A magnetic switch protects large motors by tripping when overloads occur. This manual type switch requires re-setting by hand after tripping. (C) A Fusetron allows overload for starting electric motors yet protects the running load.

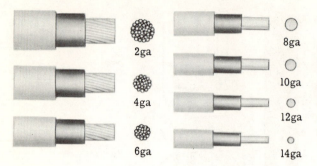

Fig. 72. Common sizes of wire used on the farm include No. 12 to No. 2 and larger. No. 14 is seldom used except for small motors and extension cords.

5. Use time-delay fuses or other appropriate devices to protect electric motors and their circuits. Regular household fuses are not satisfactory for electric motors.

6. Check the cause of blackened, overheated wires. A smoking wire or electric appliance is cause for alarm. Electric motors may become overheated for numerous reasons and may set buildings afire unless the circuit is properly protected. After continued operation, an electric motor should feel comfortable to the hand.

7. Study the electrical system at least once a year to find damaged wire, faulty switches, and other potential trouble spots. Repair worn or damaged cords as soon as they are discovered. (See Fig. 77 in project section.) In installing new electric circuits, be certain that the wire size is adequate for the load that it will carry. (See Chapter 5 for instructions on how to determine wire size.)

8. In purchasing electric appliances and materials, be certain the quality is up to standard. "Cheap" fixtures will be costly if they cause a fire. The Underwriters' Laboratories (UL) label on an appliance is good insurance even though it is no guarantee that you will not have a fire.

9. Farmers and farm boys should be capable of installing a new switch or adding new circuits to the present electrical system. For a major wiring job, however, it is wise to employ a certified electrician, unless you have had some wiring experience.

10. Install correct-size wire for all electric motors and other electric equipment.

11. Store gasoline, paint, and other inflammable materials away from the vicinity of a farm arc welder.

12. All entrance switches should be enclosed and may require locking.

What Should You Know About
National Protection Agencies?

Everybody suffers when accidents occur and when property is destroyed by fires. The national hazard from electricity is so great that the insurance companies and other professional groups have banded together to help make electric service safer for everybody. The quality of many electrical devices and materials on the market today is better because of the work of these organizations.

The Underwriters' Laboratories. If you have ever seen a label on an electrical device bearing the letters "UL," you may have wondered what this meant. These letters signify that the item has been tested by the Underwriters' Laboratories. The presence of the "UL" label means that the item measures up to safety standards for that item.

Fig. 73. The UL label on an appliance indicates that the item has been tested and approved by Underwriters' Laboratories.

The Underwriters' Laboratories organization was established by the National Board of Fire Underwriters as a national testing service. Their purpose is to eliminate or reduce fires that are started by faulty wiring and inferior electrical products. Manufacturers are not required to have their products tested by the Underwriters' Laboratories; however, increasing numbers of buyers are insisting on products that have been so tested. The result is that a majority of manufacturers are now using this service.

Products that are sent to these laboratories undergo tests of much greater severity than actual use. As an example of this, rubber-covered wire bearing the label "Approved by Underwrit-

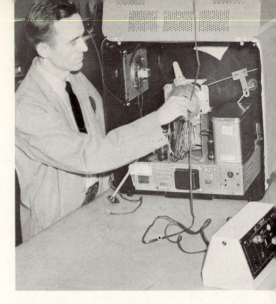

Fig. 74. An engineer tests a television set for safety. The high voltage required for the picture tube makes TV dangerous unless safety standards are met.

ers' Laboratories" has been tested by soaking in water for 12 hours, then subjected to 1,500 volts of electric pressure. Wire that stands up under such conditions would rarely break down in normal use.

In fairness to some reputable manufacturers, it should be stated that some of them do not have their products processed through UL, claiming that the expense is too great for value received. At the same time, it is only fair for the consumer to use this protection if he so desires.

To be approved by Underwriters' Laboratories means that a particular item meets the minimum standards for that type of article. The "UL" label does not claim that one article is better than another; for example, two electric motors having "UL" labels may be of different quality. The label simply signifies that safety standards have been met.

National Electrical Code. Tragic fires like the one shown in Fig. 67 may be prevented by adequate wiring. The National Electrical Code is designed to prevent or reduce such disasters. This code is a set of rules and regulations that have been drawn up by engineers, fire prevention specialists, insurance authorities, and others. The object of the code is to bring about safe and efficient electrical service. This code is revised every two years or so.

The Code sets forth minimum standards of safety for wiring and materials, but it does not guarantee adequate wiring plans.

Electricians are expected to be familiar with the rules and regulations of the National Electrical Code and should see that requirements are met with respect to materials and installation.

Many cities and other localities have their own electrical codes, which are often stricter than the National Code.

It is not practical to include in a book of this nature all regulations of the National Code. If you plan to do some electrical work around your farm, however, it would be wise to obtain a copy and study the regulations covering the type of jobs you plan to do. Some cities require that new electrical wiring be inspected for comformance with local and national codes before it can be used.

The safest policy in wiring is to follow the rules and regulations of the Code. In fact the violation of the Code is an invitation to start fires and perhaps leave yourself open to electrical injury. For example, it may seem safe to cut a wire, splice in another circuit, tape the completed joint, and leave it at that. The Code will not permit this practice unless the wire is properly spliced, soldered, taped, and enclosed in a junction box. Otherwise the splice may eventually work loose or corrode and cause a fire.

What Can You Do for a Person Who Has Received Electric Shock?

The impulse you may have to help someone who is receiving electric shock could cause you to be electrocuted. On the other hand, you may be able to save some person's life without undue hazard to yourself if you follow a few rules.

The muscles of a person receiving electric shock become paralyzed, causing him to "freeze" to the hot wire. Sometimes the victim is not able to free himself from the conductor. Getting him loose may not always be easy but may be accomplished in the following manner:

1. Look for the "live" wire or source of electric current which is causing the shock, but do not take hold of the person's body with your bare hands under any circumstances.

2. Decide immediately whether it would be easier to move the person or to move the conductor. If the conductor is to be moved, use a dry stick to push it loose; if the person's body is to be moved, use twelve to fifteen thicknesses of dry newspaper or cloth as an insulator.

3. With the cloth or paper in the hands, grasp the person's arm or leg and quickly pull him free of the conductor.

First Aid and Treatment. Have someone call a doctor or an ambulance or both. The effect of electric shock is to damage the heart and stop its action as well as to stop the breathing. Burns on various parts of the body often occur as side effects, and these may be serious in themselves. Severe burns may cause the skin to come off the entire surface of the feet, face, or both.

The only effective treatment for an electrocuted person is to use artificial respiration or a Pulmotor as a means of reviving the heart action. If it is to be effective, artificial respiration must begin almost immediately and continue for several hours or until the person is breathing normally. Refer to a first aid manual for further instructions on how to apply artificial respiration.

Summary

Each year over 1,000 persons in the United States are killed by electricity. Either carelessness or misuse is involved in most of these deaths.

The death rate of electrical accidents, in comparison with ordinary farm accidents, is about forty times greater. This is not strange when it is realized that the amount of electricity flowing through a 25w bulb is sufficient to kill a grown man.

Approximately $100 million worth of property is destroyed annually by electrically started fires and other electrical damage. Overloaded wiring often gets hot enough to start a fire. Again, carelessness and misuse are the main causes.

The best safety precaution is to be safety conscious and show a healthy respect for electricity at all times. Circuits should never be overloaded or overfused. Damaged lamp cords and other troubles should be taken care of as soon as they are found.

There are two national organizations in this country that promote safety in electrical wiring and electrical appliances. These are the Underwriters' Laboratories and a group of specialists who sponsor a National Electrical Code.

Items that have been tested by the Underwriters' Laboratories will be stamped with the letters "UL." This label indicates that the item has passed safety specifications as to materials and construction.

The National Electrical Code sets forth minimum standards for wiring materials and procedures. The object here is to reduce hazards to both life and property. This code should never be violated, since fire or death may result.

The best treatment for a person who has received electric shock is to give artificial respiration if the heart has stopped. Then the person should be covered with a blanket and kept as quiet as possible until a doctor arrives.

Questions

1. Why is electricity so much more likely to be fatal than other farm hazards?
2. Why is electricity more dangerous around water?
3. How is it sometimes possible for a wire to become hot enough to start a fire?
4. What happens in the process of reviving an electrocuted person by artificial respiration?

Additional Readings

Hamilton, C. L., *Current Follies*. Chicago, Illinois, National Safety Council, 1955.

National Safety Council, Farm Division, *Farm Safety Review*. Chicago, Illinois (All issues).

Suggested Projects for Problem-Unit Two

Electrical Demonstrations Suitable for Class Work and Programs. Your class or club can put on interesting demonstrations to illustrate electric circuits and electrical principles at very little expense by using the following ideas. The demonstrations can be used for club programs, contests, or for shop projects.

1. *Construct a Simple Circuit.* Materials needed for this project include a dry-cell battery, a laboratory-type lamp socket and a small bulb, 6 feet of No. 18 gauge single-conductor cord, and a simple knife switch. You might be able to borrow these materials from the physics laboratory at your school, or you can purchase them for about $2 at any good hardware store.

Cut the wire into three equal lengths and prepare the ends of each piece for connections, as directed on page 171. Refer to Fig. 75 and connect three lengths of wire as shown in the diagram; that is, the first length from battery to switch; the second length from switch to lamp socket; and the third length from lamp socket to battery.

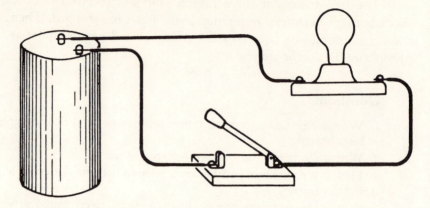

Fig. 75. A two-wire circuit operated by a dry cell battery. A knife switch opens the circuit as shown in the diagram. The bulb will light up when the switch is closed.

If the battery, bulb, switch, and wiring are in proper order, the lamp should light up when the switch is closed (in down position). Point out that the flow of current is from the battery to the switch to the bulb and back through the battery again.

Explain that a lighting circuit in the farm home is essentially the same as this simple hookup. The difference is in the higher voltage-amperage of the household current and in the larger wire required in the household circuit—preferably No. 12 gauge.

2. *Demonstrate Voltage Drop.* Voltage drop is a constant

Fig. 76. The voltage drop through 100 feet of No. 18 wire results in the slower speed of the fan.

problem on most farms; the following demonstration should be valuable as well as interesting.

Have on hand a household fan, five or six strips of 1-inch tissue paper about 12 inches in length, and a 100-foot extension cord of No. 18 gauge wire. Tie the strips of paper to the center of the fan guard and perform the test in two steps as follows:

Step 1. Plug the fan cord into a convenience outlet and turn on the fan. Observe that the strips of paper blow straight out. Remove the fan plug-in.

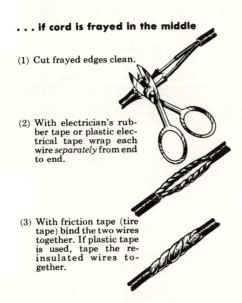

. . . if cord is frayed in the middle

(1) Cut frayed edges clean.

(2) With electrician's rubber tape or plastic electrical tape wrap each wire *separately* from end to end.

(3) With friction tape (tire tape) bind the two wires together. If plastic tape is used, tape the re-insulated wires together.

Fig. 77. Avoid fires by following the three easy steps shown here.

Step 2. In this test, first plug the 100-foot extension cord into a convenience outlet, then plug the fan cord into the extension receptacle. Now the current must flow through the extension cord before reaching the fan motor. Turn on the fan and observe the angle at which the strips are blowing outward. Notice that they do not blow straight out in this test because of voltage drop. Repeat Steps 1 and 2 to make certain that everyone in the audience sees the difference between the tests.

Explain that voltage lost in the 100-foot cord caused the fan motor to run slower in the second test, as indicated by less action of the paper strips. Explain further that the small wire and fan

. . . if cord is frayed at the plug or plug has to be replaced

(1) Release cord by loosening screw posts inside plug.

(2) Cut off frayed end of cord.

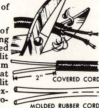

(3) Strip two inches of outer fabric covering from cord. Moulded rubber cord can be split back two inches from the end. Be sure that when the cords are split no copper wires are exposed through the protective insulation.

2"   COVERED CORD

MOLDED RUBBER CORD SPLIT APART

¾"

TWIST STRANDS OF WIRE

(4) Strip insulation from ends of cords to expose approximately three-fourths inch of bare wire. Twist strands together.

(5) Slip cord through plug and tie cord ends into an underwriter's knot. Then if cord is jerked (it shouldn't be!) there will be less chance of pulling the copper wires away from under the screw posts. Pull knot down inside plug.

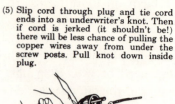

(6) Wrap wires clockwise around prongs to form an S. Loop bare copper ends clockwise around the screw posts. Hold in place and tighten screws firmly.

. . . if plug doesn't fit tightly

If the prongs of the plug slip out of the outlet or receptacle, just separate prongs a little with your fingers to get a tighter fit. Don't use too much pressure.

Fig. 78. Follow these instructions to do a good job of repairing the frayed ends of an extension cord or replacing a plug.

motor overheat and that both will be damaged unless the circuit is properly fused. Point out that the obvious cure is wire of proper size.

Safety Projects.

1. *Repair Damaged Extension Cord.* Refer to Fig. 77 and follow the self-explanatory steps in repairing a cord that is damaged in the middle. This simple job may prevent a costly fire.

2. *Repair Cord Ends and Replace Plugs.* Refer to Fig. 78 and follow the self-explanatory steps in repairing cords that are damaged at the ends; also replace the plug in accordance with instructions given in the illustration. This job too may prevent a fire.

3. *Install a Yard Light.* Remove farmstead darkness hazards by installing one or more yard lights. The project shown in Fig. 79 calls for a 20-foot length of 3- or 4-inch used iron pipe. Weld a metal bracket to the top of the pole and anchor an outside-type lamp fixture to this. Select a fixture carrying a sufficient number of PAR-38 lamps to provide light for the entire farmstead. The proj-

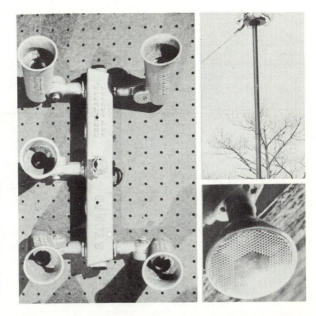

Fig. 79. One multi-unit yard-light may pay for itself many times over by preventing after-dark accidents. Materials needed include (1) a 20-foot length of 3-inch used pipe, (2) a multi-socket outside-type fixture, (3) par-38 light bulbs, and (4) a quantity of wire. The light pole at upper right could be improved by welding climbing cleats to the side.

ect shown in Fig. 79 can be improved by welding metal climbing cleats to the side of the pole. Wiring is threaded through the inside of the pipe before the light is installed. Make certain that your wire is of the proper size.

4. *Install Tractor Lights.* If you drive your tractor on the highway, you should have it equipped with night lights. These lighting sets, including fixtures and wiring, can be purchased from your implement dealer. Instructions for installing lighting equipment are furnished with the set. A workman is shown installing a night light in Fig. 80. His tractor will be safer when he is driving on the highway after dark.

Fig. 80. This workman has little trouble installing a night light on his tractor.

Fig. 81. If the mainswitch is located in a basement or other damp location, stand on a dry board when removing a blown fuse. Avoid touching anything but the fuse (right).

5. *Change a Blown Fuse.* Changing a blown fuse can be dangerous, especially in a damp location. Follow the practice of standing on a dry board when changing a fuse or setting a circuit breaker. Avoid touching metal parts of the switch or breaker box. It is also a good safety measure to disconnect the main switch before changing fuses or setting breakers. (See Fig. 81.)

Glossary for Problem-Unit Two

Ampere The measure of the rate at which electricity flows. Often abbreviated *amp.*

Volt The unit of measure of electrical pressure which causes a current to flow.

Watt A unit of electric power, equal to 1/746 hp. 1 volt × 1 ampere = 1 watt.

Kilowatt 1,000 watts, or 1.34 hp.

Kilowatthour 1,000 watts being used through one hour; often designated *kwh.* 1,000 watts × 1 hour = 1 kilowatthour.

Conductors Copper, aluminum, silver, and other metals through which electrons can be easily moved.

Insulators Glass, rubber, plastic, porcelain, and other substances through which electrons will not move. Also known as nonconductors.

Circuit A complete path providing for a continuous flow of electric current. Usually consists of two wires: one hot wire to bring the current from the source of supply, and one neutral for conducting the current back to the source.

Phase Refers to the timing of an alternating current. When two alternating currents reach their zero, maximum, and intermediate values at exactly the same instant, they are said to be in phase. A two-phase current consists of two separate alternating currents 90 degrees apart. A three-phase current consists of three separate alternating currents 120 degrees apart.

Cycle A complete series of changes that take place in the flow of an electric current and recur at regular intervals. Thus in 60-cycle alternating current, the current builds up to a positive peak and then to a negative peak 60 times each second.

NOTE: This glossary was adapted in part from a publication issued by the Tennessee Valley Authority. (Now out of print.)

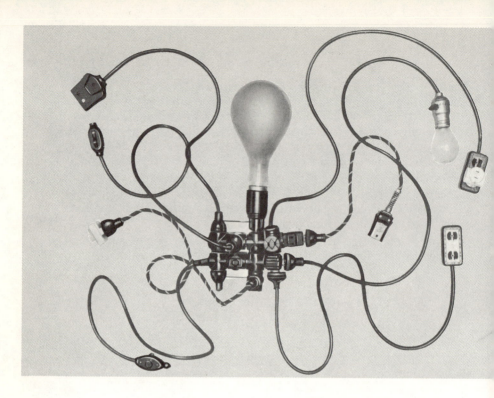

Fig. 82. Common species of "electric octopus."

PROBLEM-UNIT ||||

How to Plan and Do Farmstead Wiring

How many "wired hands" can you have for $2,000 a year? This is the approximate annual cost of a "hired hand" at the rate of $1 per hour, or $160 a month. In a recent study, the average annual cost of electricity on a group of farms in the Northwest was $157.52 per farm, as reported by the United States Department of Agriculture.* In short, one month's wages for the hired hand ($160) would pay this annual electric bill and leave eleven months' wages (about $1,800) to be invested in electric equipment.

These low-cost "wired hands" cannot work for you, however, unless you have an adequate wiring system. Every piece of electric equipment must have sufficient electricity for operation, otherwise it cannot do a good job. Since the beginning of rural electrification in this country, cheap, skimpy wiring has prevented the American farmer from using these extra "wired hands." The "electric octopus" in Fig. 82 is a sure sign of inadequate wiring. Do you have an electric octopus in your farm home or in some other farmstead building? If so, you had better get rid of it before it causes fire or other trouble.

* Joe F. Davis, *Use of Electricity on Farms,* USDA Agricultural Information Bulletin 161 (Washington, D.C., Government Printing Office, 1956), p. 2.

CHAPTER 5

*H*ow to Arrange an *Exterior Distribution System for the Farmstead*

By planning ahead for your wiring system, you can avoid some of the costly mistakes that are so common to the American farm today. A wiring plan should make provisions for the electrical needs on the farm for the next ten years or so. Wiring that is fully adequate today may become inadequate within the next few months or years. Each added appliance will increase the demand on your electrical system, and before you realize it the electrical load may exceed the capacity of your wiring. It will pay you to study your present and future needs for electrical services first, then draw up a plan to meet these needs. By avoiding one or two complete rewiring jobs, your savings on wiring could amount to several hundred dollars.

92

Fig. 83. A 20-ampere fuse for No. 12 wire = protection; a 30-ampere fuse for No. 12 wire = fire hazard.

What Caused This Farmer's "Fuse" Trouble?

The trouble reported by a farmer we will call Mr. Atwood seems to be a common complaint throughout the country. This Texas farmer reported some "fuse" trouble which started when he installed two convenience outlets to serve a new ironer and a new room heater.

When a service man arrived, he found nothing wrong with the service entrance equipment or the line voltage, so he asked Mr. Atwood to demonstrate the trouble. Here is what happened: (1) the kitchen lights were turned on; (2) the ironer was plugged in; (3) the lights dimmed; (4) the room heater was turned on; and (5) the fuse blew out.

When the service man saw that the new outlets were wired to the kitchen lighting circuit and that the blown fuse was a 20-ampere size, he asked Mr. Atwood to help add up the load that was on the circuit when the fuse blew. They found the following:

1. Two ceiling lights at 100 watts	200 watts	
2. Sink light	100	
3. Range light	100	
4. Ironer	1,450	
5. Room heater	1,600	
Total wattage load	3,450	

Converting watts to amperes, this result was obtained:

$$\frac{3,450 \text{ watts}}{115 \text{ volts}} = 30 \text{ amperes (total load)}$$

Why did the 20-ampere fuse blow? Because it had a 30-ampere load on it, and the fuse was made for 20 amperes! If it had failed to blow, the wires might have caused a fire. What would have been the result if a 30-ampere fuse had been used to make the circuit carry the 3,450 watt load? Since the No. 12 wire in this circuit was capable of carrying only 20 amperes (2,300 watts) safely, a fire would have resulted from the overheated wires.*

This farmer's trouble was caused by connecting an outlet to a circuit that was already loaded. The new appliances were large enough to require a separate circuit. The situation appeared more serious when the service man examined the service switch and

* For more information on sizes and types of wire, refer to page 155.

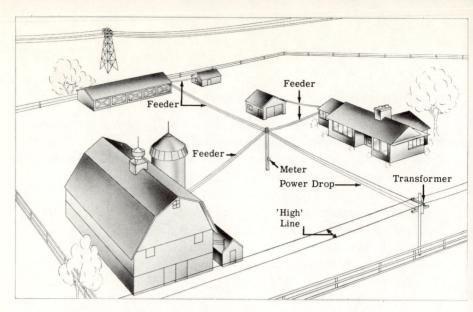

Fig. 84. A central metering system provides the most economical wiring as well as better service.

found that it was only a 60-ampere size. The only way another circuit could be obtained was to install a larger service switch. This, of course, required a larger service entrance cable as well as other changes in the farmstead wiring system.

How to Correct Mr. Atwood's Fuse Trouble. For temporary help, the service man suggested that they connect one of the new convenience outlets to an existing appliance circuit. This change would make it possible to use either the ironer or the room heater but not both at the same time.

For a more permanent solution, the service man recommended that Mr. Atwood ask the power supplier to send a farm-service specialist out to help plan a new farmstead wiring system. This service, he explained, could be obtained free of charge, and the wiring plan would take care of the electrical needs for ten years ahead.

What Should a Farmstead Wiring Plan Include?

The first thing the farm planner did when he arrived at the Atwood farm was to explain the importance and function of the main parts of the farmstead wiring system. He showed by diagram, for example, how the power supply could be "choked off" at the transformer, the power drop, the feeder circuits, or the service entrance if any of these parts were too small. The branch circuits also, he explained, could restrict the power supply. (How well Mr. Atwood knew this already!)

Next, the planning specialist asked what plans the farmer had for adding electric equipment in the farm home, the dairy, the poultry houses, the hog houses, the feed barns, the farm shop, and other service buildings on the farmstead.

After the ten-year needs had been listed, the planner helped to design a wiring system that would meet these requirements; by going ahead and installing that system Mr. Atwood saved several hundred dollars. How? He avoided one rewiring job that otherwise would have been necessary within five years.

The completed wiring plan included the following parts:

1. The power distribution system for the farmstead.

2. The size and type of service entrance for the farmstead and for each separate building.

3. The arrangement, type, and size of feeder circuits required for the farmstead.

4. The wire size, type, and arrangement of branch circuits for the farmstead. (NOTE: Branch circuits are covered in Chapter 6).

What Method of Power Distribution Is Best?

There are two general methods of distributing electricity on the farmstead: (1) metering at a yardpole and (2) metering at a farmstead building.

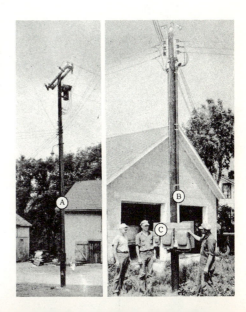

Fig. 85. Two common types of wiring for yardpole metering. The service in *A* is wired with service entrance cable; in *B,* the yardpole is equipped with conduit. A small switch (C) controls the water pump and is independent of other switches.

Metering at a Yardpole. The diagram in Fig. 84 shows how a yardpole may be set in a central part of the farmstead so that the service entrance equipment, including the meter, may be as close to the several farm buildings as possible. This arrangement makes it possible to use smaller and therefore less costly feeder wiring for serving the various buildings.

Moreover, a separate switch and circuit to serve the water pump may be tapped off the yardpole, as shown in Fig. 85-B at left. This arrangement makes it possible to operate the pump, even if all the farm buildings were to catch fire. In addition to the conduit installation, shown in Fig. 85-B, service entrance cable is also used to wire the yardpole in some sections of the country. Fig. 85-A shows a typical installation of this type. Service entrance cable is less expensive than conduit but is not acceptable by the codes in some areas. In both installations, several feeder circuits lead to the various farm buildings. (NOTE: Details of wiring the yardpole may be found in Chapter 8.)

Metering at a Building. If you have a farm building located near the load center of your farmstead, you may install the main service entrance equipment there and distribute electricity from that point. Fig. 86 shows this type of setup.

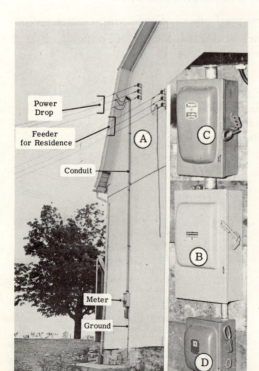

Fig. 86. Metering at a farm building. Exterior parts of the installation are mounted on the barn wall (*A*). The three switches at right are mounted inside of the barn. The 200-ampere switch (*B*) supplies a 100-ampere service for the farm home through switch C and a 60-ampere service for the barn and feed mill through switch *D*.

On a farm making heavy use of electricity, metering from a building is not satisfactory unless it is centrally located on the farmstead. Otherwise, the feeder wire would be too expensive because of the long runs required. As explained before, long runs of wire result in excessive voltage drop unless large-size wire is used. Large wire, of course, is more expensive than small wire.

More than one meter may be required for the farmstead if the buildings are widely scattered or if more than one heavy electrical service is to be installed. Sometimes it is more economical to install a separate meter for a single large electric motor; for example, where the length of feeder circuit would be more than 500 feet.

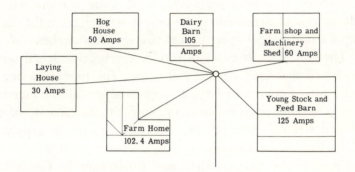

Fig. 87. The proper location for a meter pole is determined by balancing the six loads against the distances between the buildings. The meter is closer to the heaviest loads.

How to Determine the Proper Location for the Meter. For central metering, the best location for the meter is *at or near the center of the electrical load of the entire farmstead.* This location takes into account all the separate loads to be served and the distances between them. The diagram in Fig. 87 shows how the load center can be found. Simply draw a diagram of your farmstead and list the amperage loads that will likely be served in the next ten years.

The proper location for the meter, then, will be the point at which you can get the best balance between loads and distances. That is, the meter should be closer to the heaviest loads and farther from the lightest loads.

Advantages of Central Metering. In situations where electricity is to be used in farming as well as in the farm home, central metering offers the following advantages: (1) lower cost of exterior wiring; (2) better electrical service due to less voltage drop; (3) longer life of electric equipment; (4) easier wiring of future services; and (5) better fire protection.

What Size Service Entrances Will You Need?

With a central metering system, you will be concerned with two types of service entrances. These are: (1) a *master service entrance*, which supplies electricity for all farmstead buildings or services; and (2) *individual service entrances*, one for each building or service. In selecting this equipment, your problem will primarily be one of determining the proper wire size for the service entrance cable and selecting proper size service switches.

The size of both types of service entrances is based on the ampere load that each service will carry. The master service entrance must, of course, be large enough to supply all the individual buildings or other electrical services. Similarly, the capacity of each individual service entrance must be large enough to supply the needs in the building it serves.

Parts of the Service Entrance Equipment to Consider in Figuring Size. In Fig. 88 you will see an illustration of the relative capacity of 30-, 60-, 100-, and 200-ampere service entrances. These illustrations show that the amount of electricity you can draw depends primarily on the wire size and switch capacity of the entrance. In planning your service entrances, therefore, you should take account of your future needs for electrical service. To illustrate, if you select a 60-ampere service entrance for a dairy barn, the total electrical load you can have in that building will be limited to 60 amperes. One $7\frac{1}{2}$-hp motor would take approximately 40 amperes of this, leaving only 20 amperes for all other uses.

Other parts of the service entrance, such as ground wire, service head, conduit (if used), and the like, must match the size of the service entrance wires and service switch, but size of the service entrance must be determined first.

The kind of equipment required in the service entrance system is largely controlled by the kind of distribution system used.

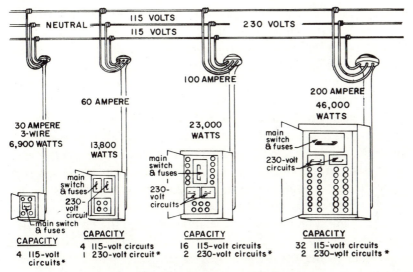

Fig. 88. Comparison of 30-, 60-, 100-, and 200-ampere capacity service entrances.

For example, where pole metering is used, a proper size meter loop and master disconnect switch are installed on the pole, and feeder circuits are run from there to the various buildings or other services. In this setup, the service switch for each building is installed in the building it serves.

Where the master service entrance is installed in a centrally located building, sub-panels for the various buildings are installed along with the master service switch; then feeders are run to each building or other service. In addition, a disconnect switch is usually installed at each building to provide for safety and convenience. This system generally costs somewhat more than does pole metering.

Where two or three buildings are to be served through one common feeder circuit, the service entrance at the first building must be large enough to carry the ampere load at all three buildings; the service entrance at the second must be large enough to supply the needs at that building plus other buildings farther along the line, and so on. Feeder circuits must be proportionately larger.

This type of distribution is usually more expensive than central metering because of the larger wire size and equipment required in the first and second buildings. A common feeder circuit for a long string of buildings is thus found to be excessively expensive if not altogether impractical.

A common feeder may be practical on small farmsteads having only limited needs for electrical services.

Ampere Loads and Their Relation to Wire Size. In figuring ampere loads, two types of loads are considered. These are (1) the total connected load, and (2) the probable maximum load. Some parts of the farmstead electrical system must be designed to carry the total connected load; other parts may be designed on the law of averages that not all of the total load will be on at one time. This is an important point to remember because the probable maximum load, being usually less than the total connected load, makes it possible to use smaller and less expensive entrance equipment. Examples later in this chapter show how this works.

The Meaning of Wire Size. At this point it is important to review the meaning of wire size since this is one of the main things you will deal with in designing your service entrances.

In Chapter 2, wire size is shown to have a similar effect on the flow of an electric current as pipe size has on the rate of flow of water in a pressurized water pipe; that is, larger electrical loads re-

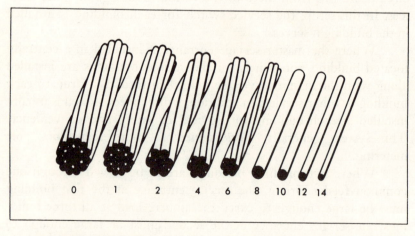

Fig. 89. Actual size of wire, No. 14 to No. 0, without insulation. Wire up to No. 8 is solid; above No. 8, it is stranded.

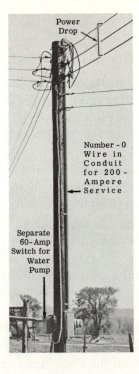

Fig. 90. A 200-ampere service entrance requires No. 0 size for the entrance wires (meter loop).

quire larger wire size, just as a greater flow of water requires a larger pipe. Therefore, it is essential to select the wire size that is large enough to carry the load that will be on the entrance equipment. On the other hand, buying larger wire than is actually needed is a waste of money.

One common measure of wire size is in AWG (American Wire Gauge) and the numbers are in reverse to the largeness of the wire; for example, No. 2 is larger than No. 4, No. 12 is larger than No. 14, and the like.

Small Wire. The samples of wire shown in Fig. 89 are actual size. Note that the smallest, No. 14, is *not* recommended for branch circuits in the farm home. No. 14 may be used in other farm buildings for circuits up to 30 feet in length where the load will not exceed 15 amperes. Generally, it is wise to use No. 12 wire for branch circuits in all farm buildings, since you may later find it necessary to operate more than 15 amperes (1,725 watts at 115 volts) on a given circuit. No. 14 wire may also be used for separate circuits to operate electric motors (up to 15 amperes) where the run is not over 80 feet at 115 volts or 150 feet at 230 volts. No. 14 and smaller wire may also be used for extension cords to operate light-load appliances. See Tables 11A and 11B for additional information on wire sizes.

Large Wire. In Fig. 89 the largest wire size shown is No. 0. This size (Type RH) will carry up to 150 amperes in an enclosed installation or up to 235 amperes (Type WP) in open air. The service entrance cable shown in Fig. 90 is No. 0 for this open-air installation.

Wire sizes larger than those shown in Fig. 89 include 2/0, 3/0, 4/0, and still larger sizes expressed in circular mils. Large central metering systems for electrified farms often require 4/0 or larger service entrance cable. (NOTE: Data in Table 12 are for copper wire. Aluminum wire will carry only 84 per cent as much load in each instance.)

The proper wire size for a service entrance must be matched by the proper size of service switch or breaker. This is discussed later.

How to Apply the Seven-Step Formula in Figuring the Size of the Service Entrances. Since the size of the service entrances are essential to the future welfare of the electrified farm, their planning should not be left to the community electrician. Despite the seeming difficulty of figuring electrical loads and selecting the proper wire size, this is a rather simple procedure. If you will study the seven steps and the examples on the following pages, you should be able to determine the proper size of your service entrances with little or no trouble at all. Ask a competent person to show you how to use this formula if you find it difficult.

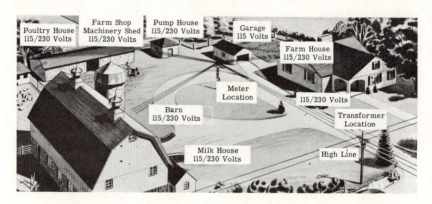

Fig. 91. The probable maximum load of the entire farmstead takes account of the load that is likely to be on at one time in every building or service on the farmstead.

Before applying the seven-step formula, remember that figuring amperage loads is a process simply of finding individual amperages and totaling them. The amperage rating of an appliance can be found by examining its label. If this is given in watts, divide wattage by 115 or 230 (volts) to obtain amperes, depending on which service is being used. Several special rules of thumb are given in the seven-step method whereby amperages can be estimated; for example, lighting is figured on a square-foot basis; farm home appliances on a flat-rate allowance, and so on.

Some loads are taken on the basis of the total; others are figured on the basis of probable maximum load, which refers to the electrical load that is likely to be on at one time; for example, only a part of the total amperage of an electric range would likely be on at once. This is more fully explained in the seven-step formula and the examples that follow:

Step 1. For each building or service on the farmstead, list each full-current load, including lighting, small appliances, large electric motors, and so on. The total is the total connected load. (See example, Table 9.)

Step 2. For each building, or service, convert the total connected load to the probable maximum load. (NOTE: Not all of the total connected load will be on at one time; therefore, you can figure a smaller load here and use smaller wire than would be required for the total connected load. The example that follows illustrates the method of figuring the probable maximum load.)

Step 3. From the list of probable maximum loads found in Step 2, write down the largest single load on the farmstead.

Step 4. List the remainder of the loads on the list found in Step 2 and total them. Take 50 per cent of this figure and write it down under item 3.

Step 5. Add items 3 and 4 and the result will be the probable maximum load for the entire farmstead.

Step 6. Refer to Table 12 and find the wire size required for your service entrance cable.

Step 7. Select a service switch of equal or larger capacity. (NOTE: If you expect to add other electrical services in the future, choose the next standard size above the probable maximum load.)

Master Service Entrance. You will now observe the method of determining the wire size and service switch for the main service entrance.

EXAMPLE: Assume that you have a farmstead with three buildings where electricity is used. Select the wire size for the entrance wires or meter loop and the proper size main service switch. The buildings and electrical loads are described as follows.

1. *Farm Home.* Assume 2,000 square feet of floor area, an adequate amount of lighting, an average number of plug-in appliances, a range, a washer-dryer, two 1-hp air conditioner units, a ¾-hp food freezer, a 60-gallon (4,200w) water heater, a 1,200w dishwasher-disposer, and a 1-hp water pump.

2. *Dairy Barn, Milk House, and Feed Unit.* Assume an adequate amount of lighting, an average number of plug-in appliances, a 5-hp feed grinder, a 3-hp feed-handling unit, a 1-hp milker, a 2-hp milk cooler, and a water heater.

3. *Farm Shop.* Assume an adequate amount of lighting, an average number of plug-in type tools (drills and the like), a ¾-hp bench grinder, a 1-hp bench saw, and a farm arc welder (37.5 amperes).

Steps 1 and 2. Notice that Steps 1 and 2 are combined in Table 9. This method saves time, and certain data derived will be used later to select each service entrance as well as feeders.

Step 3. Select the largest probable maximum load at the farmstead—104.6 amperes (dairy-milk house-feed unit).

Step 4. Add 50 per cent of the remaining probable maximum loads: 102.4 + 67.8 is 170.2 × .50 is 85.1.

Step 5. Total of Steps 3 and 4—is 189.7 amperes.

Step 6. Refer to Table 12 and select wire size that will carry 189.7 amperes. Notice that ampere capacity varies with the type of wire and the method of installation used. If your wire is to be enclosed in conduit, choose a type of wire listed in either column two or three (assume 'Type RH') and read down until you find 189.7. The nearest to this figure is 200. Next find in column one the wire size indicated for 200 amperes. This is 3/0 wire (Type RH) and is safe for loads up to 200 amperes.

Notice that a smaller wire size could be used by selecting one of the types of wire listed in either columns four or five. These figures are for feeders and other "free air" installations (wire not enclosed or buried). In some parts of the country, however, service entrances are required to be enclosed and in this case the ampere data in columns four and five will not apply.

Step 7. Select suitable master service switch. Since the ampere load is near 200, a 200-ampere or larger capacity switch or breaker should be used.

TABLE 9

Electrical Loads at Three Farmstead Buildings

Appliance or Other Use	Total Connected Load		Probable Maximum Load
FARM HOME			
Lighting, 2,000 sq ft @ 3w	6,000w	@ 50%	3,000w
Plug-in appliances, flat allowance	3,000w	@ 50%	1,500w
Range	12,000w	@ 50%	6,000w
Washer-dryer	6,000w	@ 50%	3,000w
Water heater, 60 gal	4,200w	@100%	4,200w
Dishwasher-disposer	1,200w	@100%	1,200w
Water pump, 1 hp	1,400w	@100%	1,400w
Food freezer, ¾ hp	900w	@ 50%	450w
2 Air conditioner units, 1 hp each	2,800w	@100%	2,800w
Total watts load at farm home	37,500		23,550
Total ampere load at farm home (at 230 volts)	163		102.4*
DAIRY-MILK HOUSE-FEED UNIT			
Lighting and convenience outlets, 20 @1½ amperes	30		15
Feed grinder, 5 hp (28 amperes x 1.25)**	35		35
Milker, 1 hp	6.5		6.5
Milk cooler, 2 hp	12		12
Water heater, 80 gal (4,400w)	19.1		19.1
Feed handling unit, 3 hp	17		17
Total amperes at dairy (at 230 volts)	119.6		104.6*
FARM SHOP			
Convenience and lighting outlets, 16 @1½ amperes	24		12
Bench saw, 1 hp (6.5 amperes x 1.25)**	8.1		8.1
Bench grinder, ¾ hp	5.1		5.1
Air compressor, ¾ hp	5.1		5.1
Farm arc welder	37.5		37.5
Total ampere load at farm shop (at 230 volts)	79.8		67.8*

* Ampere load shown will be used in later examples to determine the capacity and size of individual service entrances and feeder circuits.

** 25 per cent of the full-load current of the largest motor in each building is added for starting current. This is counted for only one motor in each building.

Fig. 92. A 200-ampere disconnect switch (or service entrance switch) is needed for the load in the example.

ANSWER: If little or no expansion of the electrical services is planned for the future, choose 3/0 wire for the service cable or meter loop (Type RH) and a 200-ampere master service switch or breaker. If considerable expansion of electrical service is planned, you may save money by going ahead and choosing a 400-ampere service switch and comparable wire size for the entrance wires. Using Type RH enclosed, a 400-ampere load would require a wire size of 750 circular mils.

Fig. 93. To find the full-load current required by the 5-hp motor shown, multiply its rated load of 28 amperes by 1.25; thus, 28 X 1.25 = 35 amperes. NOTE: This example assumes that the 5-hp motor is the largest motor on the farm.

TABLE 10*

Typical Computed Loads and Probable Maximum Demands

Building	Computed Load		Probable Demand	
Farm Residence.	19	kw	13	kw
Dairy Barn, medium size, including milk house and one 5-hp motor.	20	kw	12	kw
Dairy Barn, large size, including milk house and one 7½-hp motor.	27	kw	15	kw
Same, two 7½-hp motors.	36	kw	24	kw
Milking Barn with Milk House.	7.5	kw	5.8	kw
Milk House only.	6.0	kw	4.8	kw
Beef-Cattle, Horse, Sheep and Hog Barns, medium size, with 5-hp motor.	14	kw	10	kw
Same, large size, with 7½-hp motor.	20	kw	15	kw
Poultry Laying House:				
1000 sq ft	1.8	kw	1.8	kw
4000 sq ft	8.7	kw	6.4	kw
8000 sq ft	15.2	kw	11.7	kw
Brooder House, per brooder:				
Infrared	2.25	kw	2	kw
Standard brooder	1.25	kw	1	kw
Farm Shop, with welder.	17	kw	10	kw
Sweet-Potato curing and storage.	1.5	w/cu ft or	1.5	w/cu ft or
	4	w per bushel	4	w per bushel
Machinery Sheds, Stock Shelters and Miscellaneous Buildings.	1	watt per sq ft floor area	1	watt per sq ft floor area

* *The Farmstead Wiring Handbook*, New York, The Industry Committee on Interior Wiring Design, 1955, p. 39. (NOTE: Approximate amperes can be obtained by dividing kw by 230 or 115 volts as the case may be.)

TABLE 11A*

Wire Sizes for Loads up to 200 Amperes at 115 Volts, Based on 2 Per Cent Voltage Drop

Load in Amperes	Length of Run in Feet								
	30	40	50	60	70	80	90	100	125
5	14	14	14	14	14	14	12	12	12
6	14	14	14	14	14	12	12	12	10
7	14	14	14	14	12	12	12	12	10
8	14	14	14	12	12	12	12	10	10
9	14	14	12	12	12	12	10	10	10
10	14	14	12	12	12	10	10	10	8
12	14	12	12	10	10	10	10	8	8
14	14	12	12	10	10	10	8	8	8
16	12	12	10	10	10	8	8	8	6
18	12	12	10	10	8	8	8	6	6
20	12	10	10	8	8	8	8	6	6
25	10	10	8	8	8	6	6	6	4
30	10	8	8	6	6	6	6	4	4
35	10[b]	8	8	6	6	6	4	4	4
40	8	8	6	6	6	4	4	4	2
45	8[a]	8[a]	6	6	4	4	4	4	2
50	8[b]	6	6	4	4	4	4	2	2
60	6[a]	6[a]	4	4	4	2	2	2	1
70	6[b]	6[b]	4	4	2	2	2	2	1
80	6[b]	4[a]	4[a]	2	2	2	2	1	0
90	6[c]	4[b]	4[b]	2	2	2	1	1	0
100	4[b]	4[b]	2[a]	2[a]	2[a]	1	1	0	00
115	4[c]	2[a]	2[a]	2[a]	1	0	0	0	00
130	4[c]	2[b]	2[b]	1[a]	1[a]	0	00	00	000
145	4[c]	2[c]	1[b]	1[b]	0[a]	00	00	00	0000
160	4[c]	2[c]	1[b]	0[b]	0[b]	00	00	000	0000
180	2[c]	2[c]	1[c]	0[b]	00[b]	00[b]	000[a]	000[a]	0000
200	2[c]	1[c]	0[c]	00[b]	00[b]	000[a]	000[a]	0000[a]	250M

[a] Type RH or RHW in cable or raceway; all types in air. For other types of wire in cable or raceway refer to Table 12 for minimum size permissible.

[b] Weatherproof or Type TW in air. For wires in cable or raceway refer to Table 12 for minimum size permissible.

[c] Weatherproof wire in air. For all other conditions refer to Table 12 for minimum size permissible.

TABLE 11A (Continued)

Wire Sizes for Loads up to 200 Amperes at 115 Volts, Based on 2 Per Cent Voltage Drop

150	175	200	225	250	275	300	350	400	Load in Amperes
10	10	10	8	8	8	8	6	6	5
10	10	8	8	8	8	6	6	6	6
10	8	8	8	8	6	6	6	6	7
8	8	8	8	6	6	6	6	4	8
8	8	8	6	6	6	4	4	4	9
8	8	6	6	6	6	4	4	4	10
6	6	6	6	4	4	4	4	2	12
6	6	6	4	4	4	4	2	2	14
6	6	4	4	4	4	2	2	2	16
6	4	4	4	4	2	2	2	2	18
4	4	4	4	2	2	2	2	1	20
4	4	2	2	2	2	1	1	0	25
2	2	2	2	1	1	0	0	00	30
2	2	2	1	1	0	0	00	00	35
2	2	1	1	0	0	00	00	000	40
2	1	1	0	0	00	00	000	000	45
1	1	0	0	00	00	000	000	0000	50
1	0	00	00	000	000	000	0000	250M†	60
0	00	00	000	000	0000	0000	250M	300M	70
00	000	000	000	0000	0000	250M	300M	300M	80
00	000	000	0000	0000	250M	250M	300M	350M	90
000	000	0000	0000	250M	300M	300M	350M	400M	100
000	0000	0000	250M	300M	300M	350M	400M	500M	115
000	0000	250M	300M	300M	350M	350M	500M	500M	130
000	250M	300M	350M	350M	400M	400M	500M		145
250M	300M	300M	350M	400M	400M	500M	500M		160
250M	300M	350M	400M	500M	500M	500M			180
300M	350M	400M	500M	500M	500M				200

* *Farmstead Wiring Handbook,* New York, Industry Committee on Interior Wiring Design, 1955, p. 43.

† M = thousand circular mils.

NOTES: Conductors in overhead spans must be at least No. 10 for spans up to 50 feet and No. 8 for longer spans. See 1953 NE Code, Section 7314b. Feeder conductors must be at least No. 10. See 1953 NE Code, Section 2201.

TABLE 11B*

Wire Sizes for Loads up to 400 Amperes at 230 Volts, Based on 2 Per Cent Voltage Drop

Load in Amperes	*Length of Run in Feet*							
	40	50	60	70	80	90	100	125
5	14	14	14	14	14	14	14	14
6	14	14	14	14	14	14	14	14
7	14	14	14	14	14	14	14	14
8	14	14	14	14	14	14	14	12
9	14	14	14	14	14	14	12	12
10	14	14	14	14	14	12	12	12
12	14	14	14	14	12	12	12	10
14	14	14	14	12	12	12	12	10
16	12	12	12	12	12	12	10	10
18	12	12	12	12	12	10	10	10
20	12	12	12	12	10	10	10	8
25	10	10	10	10	10	10	8	8
30	10	10	10	10	8	8	8	6
35	10[b]	10[b]	10[b]	8	8	8	8	6
40	10[b]	10[b]	8	8	8	8	6	6
45	10[c]	10[c]	8[a]	8[a]	8[a]	6	6	6
50	10[c]	8[b]	8[b]	8[b]	6	6	6	4
60	8[b]	8[c]	6[a]	6[a]	6[a]	6[a]	4	4
70	8[b]	8[c]	6[b]	6[b]	6[b]	4	4	4
80	6[b]	6[b]	6[b]	6[b]	4[a]	4[a]	4[a]	2
90	6[c]	6[c]	6[c]	4[b]	4[b]	4[b]	4[b]	2
100	6[c]	6[c]	4[b]	4[b]	4[b]	4[b]	2[a]	2[a]
115	4[c]	4[c]	4[c]	4[c]	2[a]	2[a]	2[a]	2[a]
130	4[c]	4[c]	4[c]	2[b]	2[b]	2[b]	2[b]	1[a]
145	2[c]	2[c]	2[c]	2[c]	2[c]	2[c]	1[b]	0[a]
160	2[c]	2[c]	2[c]	2[c]	2[c]	1[b]	1[b]	0[b]
180	1[c]	1[c]	1[c]	1[c]	1[c]	1[c]	1[c]	0[b]
200	1[c]	1[c]	1[c]	1[c]	1[c]	1[c]	0[c]	00[b]
225	0[c]	0[c]	0[c]	0[c]	0[c]	0[c]	0[c]	00[b]
250	00[c]	00[c]	00[c]	00[c]	00[c]	00[c]	00[c]	000[b]
275	00[c]	00[c]	00[c]	00[c]	00[c]	00[c]	00[c]	000[c]
300	000[c]	000[c]	000[c]	000[c]	000[c]	000[c]	000[c]	0000[b]
325	0000[c]	0000[c]	0000[c]	0000[c]	0000[c]	0000[c]	0000[c]	0000[c]
350	0000[c]	0000[c]	0000[c]	0000[c]	0000[c]	0000[c]	0000[c]	0000[c]
375	250M[c]	250M[c]	250M[c]	250M[c]	250M[c]	250M[c]	250M[c]	250M[c]
400	250M[c]	250M[c]	250M[c]	250M[c]	250M[c]	250M[c]	250M[c]	250M[c]

[a] Type RH or RHW in cable or raceway; all types in air. For other types of wire in cable or raceway refer to Table 12 for minimum size permissible.

[b] Weatherproof or Type TW in air. For wires in cable or raceway refer to Table 12 for minimum size permissible.

[c] Weatherproof wire in air. For all other conditions refer to Table 12 for minimum size permissible.

TABLE 11B (Continued)

Wire Sizes for Loads up to 400 Amperes at 230 Volts, Based on 2 Per Cent Voltage Drop

Length of Run in Feet									Load in Amperes
150	175	200	225	250	275	300	350	400	
14	12	12	12	12	10	10	10	10	5
12	12	12	12	10	10	10	10	8	6
12	12	12	10	10	10	10	8	8	7
12	12	10	10	10	10	8	8	8	8
12	10	10	10	10	8	8	8	8	9
10	10	10	10	8	8	8	8	6	10
10	10	8	8	8	8	6	6	6	12
10	8	8	8	8	6	6	6	6	14
8	8	8	6	6	6	6	6	4	16
8	8	6	6	6	6	6	4	4	18
8	8	6	6	6	6	4	4	4	20
6	6	6	6	4	4	4	4	2	25
6	6	4	4	4	4	4	2	2	30
6	4	4	4	4	2	2	2	2	35
4	4	4	4	2	2	2	2	1	40
4	4	4	2	2	2	2	1	1	45
4	4	2	2	2	2	1	1	0	50
2	2	2	2	1	1	1	0	00	60
2	2	2	1	1	0	0	00	00	70
2	2	1	1	0	0	00	00	000	80
2	1	1	0	0	00	00	000	000	90
1	1	0	0	00	00	000	000	0000	100
1[a]	0	00	00	00	000	000	0000	250M†	115
0[a]	0[a]	00	000	000	000	0000	0000	250M	130
0[a]	00	00	000	0000	0000	0000	250M	300M	145
00[a]	00[a]	000	000	0000	0000	250M	300M	300M	160
00[b]	000[a]	000[a]	0000	0000	250M	300M	300M	350M	180
000[a]	000[a]	0000[a]	0000[a]	250M	300M	300M	350M	400M	200
000[b]	0000[a]	0000[a]	250M[a]	300M	300M	350M	400M	500M	225
0000[b]	0000[b]	250M[a]	300M[a]	300M[a]	350M	350M	400M	500M	250
0000[b]	250M[b]	300M[a]	300M[a]	350M[a]	350M[a]	400M	500M		275
250M[b]	250M[b]	300M[b]	350M[a]	350M[a]	400M[a]	500M	500M		300
250M[b]	300M[b]	300M[b]	350M[b]	400M[a]	500M[a]	500M[a]			325
250M[c]	300M[b]	350M[b]	400M[b]	400M[b]	500M[a]	500M[a]			350
300M[b]	350M[b]	350M[b]	400M[b]	500M[b]	500M[b]				375
300M[c]	350M[b]	400M[b]	500M[b]	500M[b]					400

* *Farmstead Wiring Handbook,* New York, Industry Committee on Interior Wiring Design, 1955, p. 42.

† M = thousand circular mils.

NOTES: Conductors in overhead spans must be at least No. 10 for spans up to 50 feet and No. 8 for longer spans. See 1953 NE Code, Section 7314b. Feeder conductors must be at least No. 10. See 1953 NE Code, Section 2201.

TABLE 12*

Allowable Current-Carrying Capacities of Insulated Copper Conductor in Amperes**

	Not More Than Three Conductors in Raceway or Cable, or Direct Burial		*Single Conductors in Free Air*	
Size AWG or MCM	*Rubber Insulation, Type R, RW, RU, RUW Thermoplastic Insulation, Type T, TW*	*Rubber Insulation, Type RH, RHW*	*Weatherproof Insulation, Type WP*	*Thermoplastic Insulation, Type TW*
14	15	15	* * *	* * *
12	20	20	* * *	* * *
10	30	30	55	40
8	40	45	70	55
6	55	65	100	80
4	70	85	130	105
3	80	100	150	120
2	95	115	175	140
1	110	130	205	165
0	125	150	235	195
00	145	175	275	225
000	165	200	320	260
0000	195	230	370	300
250	215	255	410	340
300	240	285	460	375
350	260	310	510	420
400	280	335	555	455
500	320	380	630	515
600	355	420	710	575
700	385	460	780	630
750	400	475	810	655

* *Farmstead Wiring Handbook*, New York, The Industry Committee on Interior Wiring Design, 1955, p. 39.

** These are limiting capacities of these conductors beyond which excessive temperatures may damage the insulation. Data from 1953 NE Code, Chap. 10, Tables 1 and 2. For Aluminum Conductors take 84% of capacities given above. If bare conductors are used with insulated conductors, their allowable current-carrying capacity shall be limited to that of insulated conductors with which they are used.

*** No. 10 is minimum permissible in overhead spans up to 50 ft in length. For spans over 50 ft in length No. 8 is minimum permissible. See 1953 NE Code, Section 7314b.

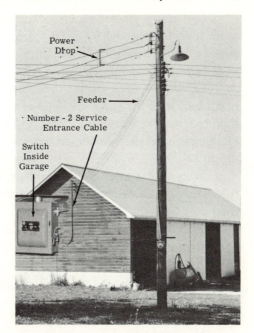

Fig. 94. No. 2 service entrance cable is the size required for the garage-feed mill here. The service switch (inset) is 100-ampere capacity.

Service Entrance for Each Farmstead Building. Fig. 94 illustrates the use of a central pole metering setup and individual service entrances for the several farmstead buildings. In the preceding example you observed the method of selecting the proper size service equipment for a pole metering setup of this type or for a service entrance installed in a centrally located building.

The next step is to select the service entrance equipment for individual farm buildings.

EXAMPLE: (1) Figure the proper wire size and service switch for the farm home used in Table 9; (2) repeat this for the dairy; and (3) repeat this for the farm shop.

SOLUTIONS: (1) *Farm Home*—Table 9 shows that the probable maximum load for the farm home is 102.4 amperes. Next refer to Table 12 and find under the column containing "Type RH" wire the figure 102.4. The figure nearest to 102.4 is 115. (NOTE: You cannot use a figure lower than your load.) Next find the wire size indicated in column one for 115 amperes.

ANSWER: No. 2 wire may be used for "Type RH." Select either a 150-ampere circuit breaker or a 200-ampere fused service switch for the farm home.

(2) *Dairy*—Refer to Table 9 and note that the probable maximum load for the dairy is 104.6 amperes; therefore the wire size and service switch for this building should be the same as that selected for the farm home.

(3) *Farm Shop*—Refer to Table 9 and note that the probable maximum load for the farm shop is 67.8 amperes. Table 12 shows that No. 4 wire is required where "Type RH" is used. Select a 100-ampere service switch or equivalent circuit breaker for the shop.

Notice that in all three problems here, the wire size required is closely related to the type of wire and the method of installation used.

By following the method used in the preceding example you can easily determine the size of each farmstead service entrance.

What Type of Service Switch and Protection Devices Will You Need?

Notice the four different sizes of combination switch-distribution panels in Fig. 95-A; four sizes of circuit breakers are shown in Fig. 95-B.

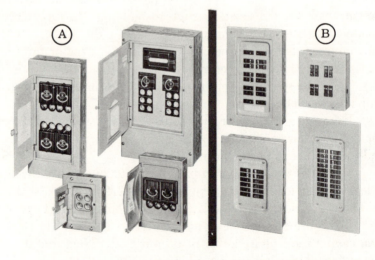

Fig. 95. The four boxes at left (A) are fuse-type distribution panels. A circuit can be broken by removing the plug or block fuses. The four boxes at right (B) are circuit breakers. An automatic trip breaks the circuit if it becomes overloaded.

Fig. 96. Breaker units are available in ampere sizes comparable to fuses.

The combination fused-main switches in Fig. 95-A serve as the disconnecting means, as distribution panels, and as protection devices. The removable fuses, both plug and block type, provide a means of disconnecting the current.

A 50-ampere cartridge fuse is mounted at the back of the removable blocks in three of the switches in Fig. 95-A. These blocks plug into the range circuit or other 230-volt circuits requiring heavy protection. The fuse in the main switch eliminates the necessity of having a separate safety switch for each 230-volt appliance. The size of the fuse must match the appliance load however. For example, a 40-ampere (9,200w) range requires a 40-ampere fuse and so on.

The four sizes of circuit breakers in Fig. 95-B are designed to eliminate the need for removable fuses. An overloaded circuit causes the disconnecting device to trip and thus breaks the circuit. The individual breaker for each circuit must be of the proper size to protect that circuit.

Notice the individual breakers shown in Fig. 96. These can be bought in sizes comparable to fuses. Thus, you could install a 20-ampere breaker for each appliance circuit, a 50-ampere breaker for the range, and so on.

When a breaker trips, the first thing to do is to find the cause. Then, after the trouble has been corrected, you can restore the service by resetting the switch button. (See Fig. 81.)

Another common type of switch found on the farm is the disconnect switch. This type may be fused or fuseless. The fuseless type is sometimes used on the meter pole to provide a convenient means of breaking the main circuit. Generally, it is best to have a fused switch if a switch is used at all. In Fig. 97 are six disconnect-type switches. All of these are fused.

Fig. 97. The large switch (200 ampere) to the right of the meter is a disconnect type. The other five switches are of the disconnect type also.

Type and Size of Fuses Needed. There are several types and sizes of plug and cartridge fuses available for special needs. Fig. 98 shows a collection of both types.

An ordinary plug fuse is rather simple in construction. It consists of a base or shell containing a small ribbon of metal through which the current must flow. This little ribbon is designed to burn in two at a certain temperature, a point that is reached when about 15 per cent overload (in amperes) occurs for more than a few seconds. Plug fuses come in sizes ranging from 5 to 30 amperes.

Observe how this would work. Assume that you have installed a 20-ampere fuse for protecting an appliance circuit which is designed to stand 2,300 watts. Now suppose your circuit is already loaded with 2,300 watts and you plug in an additional

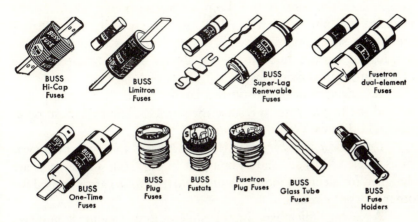

BUSS
Hi-Cap
Fuses

BUSS
Limitron
Fuses

BUSS
Super-Lag
Renewable
Fuses

Fusetron
dual-element
Fuses

BUSS
One-Time
Fuses

BUSS
Plug
Fuses

BUSS
Fustats

Fusetron
Plug Fuses

BUSS
Glass Tube
Fuses

BUSS
Fuse
Holders

Fig. 98. Assortment of plug and cartridge fuses for farm use.

600w toaster. The resulting 2,900 watts is considerably more than the 15 per cent overload allowed. The fuse should blow.

Some cartridge-type fuses have a renewable link, while others are the throwaway type. Fig. 99 shows how to replace a blown link in a 30-ampere cartridge fuse. Some switches carry the knife-type of cartridge fuse, usually for loads above 60 amperes. A fuse of this type is shown in Fig. 98.

Since a blown fuse is an indication of trouble, you should make a habit of finding and correcting the source of trouble before

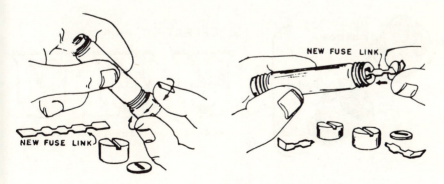

NEW FUSE LINK

NEW FUSE LINK

Fig. 99. To replace a blown link in a renewable cartridge fuse, unscrew the end caps, insert a new link, and replace the caps. A new link must be the correct size.

you replace the fuse. If you keep a diagram handy, showing the electrical circuits in each building, you can usually trace "fuse" trouble in short order. Often a blown fuse can be traced to an overloaded circuit, but this is not always so. Short circuits and other faults can and do cause fuses to burn out.

It is dangerous to substitute a larger fuse or to place a penny behind the blown fuse to restore the service. Either of these practices will destroy your protection.

Protection for Electric Motors. Notice the two plug-type fuses labeled "Fustat" and "Fusetron" in Fig. 100. These fuses are designed for electric motor circuits. (NOTE: *Fustats* are also used for other types of circuits.)

A ⅓-hp split-phase motor should draw about 8 amperes while running under a normal load, but the same motor would draw from 20 to 40 amperes while getting started.

How does this wide fluctuation affect fuse protection for electric motors? It means that an 8-ampere fuse, which would be correct for this motor, would burn out every time the motor attempts to start. On the other hand, if you were to install a 20-, 30-, or 40-ampere fuse to enable the motor to start, the 8-ampere motor would no longer be protected. It would "burn out" before a 20-, 30-, or 40-ampere fuse would blow.

An 8-ampere Fustat or Fusetron will solve this problem. These fuses are built to stand a heavy overload long enough for an electric motor to start. If the overload persists, however, the Fustat or Fusetron burns out the same as other types. Fig. 101 shows a

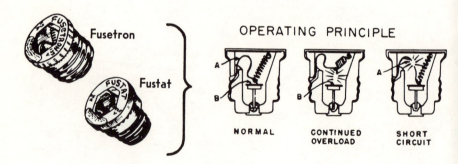

Fig. 100. The Fusetron at upper left is designed for electric motors. The Fustat at lower left is said to be tamper proof because it will fit only the correct size of adapter.

Fig. 101. A Fusetron installed in a water-pump circuit allows heavy overload for a few seconds to enable the motor to start. Fuse blows if overload continues.

Fusetron installed in a separate electric motor circuit. It is necessary to select the fuse to match the ampere load of the motor, and this fuse must serve nothing but the motor it is to protect.

Fustats require a special adapted base that prevents the use of fuses larger than the base is built to carry.

What Size Feeder Circuits Should You Have?

You may find some disagreement in wiring manuals as to the definition of a *feeder* circuit. In this book, two types of circuits are considered feeders: (1) circuits that carry electricity beyond the farmstead meter to all farm buildings or other points of major use, and (2) circuits that carry electricity from a distribution panel to another service entrance, even though this may be in the same building. Fig. 102 shows a farmstead distribution system having several feeder circuits. The main wires from the high-line to the yardpole are called the *service drop*, not feeders.

You will find it easy to determine the wire size needed for each feeder circuit by following three steps:

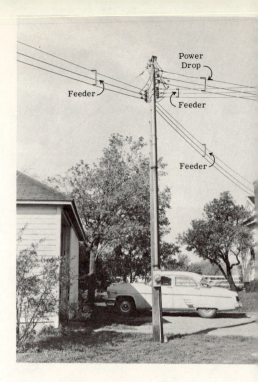

Fig. 102. Electric lines carrying electricity from the meter or fused switch to another service are called *feeders.*

Step 1. List the probable maximum load for each farmstead building to be wired. (NOTE: Use the same data you used in selecting the service entrance for each farmstead building.)

Step 2. Measure the distance from the service switch to the building that is to be wired. This is called the *length of run.*

Step 3. Refer to Table 11B (230-volt service) and select the proper wire size. The sizes in these tables are designed for a maximum of 2 per cent voltage drop. For brooders or other equipment involved in life processes you should increase the wire size indicated in Tables 11A and 11B by one commercial size; that is if No. 3 is indicated, use No. 2, and so on.

EXAMPLE: Select the feeders for the farm home used in the previous example, assuming that the length of run is 140 feet.

SOLUTION: *Step 1:* The probable maximum load was found to be 102.4 amperes.

Step 2: The run is 140 feet.

Step 3: Refer to Table 11B (for 230-volt service). Note that you must use the column for "150 feet" since this is the nearest run stated above 140 feet. Read down column one until you find the bracket containing 102.4 amperes. This falls on the 115-ampere bracket. Read across from "115 amperes" directly under "150 feet." The size indicated is No. 1. This must be checked against Table 12, however, for a safety check, and the data there show that No. 1 WP wire will carry up to 205 amperes in open air; less in enclosed installations.

ANSWER: No. 1 wire is required for the two hot feeders to the farm house, and you may use one standard size smaller (No. 2) for the neutral.

In selecting feeders, remember that additional loads may be added in the future. If you select feeders just large enough to carry your present load, no other electrical services can be added until larger feeders are installed. New feeders would entail the expense of tearing down the old ones, cost of new wire, and the cost of installation. In the long run, it would be less expensive to install adequate size feeders and thus provide for future expansion without re-wiring.

By following the steps presented in the preceding example you can determine the proper size feeders for each farmstead building you wish to wire, and do so with little difficulty. In the main, this job consists of adding amperage loads, measuring distances between buildings, then reading a table—nothing technical or complicated at all.

Summary

One of the most costly mistakes you can make in farmstead wiring is to use cheap or undersize materials. Skimpy wiring prevents the addition of needed electric equipment later.

The first consideration in wiring is to install an adequate system for the exterior distribution of power for the entire farmstead. Pole metering is one of the most economical and efficient methods used. In this system, the meter is located near the center of the electrical load of the farmstead and therefore provides the lowest possible cost of wire for feeder circuits. Also, central metering provides quality service. Central metering can be installed in a building if it is centrally located on the farmstead.

The choice of wire size is an important matter in farmstead wiring. The smallest wire recommended for branch circuits is No. 12, except for small motors. The main service entrance, where a 200- to 400-ampere load may be carried, may require 4/0 wire or larger.

The most accurate method of figuring the sizes of wire and service switches required for a farmstead, or for each farm building, is to total the electrical loads, convert this to the probable maximum load, then refer to wire size tables and select the size indicated. A seven-step formula for determining the wire size is the simplest way to do this. An example using this formula is included in this chapter.

The size of service switches for the average farmstead ranges from 60 to 400 amperes. A rather common size for the main service entrance is 100 or 200 amperes without electric house heating. The size of the service cable for a 200-ampere service switch would likely be 3/0 or 4/0.

A typical service entrance for an electrified 30-cow dairy is a 100-ampere service switch and No. 2 entrance cable. If two 7½-hp motors are added, a 200-ampere switch is needed.

Three types of switches and protection devices are widely used in house wiring. These are (1) the block or plug fuse panel, (2) the circuit breaker, and (3) the disconnect switch, which may be either a fuse type or a fuseless type.

For electric motor protection, a Fusetron is recommended. This type of fuse allows overloads while the motor is starting but blows if the overload continues.

The wire size required for feeder circuits is found by following a method similar to that used in determining the size of the service entrance. Figure the probable maximum load at the building or other service to be supplied by that feeder, measure the length of run, and select the wire size from the proper table.

Questions

1. How can you show that the wiring in a pole metering system is usually less expensive than metering from a building? More efficient?
2. In counting the total load in a farm building, why must the amperage of the largest electric motor be multiplied by 1.25?
3. Why is only 50 per cent of the total amperage of a range counted in totaling the load at the residence?
4. Why will "enclosed" wire carry less amperage than wire in "open air"?
5. Why is it wise to choose the next standard size above that indicated for the entrance service for a farmstead?

Additional Readings

Brown, R. H., *Farm Electrification*. New York, McGraw-Hill, 1956.

Davis, Hollis R., *Adequate Farm Wiring Systems*, Extension Bulletin 849. Ithaca, New York, Cornell University, 1956.

Henderson, G. E., *Planning the Home Wiring System*. Southern Association of Agricultural Engineering and Vocational Agriculture. Athens, Georgia, University of Georgia, 1951.

Industry Committee on Interior Wiring Design, *Farmstead Wiring Handbook*. New York, 1955.

————, *Residential Wiring Handbook*. New York, 1954.

Montgomery Ward & Co., *Modern Wiring*. Chicago, Illinois, 1955.

Richter, Herbert P., *Practical Electricity and House Wiring*. Wilmette, Illinois, Fredrick J. Drake & Co., 1952.

Sears Roebuck & Co., *Electric Wiring*. Chicago, Illinois, 1955.

Wright, Forrest B., *Electricity in the Home and on the Farm*, 3rd ed. New York, John Wiley and Sons, 1950.

CHAPTER 6

*B*ranch Circuits and Outlets for the Farm Home and Farm Service Buildings

After planning the feeder circuit and service entrance for each farmstead building, the next step is to plan the *branch circuits* and *outlets* for each. The purpose of a branch circuit is to carry the proper amount of electricity from a source, usually a fused switch, to the outlets where the electricity is to be used. A branch circuit, then, is the final link in the distribution system.

One farmer made the mistake of using No. 14 wire for a 250-foot branch circuit to operate his 1,150w pig brooder. He thought the two-wire, 115-volt circuit would provide 115 volts times 10 amperes, or 1,150 watts. However, he forgot to figure the voltage drop; so when the brooder failed to operate properly, five pigs died from chilling. A test showed that the voltage at the brooder was 100 volts, not 115; the amperage, at 100 volts, had dropped from 10 to 8 amperes. This was 100 volts times 8 amperes or 800 watts,

Fig. 103. The proper size of wire for a heat lamp insures correct operation.

124

not 1,150 watts as the brooder required. This amounted to 350 watts loss between the fused switch and the brooder. Besides paying for that loss, the farmer lost his profit on the litter. The purchase of the No. 14 wire was false economy. There was only about $2 difference between the cost of No. 14 and the cost of No. 12 wire.

Before you plan your branch circuits, it will pay you to study your present and future needs for electricity. Also, study the most common troubles and faults that are associated with branch circuits as summarized in the following table.

TABLE 13

Summary of Common Faults and Results in Branch Circuits

Circuit Fault	*Usual Result*
Too few circuits	Overloading, poor service
Use of undersize wire	Loss of power; voltage drop; high cost of energy used
Use of 115-volt circuits where 230 volts are required	Loss of power; poor service; reduced life of equipment
Circuits too long	Voltage drop; high cost of wire; high cost of energy used; reduced life of equipment
Too few outlets	Inconvenience; restricted use of electrical equipment; overloading
Too few switches and other controls	Inconvenience; hazard to life and property
Improper controls	Hazard to life and property
Improper junction boxes and connections	Hazard to property; poor service
Miscellaneous unsafe wiring practices	Hazard to life and property; poor electrical service; reduced life of equipment; restricted use of equipment

What Recommendations Should You Follow in Planning All Branch Circuits?

You can profit from the mistakes of others by applying the following recommendations:

1. Plan for a sufficient number of circuits and outlets for each building. Fig. 104 shows a layout of a 200-ampere breaker with thirteen branch circuits serving a modern farm home. A little later you will find a discussion of the types of circuits shown.

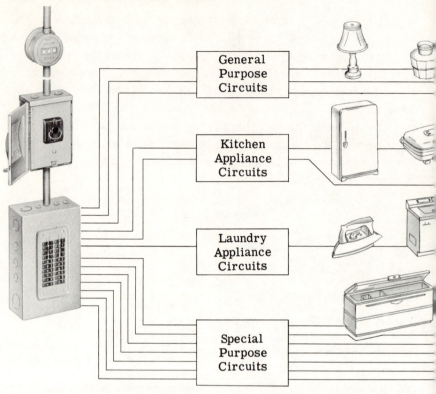

Fig. 104. Thirteen branch circuits are needed for adequate electrical service for the modern farm home.

2. A common rule of thumb is to limit the number of lighting outlets on one circuit to ten and preferably not more than eight. Five or six convenience outlets constitute a load for one branch circuit. Even then, the total load on a two-wire circuit of No. 12 wire should not exceed 2,300 watts. If you already have some circuits wired with No. 14 wire, the total load on any two-wire circuit should not exceed 1,725 watts. Remember, however, that No. 14 wire is *not* considered suitable for branch circuits in a farm home. Always insist on No. 12 gauge or larger, as the load may require.

3. With few exceptions, appliances rated at 1,000 watts or above, and all electric motors ½-hp and over, should be permanently connected. The exceptions are heavy-duty portable motors, room heaters, or other appliances that are used in several locations.

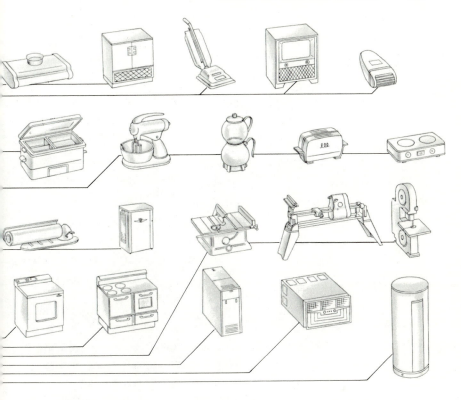

See that the wiring for these appliances is adequate. For example, a 1,500w room heater ordinarily will not operate successfully on a general-purpose circuit; provide a separate appliance circuit.

Fig. 105. This ¾-hp motor is wired in, not plugged in.

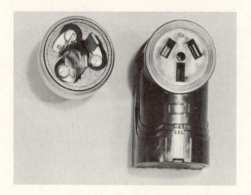

Fig. 106. Three-prong plug and 50-ampere receptacle for a 230-volt range circuit. Cable for this circuit should be at least No. 6, three-wire style.

4. Your range, food freezer, water heater, and other high-wattage equipment should be wired for 230-volt (three-wire) service. Put your food freezer and brooders on an individual circuit to reduce the danger of interruption of the current.

5. For high-wattage equipment requiring a circuit longer than 50 feet, select the wire size by reference to Tables 11A and 11B. No. 12 wire is usually adequate for most household appliances if the run is under 50 feet. Your range, dryer, and water heater, however, may require a wire size larger than No. 12.

6. Insist on standard wiring supplies and good wiring practices. For example, make certain that every splice is properly joined and is protected by junction boxes. Wiring supplies should carry

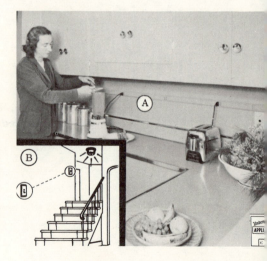

Fig. 107. A Plugmold wiring system in the kitchen (*A*) provides plenty of plug-ins, one every 18 inches in the metal channel. A three-way switch at the head and foot of the stairs (*B*) reduces the falling hazard; the UL label (*C*) is a guarantee of safe wiring materials.

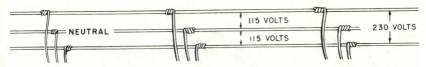

Fig. 108. One hot wire and a neutral = 115 volts; two hot wires with or without a neutral = 230 volts.

the UL label. Also insist on having plenty of wall switches (two- and three-way, as needed) and plan for an adequate number of convenience outlets. Remember that it is less expensive to install adequate wiring at the time your wiring job is done than it is to re-wire.

7. Determine the proper type and size of protection devices for each circuit and follow the strict rule of never over-fusing.

What Types of Branch Circuits Will You Need?

Branch circuits are classified according to (1) voltage rating, and (2) use or purpose.

How to Plan Your Branch Circuits to Meet Voltage Requirements. The voltage of a two-wire circuit may vary from 110 to 120

Fig. 109. Fuses and circuit breakers for the farm home.

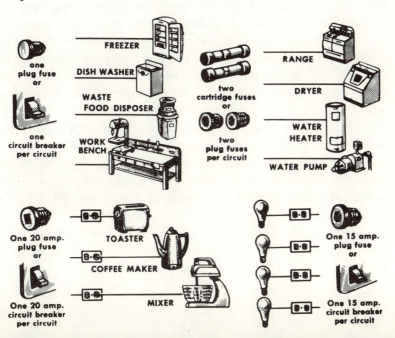

Fig. 110. This carpet sweeper operates on a general-purpose circuit of No. 12 wire, fused at 15 or 20 amperes.

volts, and a three-wire circuit may vary from 220 to 240 volts. To simplify examples, however, this book uses 115 volts for two-wire circuits and 230 volts for three-wire circuits. This voltage is considered average at the point of entry at farm buildings.

Almost every farm wiring system requires both 115- and 230-volt circuits. Two-wire circuits are adequate for lighting and low-wattage appliances. Three-wire service should be provided, however, for all single loads of 1,000 watts and higher. Also, three-wire, 230-volt service is needed for motors rated at ½ hp or more.

Protection Should Match the Type of Circuit. A two-wire circuit should be protected with a 15- or 20-ampere fuse if the wire size is No. 12. If you already have some No. 14 wire in your buildings, fuse these circuits with 10- to 15-ampere fuses. A range usually requires a 50-ampere fuse. Other equipment should be fused according to the amperage rating. Fig. 109 shows common types of fuses for circuits and appliances in the farm home.

Electric motors will draw from two to six times their normal amperage while starting; therefore, circuits that serve electric motors should be protected with a *time-delay fuse*. (See Chapter 5 for a discussion of protection for electric motors.)

How to Plan Branch Circuits According to Purpose. Branch circuits are designed for three purposes: (1) general purpose, (2) appliance, and (3) individual equipment.

Fig. 111. This clothes washer operates on a 20-ampere appliance circuit, No. 12 wire.

1. *General-purpose circuits* serve outlets for lighting, vacuum cleaners, small fans, radios, table lamps, clocks, and other portable household equipment.

2. *Appliance circuits* operate most of the portable equipment in the laundry, dining room, and kitchen with the exception of the range, the high-speed dryer, the food freezer, and other high-wattage equipment.

3. *Individual-equipment circuits* serve high-wattage equipment that is usually installed in a permanent location. The range, dryer, water pump, air conditioner, water heater, and food freezer should have individual circuits for satisfactory service.

The individual circuit may be two-wire, 115-volt, but it is usually three-wire, 230-volt. A special-purpose receptacle is usually

Fig. 112. This food freezer requires an individual-equipment circuit. The motor should be wired in instead of plugged in.

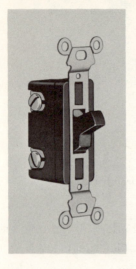

Fig. 113. Yard light controlled by a three-way switch inside the farm home and another three-way switch at the barn.

installed to serve the range; however, individual circuits are usually wired directly to the piece of equipment being served.

Circuit accessories include wall switches, pull-chain switches, convenience outlets, ceiling outlets, special-purpose outlets, junction boxes, outlet boxes, and other miscellaneous items.

A two-way wall switch will control lighting outlets at one location, and a three-way* wall switch will provide control from two different locations. Three-way switches are needed to control outlets at two entrances to a room, to control a yard light or garage light, to control lights for a stairway, and to operate lights in out-of-way places.

Use four-way switches wherever you may need to control a light from three different locations. A room having three entrances or a yard light would be an example of this need.

Use a pull-chain switch to control lights in a closet or bathroom. A pull chain must have an insulated, nonconducting link in it to protect against shock. Never install any pull chain or other electric fixtures in a location that can be reached from the bath tub or shower.

Most convenience outlets should be of the duplex receptacle type, which provide two places for plugging in at one outlet. (See

_____

* The term "three-way" indicates that a switch has three terminals on it and will control a circuit at two locations. A four-way switch has four terminals on it and will control a circuit at three locations.

Fig. 114. A pull-chain light fixture is suitable for use in closets, bathrooms, and other small spaces.

Fig. 115.) Your range will probably be equipped with a special-purpose plug having three blades arranged in such a way that it can be plugged into the outlet in only one position. Your 230-volt air conditioner, and perhaps other high-wattage equipment, may have a 230-volt polarized plug-in.

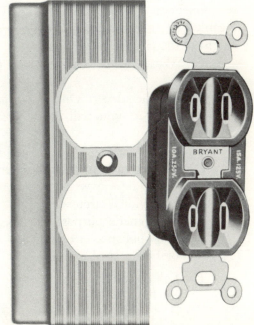

Fig. 115. A duplex receptacle has two plug-in positions.

How Many Circuits of Different Types Will Be Needed for the Farm Home?

In a previous example, you selected a 200-ampere entrance switch for your residence and selected the service entrance cable and the feeder circuit for a maximum demand of 102.4 amperes. Using the same 2,000-square-foot residence, design the number and type of the branch circuits needed.

General-Purpose Circuits. Allow one general-purpose circuit for each 500 square feet of floor area as a minimum; for extra-heavy use of electric equipment, this should be increased by one circuit.

2,000 sq ft ÷ 500 = 4 (minimum) or 5 (heavy usage). Total 4

Appliance Circuits. Allow at least two 115-volt, 20-ampere circuits for kitchen and dining room appliances.

Sub-total   2

Allow at least one appliance circuit for the laundry.

Sub-total   1

Total number of all appliance circuits: Total   3

Individual Circuits. Each of the following high-wattage appliances should have a separate circuit:

(a) Air conditioner: One 115-230-volt circuit, No. 12 wire minimum.   Sub-total   1

(b) Range: One 230-volt circuit, using fuse and wire size as recommended by the manufacturer. This will be three-wire, No. 6 cable or larger, depending on the wattage of the range and the length of the circuit.   Sub-total   1

(c) Water heater: One 230-volt circuit.

Sub-total   1

(d) Washer-dryer: One 115-230-volt circuit. If you have a high-speed dryer, you will need No. 8 or No. 6 cable for the circuit.   Sub-total   1

(e) Food freezer.   Sub-total   1

(f) Shop equipment and other items in the basement.

Sub-total   1

Total individual circuits: Total   6

1. Total general purpose circuits: 4
2. Total appliance circuits: 3
3. Total individual circuits: 6

Total all circuits: 13

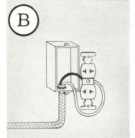
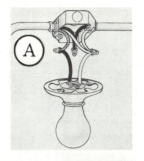
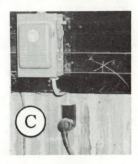

Fig. 116. Outlets for the farm home: (A) lighting outlet, one for each 150 square feet of floor area; (B) convenience outlet, no point on wall more than 6 feet from an outlet; (C) special purpose, three-wire, 230-volt outlet for a range or other high-wattage equipment.

Circuits for Smaller Homes. For a small farm home having less need for electricity, a 60-ampere service entrance may be satisfactory. This will provide for a range, a water heater, two general-purpose circuits, and two appliance circuits. No major appliances can be added.

A 100-ampere service entrance provides for sixteen branch circuits, but the total capacity is 23,000 watts as compared to 46,000 for the 200-ampere size.

If there is a chance that you will increase your present use of electricity, you should select a service entrance capacity of not less than 100 amperes, leaving spare circuit positions for future use.

What Outlets and Accessories Will Be Needed for the Farm Home?

The data contained in Table 14 will help you to complete the plan for the electrical system in your farm home.

An *outlet* is a place in a circuit from which electricity may be taken and used for an appliance. It may be a box in which the wires for a ceiling light are terminated and connected to a ceiling lamp

Fig. 117. Symbols used in wiring plans.

These symbols have been extracted or adapted from American Standards Association Standard, ASA Z32 9-1943, wherever possible. Adaptations and new symbols included in this list have been proposed for inclusion in the next revision of that standard.

General Outlets

○ — Lighting Outlet

▢Ⓞ▢ — Ceiling Lighting Outlet for recessed fixture (Outline shows shape of fixture.)

— Continuous Wireway for Fluorescent Lighting on ceiling, in coves, cornices, etc. (Extend rectangle to show length of installation.)

Ⓛ — Lighting Outlet with Lamp Holder

Ⓛ$_{PS}$ — Lighting Outlet with Lamp Holder and Pull Switch

Ⓕ — Fan Outlet

Ⓙ — Junction Box

Ⓓ — Drop-Cord Equipped Outlet

Ⓒ — Clock Outlet

To indicate wall installation of above outlets, place circle near wall and connect with line as shown for clock outlet.

Convenience Outlets

⊖ — Duplex Convenience Outlet

⊖$_3$ — Triplex Convenience Outlet (Substitute other numbers for other variations in number of plug positions.)

⊖ — Duplex Convenience Outlet – Split Wired

⊖$_{GR}$ — Duplex Convenience Outlet for Grounding-Type Plugs

⊖$_{WP}$ — Weatherproof Convenience Outlet

⊖ X″ — Multi-Outlet Assembly (Extend arrows to limits of installation. Use appropriate symbol to indicate type of outlet. Also indicate spacing of outlets as X inches.)

⊖–S — Combination Switch and Convenience Outlet

⊖Ⓡ — Combination Radio and Convenience Outlet

⊙ — Floor Outlet

⊖$_R$ — Range Outlet

▲$_{DW}$ — Special-Purpose Outlet. Use subscript letters to indicate function. DW-Dishwasher, CD-Clothes Dryer, etc.

Switch Outlets

S — Single Pole Switch

S$_3$ — Three-Way Switch

S$_4$ — Four-Way Switch

S$_D$ — Automatic Door Switch

S$_P$ — Switch and Pilot Light

S$_{WP}$ — Weatherproof Switch

S$_2$ — Double-Pole Switch

Low-Voltage and Remote-Control Switching Systems

$\underline{S}$ — Switch for Low-Voltage Relay Systems

$\underline{MS}$ — Master Switch for Low-Voltage Relay Systems

○$_R$ — Relay–Equipped Lighting Outlet

– – – – – Low-Voltage Relay System Wiring

Auxiliary Systems.

▣ — Push Button

▽| — Buzzer

◁ — Bell

◁▽ — Combination Bell-Buzzer

CH — Chime

◇ — Annunciator

Ⓓ — Electric Door Opener

Ⓜ — Maid's Signal Plug

▢ — Interconnection Box

Ⓣ — Bell-Ringing Transformer

▶ — Outside Telephone

▷ — Interconnecting Telephone

Ⓡ — Radio Outlet

TV — Television Outlet

Miscellaneous

▨ — Service Panel

▬ — Distribution Panel

– – – – Switch Leg Indication. Connects outlets with control points.

○$_{a,b}$
⊖$_{a,b}$
▲$_{a,b}$
▢$_{a,b}$ — Special Outlets. Any standard symbol given above may be used with the addition of subscript letters to designate some special variation of standard equipment for a particular architectural plan. When so used, the variation should be explained in the Key of Symbols and, if necessary, in the specifications.

fixture, or it may refer to a receptacle where electric devices can be plugged in for using electricity.

For wiring the residence, three types of outlets will be needed: (1) ceiling or lighting outlets; (2) convenience outlets; and (3) special-purpose outlets such as range receptacles and other polarized plug-ins.

The general rule for determining the number of lighting outlets needed in a residence is one outlet for each 150 square feet of floor area. A 14 x 14 room would contain 196 square feet and would need two lighting outlets. Convenience outlets are specified on the basis of linear feet of usable wall lines. (See Table 14 for specifications.)

In addition to an adequate number of switches needed inside your farm home, you should have three-way switches for your yard lights and garage lights so that they can be turned on or off at both ends of the circuit.

Before studying the information in Table 14, you will find it helpful to familiarize yourself with the electrical symbols in Fig. 117. Then refer to the typical wiring plan for a farm home in Fig. 118 and see whether you can read the symbols. Later, when you begin to make wiring plans yourself, you will need to use these symbols quite often.

Fig. 118. Typical wiring plan for three-bedroom farm home.

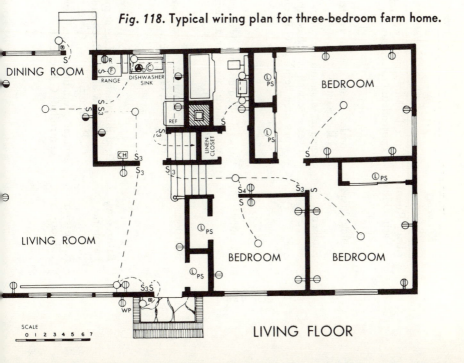

DINING ROOM

RANGE   DISHWASHER SINK

REF

LINEN CLOSET

CH

BEDROOM

BEDROOM

BEDROOM

LIVING ROOM

WP

SCALE
0 1 2 3 4 5 6 7

LIVING FLOOR

TABLE 14*

Summary of Electric Outlets for the Farm Home

Room or Space	Lighting Outlets	Convenience Outlets	Special-Purpose Outlets
Living Room, Farm Office	General illumination, wall switch controlled; G.P. circuit.	No point at wall line more than 6 feet from an outlet; outlet in mantel shelf; 2 or more outlets, switch controlled; G.P. circuit.	1 for room air conditioner; Ind. circuit.
Dining Areas	1 outlet, wall switch controlled; G.P. circuit.	No point at wall line more than 6 feet from an outlet. App. circuit.	
Kitchen	General illumination plus light over sink, wall-switch controlled; work area lighting; G.P. circuit.	1 for every 4 feet of kitchen work surface frontage; 1 at refrigerator location; 1 at table space; App. circuit.	1 for range, Ind. circuit; 1 for clock, G.P. circuit; 1 for fan, G.P. circuit; 1 for dishwasher-waste disposal unit (if plumbing facilities are installed), Ind. circuit.
Laundry	General illumination, wall switch controlled; work-area lighting; G.P. circuit.	1 outlet, at least; App. circuit.	1 for washer, Ind. circuit; 1 for hand iron or ironer, App. circuit; 1 for clothes dryer, Ind. circuit; 1 for water heater, Ind. circuit.
Bedrooms	General illumination, wall switch controlled; G.P. circuit.	No point at wall line more than 6 feet from an outlet; Outlet on each side and within 6 feet of center line of each bed location; G.P. circuit.	1 for room air conditioner, Ind. circuit.
Bathrooms, Lavatories	Good illumination of face at mirror essential, wall switch controlled; G. P. circuit.	1 near mirror; G.P. circuit.	1 for built-in space heater, Ind. circuit; 1 for built-in fan, wall switch controlled, G.P. circuit.
Recreation Room	General illumination, wall switch controlled, G.P. circuit.	No point at wall line more than 6 feet from an outlet; outlet in mantel shelf; G.P. circuit.	

Location			
Hall	General illumination, wall switch controlled; G.P. circuit.	1 for each 15 feet of hallway; halls over 25 sq ft at least one outlet; G.P. circuit.	
Stairways	Outlets for adequate illumination of each stair flight. Multiple control at head and foot of stairway; G.P. circuit.	1 at intermediate landings; G.P. circuit.	
Closets	1 outlet; G.P. circuit.		
Exterior Entrances	1 or more outlets, wall switch controlled; G.P. circuit.	1 preferably near front entrance; G.P. circuit.	
Porches	Outlet for area greater than 75 sq ft, wall switch controlled; G.P. circuit.	1 for each 15 feet of wall bordering porch; G.P. circuit.	
Terraces and Patios	General illumination, wall switch controlled; G.P. circuit.	1 for each 15 feet of wall bordering terrace or patio; G.P. circuit.	
Basement and Utility Space	General illumination of work areas, equipment, and stairways; G.P. circuit.	2 outlets, one at work-bench location; G.P. circuit.	1 for electrical equipment in connection with furnace, Ind. circuit; 1 for freezer, Ind. circuit.
Accessible Attics	1 outlet, wall switch controlled; 1 for each enclosed space; G.P. circuit.	1 for general use; G.P. circuit.	1 for cooling fan, with switch control, Ind. circuit.
Garage	1 for one or two-car garage, wall-switch controlled; 1 for exterior lighting, multiple-switch controlled if garage is detached from house; G.P. circuits.	1 for one or two car garage; G.P. circuit.	If food freezer, work bench or automatic door opener is planned, provide appropriate outlets, Ind. circuits.

* Farmstead Wiring Handbook (New York, The Industry Committee on Interior Wiring Design, 1955), pp. 23, 24. (Slightly condensed.)

Codes used to designate circuit types: G.P. = General-purpose circuit; App. = Appliance circuit; Ind. = Individual-equipment circuit.

A convenience outlet should be of the duplex type (two or more plug-in positions) at least, except as otherwise specified.

All spaces for which wall switch controls are required, and which have more than one entrance, should be equipped with multiple-switch control at each principal entrance. If this requirement would result in the placing of the switches less than 10 feet apart, one of them may be eliminated.

139

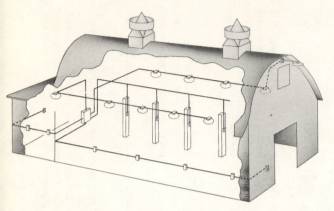

Fig. 119. A modern dairy barn containing five circuits.

What Branch Circuits and Outlets Will Be Needed
for Each Farm Service Building?

For general recommendations on branch circuits refer to the first part of this chapter. Code requirements and other suggestions may be found in that section of the book. The demand for electric energy to do farm chores is becoming so great that the only satisfactory wiring arrangement for the future will be a separate service entrance for each major farm service building. This will involve not only a service entrance for the building, but will also require

Fig. 120. The cover of an authoritative book on standards and recommendations for farmstead wiring.

Farmstead
Wiring
Handbook

A
Guide
to
Electrical
Planning
for
Farmsteads

Industry Committee on Interior Wiring Design

one or more branch circuits according to the needs in that particular building. For example, a modern dairy may require five or more branch circuits, whereas a potato storage house might require only one or two. But separate service entrances will be needed for both.

Ordinarily, the least expensive type of wiring you can use in farm buildings is non-metallic sheathed cable. In barns, however, where strong fumes and extreme dampness are present, you may save money in the long run by choosing neoprene-covered wire. Chapter 7 contains a discussion of the major types of wiring.

The specifications in Table 15, along with the wiring diagrams, are typical for farm service buildings throughout the country. By studying these diagrams and referring to Table 15, you should be able to plan the branch circuits and outlets for each farm building.

TABLE 15*

Summary of Electric Outlets for Farm Buildings

Type of Outlet	Location of Outlet	Conditions to Observe
	DAIRY BARN	
Lighting	Every 12 feet in litter alley and 15 feet in feed alley	
Convenience	Every 20 feet in litter alley	For portable milkers, clippers, immersion heaters, infrared lamps, sprayers, etc.
	At certain windows and doors	For electric fly screens
	At ventilating fans	Less than ½ hp
Special	At ventilating fan	½ hp and larger
Purpose	At pipe-line milker	½ hp and larger (230 volts)
	At gutter cleaner	1 or 2 large motors required

* *Farmstead Wiring.* Pittsburgh, Pennsylvania, Westinghouse Electric Corporation, 1943.

Fig. 121. Wiring plan for a dairy barn.

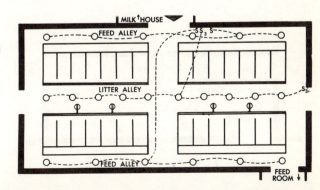

TABLE 15 (Continued)

Summary of Electric Outlets for Farm Buildings

Type of Outlet	Location of Outlet	Conditions to Observe
LOAFING BARN (COWS NOT IN STANCHIONS)		
Lighting	1 for every 150 sq ft open pen area	Place outlets in feed alley, every 20 feet
Convenience	At convenient locations	For clippers, immersion heaters, sprayers, etc.
Special Purpose	At water pipes	For heating cable to protect water system
BOX STALLS AND PENS		
Lighting	1 per stall	In low-partitioned stalls, one outlet located over separating partition may serve two stalls
Convenience	1 per stall	In low-partitioned stalls, one outlet may serve two stalls
Special Purpose	At water pipes	For heating cable to protect water system
MILKING BARN OR MILKING ROOM		
Lighting	1 for every 3 cows, in passage front of cows 1 for every 2 cows, in passage back of cows	
Convenience	1 for every 5 cows	For portable milkers, clippers, immersion heaters, sprayers
	At ventilating fans	Less than ½ hp
Special Purpose	At ventilating fan	½ hp and larger
	At milking machine	½ hp and larger (230 volts)
MILKING PARLOR		
Lighting	At rear of each cow on center line of pit	Light for cleaning cow's udder and for milking
	At each entrance and exit	Light for entering and leaving

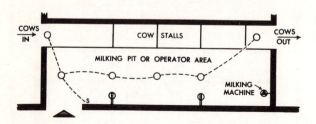

Fig. 122. Wiring plan for a milking parlor.

TABLE 15 (Continued)

Summary of Electric Outlets for Farm Buildings

Type of Outlet	*Location of Outlet*	*Conditions to Observe*
Convenience	Every 2 cows on either side of pit	For clippers, immersion heater, lamp, clock, radio, portable milker (if used)
Special Purpose	1 outlet at one end of milking parlor or milker may be located in separate room	For operating milking machine
	1 outlet at window	For ventilating fan

MILK HOUSE OR MILKROOM

Lighting	1 for every 100 sq ft floor area, and at loading platform	
Convenience	At each work area	For portable appliances, such as plug-in water heaters and motor-driven devices of less than ½ hp
	At ventilating fans	Less than ½ hp
Special Purpose	At ventilating fan	½ hp and larger
	At milk cooler	½ hp and larger (230 volts)
	At water heater	Omitted where 115-volt plug-in heaters are used
	At utensil sterilizer	

Fig. 123. Wiring plan for a milk house.

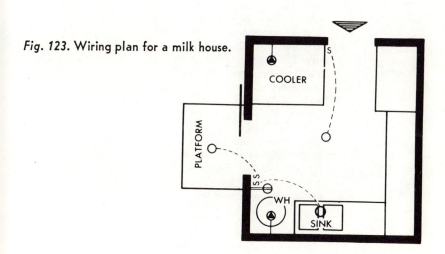

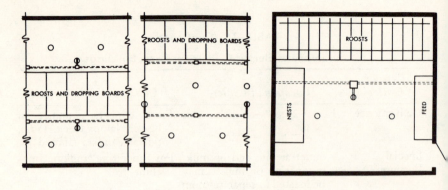

Fig. 124. Wiring plans for three types of laying houses.

TABLE 15 (Continued)

Summary of Electric Outlets for Farm Buildings

Type of Outlet	Location of Outlet	Conditions to Observe
	LAYING HOUSE	
Lighting	1 for every 200 sq ft floor area	Time switch controlled (Reflectors desirable for all lighting units)
	(a) 20 ft deep house—one row of outlets 10 feet apart on center line between dropping board and front of house	
	(b) Greater than 20 feet in depth: with roosts at back of pen; two rows of outlets on 10 feet centers, staggered. With roosts in center; two rows of outlets on 10 feet centers, one row on center line between dropping board and front of house, the other between dropping board and rear	

TABLE 15 (Continued)

Summary of Electric Outlets for Farm Buildings

Type of Outlet	Location of Outlet	Conditions to Observe
Lighting (With Dimmers)	Bright lights: 1 for every 200 sq ft floor area (Locate same as outlined under Item 27)	Time switch controlled (Reflectors desirable for all lighting units)
	Dim lights: 1 for every 400 sq ft floor area. Placed in a row slightly back of bright light outlets, toward roosts	Time switch controlled
Lighting (All Night)	One 10-15w unit for every 200 sq ft floor area (Locate same over feeding areas)	Wall switch control outlets in each pen (Time switch controlled if desired)
Convenience	1 for every 400 sq ft floor area, but at least one in every pen (On post in center or on wall)	For portable poultry water heaters and for small manually-controlled ventilating fans
Special Purpose	At ventilating fan	Automatic control desirable

(NOTE: See local authorities for wiring plans.)

BROODER HOUSE (PORTABLE OR INDIVIDUAL TYPE)

Lighting	On ceiling or wall	
Convenience	On ceiling in center of space	To serve brooder (also water warmer if needed—1,150 watt)

BROODER HOUSE (COLONY TYPE)

Lighting	1 per brooder pen	Controlled individually or in groups
Special Purpose	1 in each pen for brooder	1,000w brooder and 150w for water warmer

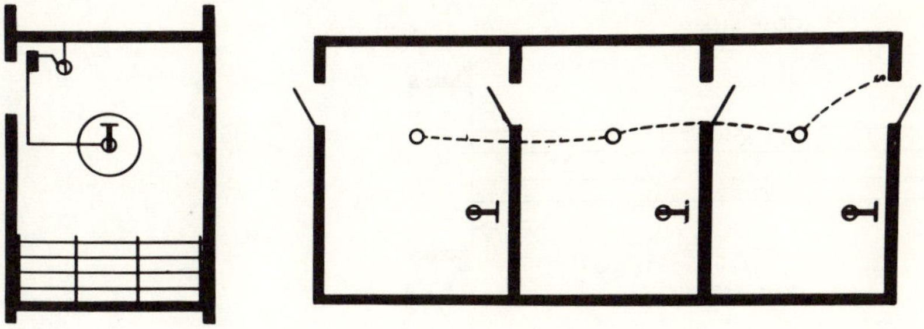

Fig. 125. Wiring plan for two types of brooder houses.

TABLE 15 (Continued)

Summary of Electric Outlets for Farm Buildings

Type of Outlet	Location of Outlet	Conditions to Observe
EGG STORAGE AND HANDLING ROOM		
Lighting	1 for every 200 sq ft floor area, and 2 over each working surface	
Convenience	At egg cooler or humidifier fan	
	At egg candler, egg cleaner and egg grader	
Special Purpose	At refrigeration unit	½ hp and larger (230 volts)
POULTRY DRESSING ROOM		
Lighting	1 for every 200 sq ft floor area and 2 over each working surface	
Convenience	1 for every 400 sq ft floor area	For general-purpose use
Special Purpose	At poultry scalder	1,000 to 4,500 watts (230 volts)
	At waxer	1,000 watts (230 volts)
	At picking machine	¾ to 1½ hp (230 volts)
	At refrigerator	½ hp and up (230 volts)
BEEF CATTLE BARN		
Lighting	1 for every 250 sq ft pen area	Place outlets in feed alley, every 20 feet
Convenience	At convenient locations	For clippers, sprayers, etc.
Special Purpose	At ventilating fan	½ hp and larger (230 volts)
	At feed mixer and conveyer	½ hp and larger (230 volts)

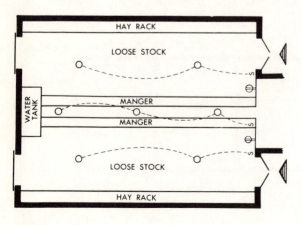

Fig. 126. Wiring plan for a beef cattle barn.

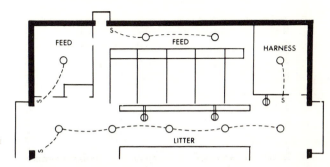

Fig. 127. Wiring plan for a horse barn.

TABLE 15 (Continued)

Summary of Electric Outlets for Farm Buildings

Type of Outlet	Location of Outlet	Conditions to Observe
	HORSE STABLES (TIE STALLS)	
Lighting	1 in back of each pair tie stalls	
	1 per box stall	Where partition separates stalls, one outlet may be located over partition to serve two stalls
	HORSE STABLE (INDIVIDUAL STALLS)	
Lighting	Every 20 feet in feed alley, and 1 for each pair of stalls (Locate outlet over partition)	If partition is high, provide one for each stall
Convenience	1 for every four stalls in service alley	
	SHEEP BARN AND LAMBING SHED	
Lighting	Every 20 feet of feed alley and 1 for every 250 sq ft of pen area	
Convenience	1 for each pair of pens (located over partition)	For lamb brooders
	At shearing location	For sheep shearing

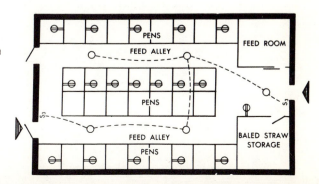

Fig. 128. Wiring plan for a lambing shed.

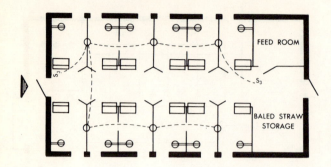

Fig. 129. Wiring plan for a farrowing house.

TABLE 15 (Continued)

Summary of Electric Outlets for Farm Buildings

Type of Outlet	Location of Outlet	Conditions to Observe
	Hog and Farrowing House	
Lighting	1 at each pair of pens (located over partition)	
Convenience	At each farrowing pen	For pig brooders; where building structure permits, one outlet may serve two pens
	Farm Shop	
Lighting	1 for every 200 sq ft floor area	
	1 for each item of permanently placed equipment, such as drill press, saw, anvil; 1 for each 10 feet of bench length	Reflector units desirable
Convenience	1 for each 10 feet bench length (also on post in center of room, if desired)	
	1 for each permanently placed piece of equipment	Less than ½ hp
Special Purpose	At drills, grinders and forges	½ hp and larger (230 volts)
	Arc welder	Only special farm-size welders should be considered. Welders are being developed with electrical characteristics especially suited for use on rural electric lines. Also, most utility companies have regulations concerning the use of welders on rural lines.

TABLE 15 (Continued)

Summary of Electric Outlets for Farm Buildings

Type of Outlet	Location of Outlet	Conditions to Observe
		To assure the most satisfactory results, it will be advantageous for the planner of the wiring system to consult the local utility company
	MACHINERY SHEDS	
Lighting	1 for every 300 sq ft floor area	
Convenience	1 for every 500 sq ft floor area (at least 1 per building)	For portable tools for doing minor repairs
	GARAGE	
Lighting	1 for every 200 sq ft and 1 over each workbench	
Convenience	1 at each workbench	
	At least 1 between each two vehicles	For charger, trouble lamp, etc.
	STAIRS AND PASSAGEWAYS	
Lighting	2 outlets at each stairway, 1 at head and 1 at foot (Locate outlets to avoid shadows and glare)	3-way switches where exit is normally made without retracing steps
	1 for every 25 linear feet of passageway (Locate outlets to avoid shadows and glare)	3-way switches where exit is normally made without retracing steps
	FEED HANDLING ROOM	
Lighting	1 for every 200 sq ft floor area	Reflector units desirable
Convenience	At fan, small corn sheller, fanning mill, etc.	Less than ½ hp
Special Purpose	At feed grinder	½ hp and larger (230 volts)
	At feed mixer	½ hp and larger (230 volts)
	At corn sheller	½ hp and larger (230 volts)
	At grain elevator	½ hp and larger (230 volts)
	CROP STORAGE ROOMS AND CRIBS	
Lighting	1 for every 400 sq ft floor area. Spaces less than 20 sq ft need not be provided with outlet	
Special Purpose	Grain elevators and blowers	½ hp and larger (230 volts)

TABLE 15 (Continued)
Summary of Electric Outlets for Farm Buildings

Type of Outlet	*Location of Outlet*	*Conditions to Observe*
	BARN FLOOR AREA	
Lighting	1 for every 400 sq ft floor area	
Convenience	1 for every 1,000 sq ft floor area	For general-purpose use
Special Purpose	At hay hoist	2 hp and larger (230 volts)
	At hay dryer	3 to 7½ hp (230 volts)
	At portable elevator	1 hp and larger (230 volts) (with portable motor, one outlet may serve various machines)
	HAYMOW OR HAYLOFT	
Lighting	At least 1 for haymow	Glass or metal protector for bulb
Special Purpose	At hay hoist	2 hp and larger (230 volts)
	At hay dryer	3 to 7½ hp (230 volts)
	SILO	
Lighting	1 at roof of silo; 1 at top; and 1 at bottom of chute	Outlets in chute to be controlled at foot of chute or at entrance to chute tunnel
Special Purpose	At ensilage cutter, blower	5 to 7½ hp (230 volts)
	At silo unloader	1 hp and larger (230 volts)
	FRUIT AND VEGETABLE STORAGE	
Lighting	Every 20 feet of alley	
Convenience	1 for every 400 sq ft floor area	
Special Purpose	At refrigeration equipment	½ hp and larger (230 volts)
	At ventilating fans	½ hp and larger (230 volts)
	ROADSIDE STAND	
Lighting	1 pair for every 50 sq ft display area and at floodlights and signs	
Convenience	At convenient locations	For space heater, refrigerator, etc.
Special Purpose	At convenient locations	For refrigeration, ½ hp and larger (230 volts)
	PUMP HOUSE	
Lighting	1 centrally located	
Convenience	At pump	
Special Purpose	For pump	½ hp and larger (230 volts)

Summary

The circuits leading from the service switch to the various lighting fixtures, plug-ins, and appliances are referred to as branch circuits. In a modern farm home there may be from twelve to fifteen of these. Usually, there are three types of branch circuits according to use: (1) general-purpose, (2) appliance, and (3) individual-equipment circuits. A 2,000-square-foot farm home would likely need four general-purpose circuits, three appliance circuits, and six for individual equipment. The latter group includes circuits for the range, the washer, and other high-wattage items.

According to wattage or amperage load carried, branch circuits are classified as two-wire, 115 volts; and three-wire, 230 volts. For single loads of 1,000 watts or more, and for motors of ½ hp or higher rating, individual circuits should be used.

No. 12 wire is the smallest that should be used in a branch circuit in the farm home, and 2,300 watts is the maximum load for a two-wire circuit. Also, a 20-ampere fuse is the largest that is safe for a two-wire circuit of No. 12 wire.

Three types of outlets are used in farmstead wiring including (1) lighting, (2) convenience or plug-in, and (3) special purpose.

No more than ten (preferably eight) outlets of any kind should be on a two-wire circuit of No. 12 wire. Usually only one special-purpose outlet is installed in a circuit for an individual piece of equipment. A special-purpose outlet usually has a three-blade plug-in that polarizes an appliance with the hot and neutral wires by the way the blades fit in only one position in the receptacle.

All convenience outlets should have at least two plug-in positions. This type of outlet is called a duplex receptacle. Generally, plug-ins should be installed 12 inches above the floor level or at convenient heights in the kitchen, the workshop, the milk room, and in other work areas. In the farm home, there should be no wall line longer than 6 feet without a plug-in. Doors do not count here, but windows do.

Generally, lighting outlets should be controlled by wall switches installed about 48 inches above floor level. Lighting outlets in closets and other narrow spaces, where pull-chain switches can be used, are exceptions to this rule. Switches of the three- or four-way type should be used where lighting outlets need to be controlled from two or three locations.

Questions

1. Why may a long branch circuit of small wire deliver less wattage than is required for an appliance to operate properly?
2. What is the advantage in using three-wire circuits for electric motors larger than ½ hp?
3. Why should a two-wire branch circuit be limited to ten outlets of any kind?
4. Why is No. 12 wire now recommended instead of No. 14 for both general-purpose and appliance circuits?
5. How many two-wire branch circuits could be wired from a 200-ampere service switch?

Additional Readings

Brown, R. H., *Farm Electrification*. New York, McGraw-Hill, 1956.

Davis, Hollis R., *Adequate Farm Wiring Systems*, Extension Bulletin 849. Ithaca, New York, Cornell University, 1956.

Henderson, G. E., *Planning the Home Wiring System*. Southern Association of Agricultural Engineering and Vocational Agriculture. Athens, Georgia, University of Georgia, 1951.

Industry Committee on Interior Wiring Design, *Farmstead Wiring Handbook*. New York, 1955.

————, *Residential Wiring Handbook*. New York, 1954.

Richter, Herbert P., *Practical Electricity and House Wiring*. Wilmette, Illinois, Fredrick J. Drake & Co., 1952.

Sears Roebuck & Co., *Electric Wiring*. Chicago, Illinois, 1955.

Westinghouse Electric Corporation, *Farmstead Wiring*. Pittsburgh, Pennsylvania, 1943.

Wright, Forrest B., *Electricity in the Home and on the Farm*, 3rd ed. New York, John Wiley and Sons, 1950.

CHAPTER 7

How to Get
Ready for a
Wiring Job

Before purchasing any wiring supplies or electricians' tools check the following:

1. Be certain that you understand the important national and local code regulations that may affect your wiring plans. For example, will you be required to have conduit for the service entrance? Will you be allowed to use pole metering? Will the local inspector approve a wiring job done by you personally? Will the local power company serve your new job? May you use galvanized water pipe for your ground rod?

2. What type of wiring is best for your situation?

3. What tools are needed? Can you have them available?

4. What kind of wiring plans are needed? How can you use them?

What Wiring Regulations Should You Observe?

Your wiring plans are controlled by certain regulations:

1. *The National Electrical Code.* The nature of the National Electrical Code is covered in detail in Chapter 4. The purpose of this code is to protect property by preventing dangerous wiring. Instructions throughout this book conform to the National Electrical Code and, if you follow them, your wiring plan should pass all inspections. However, it is advisable to check your final wiring plans with your power supplier to make certain that your diagram meets all requirements.

2. In some rural areas, especially in communities near large cities, a *local electrical code* may apply also. Local codes are often stricter than the National Electrical Code. If you comply with the local code, this will usually satisfy the requirements of the National Code also. Power suppliers in some areas will not serve a newly-wired building unless it is covered by a permit from city officials showing that the wiring materials and installation are in accordance with the local code. Sometimes this procedure requires the payment of an inspection fee. Therefore, it is wise to determine the nature of the code requirements that apply to you before you start your wiring job. Finally, determine whether you will be permitted to install your own wiring system. In some areas, only licensed electricians are permitted to wire a building.

3. The power supplier serving your farm should be consulted in planning a large wiring job, because your plan might require a new power drop or a new transformer; there is a possibility also that the present high line will not be adequate. If your power supplier cannot provide the new service you need, it would be foolish to go to the expense of buying and installing wiring that you cannot use.

Fig. 130. A new transformer and larger power-drop wire were required when this farm was re-wired.

Fig. 131. The UL label on switches tells you that they meet safety standards.

What Kind of Wiring Materials Should You Choose?

Of the hundreds of different types and styles of wire on the market only about two dozen are used on the farm. You will find it to your advantage to choose the right wire for the job, because this is the best way to combine economy, good service, and long life for your wiring. For example, it is poor economy to wire a light-duty motor with expensive heavy-duty portable cable. Yet it is poor management to skimp on buying light-duty cord for a heavy-duty motor, since the result will be poor service and perhaps a "burned out" motor too.

To make certain that you always get the right wiring, select wiring supplies and equipment that are stamped with the UL label. Also, learn the characteristics of the types of wire commonly used on the farm.

You will need to become familiar with four classifications of wiring: (1) styles of wire, (2) types of wire for outside use, (3) wire for special purposes, and (4) wire for interior use.

How to Choose the Proper Style of Wire. Seven styles of electric wire most commonly used on the farm are shown in Fig. 132 and are described below.

1. *Single-Conductor Wire.* The first sample of wire in Fig. 132 is a single-conductor style composed of small strands twisted together. This style also comes in a solid-wire conductor and is finished in numerous ways. The sample shown here is a well-constructed cord finished with (1) a fabric wrap on the wire (nylon, silk, cotton, etc.); (2) a course of heat-resisting rubber insulation

1.

2.

3.

4.

5.

6.

7.

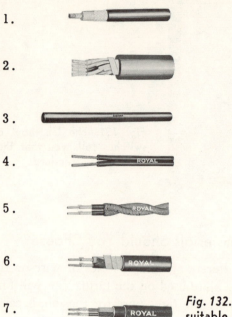

Fig. 132. Seven styles of wire
suitable for use on the farm.

over the fabric; (3) a second course of fabric over the rubber; and
(4) an outer jacket of heat-resisting rubber.

2. *Cable.* A conductor containing two or more separate conductors is referred to as cable. The lighter weight wiring materials
of this style are usually called cords or lamp cords instead of cable.
Sample 2 shows a piece of heavy-duty rubber-covered cable (also
referred to as cord) containing four conductors.

(NOTE: The letter *R* refers to rubber covering and *RH* refers to a better grade of rubber; that is, a heat-resisting rubber.)

3. *Bare Ground Wire.* Sample 3 shows a piece of bare copper
ground wire. This is used for grounding the electrical system, generally at the service entrance.

4. *Parallel Lamp Cord.* Sample 4 is a piece of No. 18 gauge,
two-conductor lamp cord. Numerous small strands are twisted together to form the conductors. The sample shown is covered with
plastic, but rubber covering is often used for this type of wire.

5. *Braided Lamp Cord* (*Twisted*). Notice the better construction of this lamp cord in comparison with sample 4. The additional courses of inner and outer fabric make this style more
durable.

6. *Portable Cord.* The sample of wire shown here is widely used for extension cord where the wire is not subjected to mechanical abuse. Notice the order of construction: (1) fabric wrap, (2) rubber insulation, (3) reinforcing fibers, (4) paper wrap, and (5) rubber jacket.

7. *Reinforced Portable Cord.* This cord is more durable than plain portable cord. Notice the two jackets of rubber in addition to the fabric wrap, rubber insulation, and braid.

How to Choose Wire for Outside Use. The common types of wire for outside use on the farm are shown in Fig. 133.

1. *Overhead Weatherproof Wire* (*WP*). The sample of WP wire shown here is the type most widely used for overhead wiring on the farm. This is a single-conductor wire, insulated with asphalt compound and covered with a tough fibrous outer jacket. Weatherproof wire is not safe for use inside buildings.

2. *Service Entrance Cable* (*SE*). Service entrance cable is a durable wire used for connecting the meter to the service switch. Notice the durable construction consisting of (1) stranded conductor, (2) rubber insulation, (3) fibrous wrap, (4) bare stranded neutral, (5) paper wrap, and (6) outer jacket.

3. *Conduit Service Wires; Red, Black, and White.* The three wires shown here are single-conductor style with three colors of outer jackets to provide for polarity. Wires are rubber insulated.

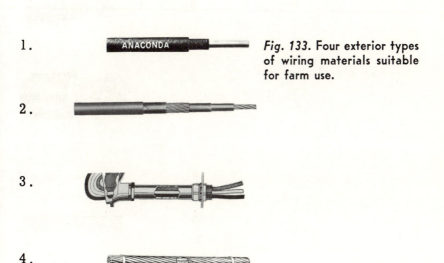

1.

2.

3.

4.

Fig. 133. Four exterior types of wiring materials suitable for farm use.

4. *Stranded Ground Wire.* This type of wire serves as the grounding conductor for service entrances. (See also Fig. 132 (sample 3) for solid ground wire.)

How to Choose Wire for Special Purposes. Fig. 134 shows seven samples of wire for special purposes.

1. *Heater Cord.* This is a sample of heater cord, used for irons and other heating devices. The construction consists of (1) a fabric wrap, (2) rubber insulation, (3) an additional fabric wrap, and (4) a braided cover.

2. *Kitchen-Unit Cord.* This three-conductor cord is used for roasters and other high-wattage equipment. Its construction is similar to heater cord.

3. *Type-W Cable.* This heavy-duty, rubber-covered cord is designed for welders and heavy motors. Rubber insulation is covered first with fabric and finally with a thick rubber jacket. Notice the bare, stranded neutrals.

4. *Thermo-Cord.* This type of wire is suitable for wiring thermostats. The covering is black and white plastic.

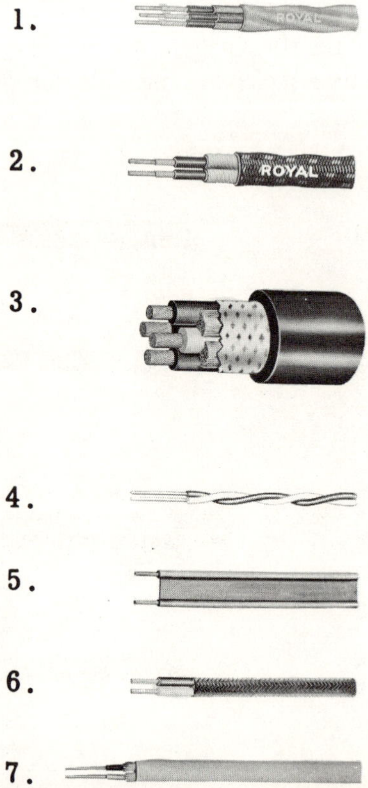

Fig. 134. Seven special-purpose types of wire common to the farm.

1.

2.

3.

4.

5.

6.

7.

5. *TV Cord.* This special TV wire should be used for a television antenna. High-voltage lead-in current is dangerous if improper wire is used.

6. *Asbestos Heat-Resisting Cord.* In locations where electric wires become extremely hot, this asbestos wire will stand up where rubber would break down.

7. *Plastic Cable.* This acid-resistant wire can be buried directly in the ground or used inside buildings. It is more expensive than ordinary types and grades of interior wiring. Note the solid conductors with plastic insulation followed by fiber filling and an outer jacket of tough plastic. Several other types of wire on the market are suitable for underground wiring.

What Types of Interior Wiring Should You Choose?

The three types of interior wiring that are widely used on the farm are (1) non-metallic sheathed cable, (2) conduit, and (3) flexible armored cable.

Another type of wire that is gaining in popularity is called Plugmold, Wiremold, and other similar trade names. Fig. 135 shows a sample of this "pre-wired" type that is easy to install.

Metallic raceway with surface outlets, used in farm service buildings, is another type of wiring that is easy to install. Fig. 136 shows this type.

Fig. 135. Plugmold wiring consists of a metal channel and pre-wired duplex plug-ins spaced 12 inches apart.

Fig. 136. Metallic raceway, outlet box, and plug-in. This type of wiring is easy to install since no carpentry work is required.

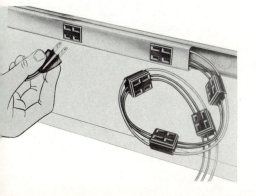

Fig. 137. Sample of non-metallic sheathed cable.

When to Choose Non-Metallic Sheathed Cable (Romex). Non-metallic sheathed cable is also referred to as Romex. It is easy to install, is low in cost, and is lightweight.

The sample of Romex in Fig. 137 has two insulated wires, one black and one white. A course of paper tape is applied over the insulation, then the whole is covered with a tough, fibrous, outer jacket. The rip cord makes it easy to remove the outer jacket.

This covering is treated to resist heat, moisture, and acid but is not suitable for use outdoors, underground, or in masonry. Romex is also available in three- and four-wire styles (cable).

More Romex is used in farmstead wiring than any other type of wire. It is suitable for indoor use in farm homes, garages, and in most farm buildings. It can be used in exposed runs as well as in concealed wiring. If exposed, it must be protected from mechanical damage by fastening it to a baseboard or other rigid support. Local codes in some areas prohibit the use of Romex; therefore you should ask before buying wire. For details on installing Romex, see page 187.

Fig. 138. Sample of single-conductor wire and a conduit ceiling outlet. Conduit wire comes in black, red, and white covering. In wiring, *conduit* refers to both wire and tubing.

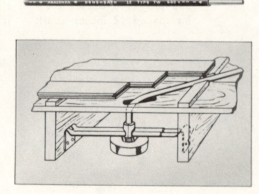

When to Choose Thin-Wall Conduit. In the farm shop and other locations where your wiring is likely to be subjected to severe mechanical abuse, special protection for the wire is required. Of the three common types of interior wiring, thin-wall conduit is best, although it is the most expensive and the most difficult to install. The tubing serves the dual purpose of protecting the wire and grounding the electrical system. Conduit is usually galvanized but is sometimes finished with a special enamel. These special finishes make it suitable for use outdoors, indoors, or in wet locations. Conduit ordinarily comes in 10-foot lengths but is easily cut to desired dimensions.

Electrical wires must be "fished" through the conduit, and for that reason the size of the tubing must be large enough to fit the size of wire used. Connections to boxes are made with threadless fittings and the entire system is grounded when properly installed.

When to Choose Flexible Armored Cable (BX). In permanently dry locations where your wiring is likely to be damaged, flexible armored cable is an excellent material and has two distinct advantages over conduit in that it is less expensive and easier to install. Flexible armored cable provides a grounded system when properly installed.

The illustration in Fig. 139 shows that armored cable is simple in construction. It consists of two insulated copper wires encased in a metal shield. Armored cable may be imbedded in plaster or concrete inside buildings that are permanently dry, but should not be used in cellars, dairy barns, basements, or outdoors where dampness prevails. Armored cable is used to extend runs of conduit and is easy to install because of its flexibility. This type of cable is more difficult to install than Romex, however. This is due largely to the special finishing job required wherever the armor is cut. Instructions for installing flexible armored cable are given on page 190.

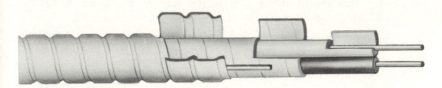

Fig. 139. Sample of flexible armored cable.

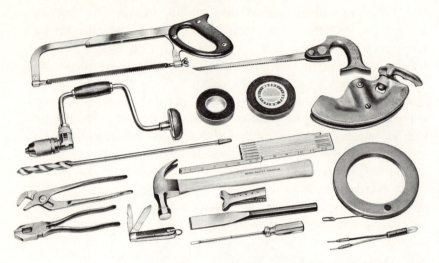

Fig. 140. Tools needed for farmstead wiring.

What Tools and Equipment Are
Needed for a Wiring Job?

A collection of tools needed in doing farm wiring is shown in Fig. 140. You may already have most of the items in this collection in your farm shop. The entire collection can be purchased for $40 or less.

A hacksaw is needed for cutting metallic armored cable, nails, bolts, and other metals encountered in a wiring job, and a brace and bit is necessary for boring holes. An extra-long bit, as illustrated in this collection, comes in handy for reaching difficult locations. A keyhole saw is indispensable for sawing openings for outlet boxes and for working in close places.

A pair of slip-joint pliers comes in handy for turning large locknuts on electrical fittings. You will also need a pair of electricians' pliers for cutting wire and loosening insulation; for cutting insulation and doing numerous other wiring tasks, an ordinary pocket knife is essential.

A screwdriver is needed for tightening screws on electrical fittings and for other uses. A cold chisel comes in handy for cutting cable, nails, bolts, and other pieces of metal.

Notice the roll of wire at lower right in Fig. 140. This is a special "fish tape," which is used for fishing wires into conduit.

The conduit bender at upper right is used for bending and shaping tubing without crushing it. A folding rule is essential in measuring, and a hammer must be available for all types of pounding.

A neon test lamp, which costs about $2, makes it possible to trace circuits in both old and new work. This is an essential item in finding faults in the wiring system. You will find plans for a homemade test lamp on page 208.

Notice the cable stripper, which is located between the hammer and cold chisel. This is an excellent, but not expensive, tool for stripping the insulation from wires. The rubber and friction tapes in this collection are needed for finishing splices and for repairing damaged wires. Plastic tape can often be used alone, for it serves the purpose of both rubber and friction tapes.

How Can You Work Up a Wiring Diagram and a Bill of Materials?

To be accurate, a bill of materials must be worked up from a wiring diagram made to scale. You can prepare your own diagram by following two steps: (1) draw to scale a floor plan of the building to be wired, and (2) sketch in the electrical system, using the proper electrical symbol for each item.

How to Draw a Floor Plan. A floor plan is easy to draw on graph paper. A size 30 x 36 inches, laid off in half-inch squares, is suitable for a wiring plan. Thus for a scale of 1 inch equals 2 feet, lay off 1 inch on the paper for each 2 feet of building. For example, if the width of your residence is 40 feet, lay off 20 inches on the graph paper; that is, count off 40 half-inch squares.

Use standard building symbols for walls, windows, floors, stairs, closets, and other features of the building. Complete the floor plan. Check for accuracy before sketching in the electrical system.

How to Sketch in the Electrical System. Before attempting to sketch in the electrical system, you will find it helpful to study the wiring diagram in Fig. 141. Locate circuits number 2 and 3 and refer to the bill of materials for these circuits. Take note of the name of each item and see that you can identify it by its symbol. You may also wish to review the list of electrical symbols in Fig. 117.

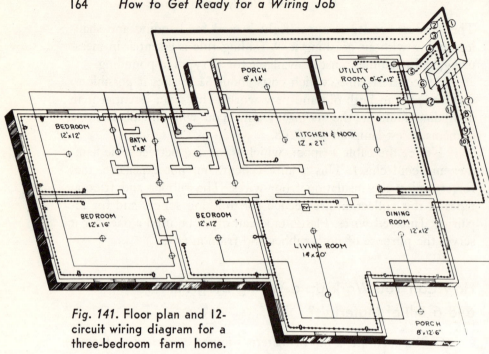

Fig. 141. Floor plan and 12-circuit wiring diagram for a three-bedroom farm home.

Generally, the following steps are observed in sketching in the electrical system:

1. Determine the location of the service-entrance equipment and sketch it in, using the proper symbol of course. The size of the service cable and service switch will have been determined beforehand. Specify the number of circuit connections in the switch.

2. Sketch in the lighting outlets and wall switches throughout the building. Note that the symbols for two- and three-way switches are different.

3. Starting at the service switch, sketch in the lighting circuits, making certain that each wall switch is connected to the proper circuit. Remember that no more than ten outlets may be wired to one circuit. More than this number on one circuit ordinarily results in poor service as well as safety hazards.

4. Determine the location of the convenience outlets throughout the building. Sketch them in.

5. Starting at the service switch again, sketch in the circuits for the convenience outlets. Up to ten outlets may be wired to each general-purpose circuit but five is the maximum for appliance circuits.

6. Sketch in the special-purpose outlets (for range, food freezer, water heater, and the like) after determining their locations.

7. Sketch in each circuit for individual equipment. Indicate the type and size of wire to be used for each circuit.

8. When you have completed your wiring diagram, have it examined by a competent person. If it is approved, you may then work up the bill of materials.

How to Prepare a Bill of Materials.

1. Starting at the service switch, measure the length of run of each circuit. Include vertical runs to wall switches and convenience outlets. Add 8 inches for making each connection.

2. Convert inches to feet and list the result. This is the amount of wire required for that circuit.

3. Count the number of junction boxes, switch boxes, "plug-in" boxes, toggle switches (two- and three-way), receptacles, cover plates, connectors, and other wiring supplies. List the totals for this circuit.

4. Likewise trace all other circuits and list the wiring supplies required.

5. Combine like items and list the total bill of materials. (See sample bill for a twelve-circuit farm home, page 166.)

How to Use a Wiring Diagram. A completed wiring diagram and bill of materials serves two purposes. First, the diagram is a wiring plan or blueprint for the actual wiring job; second, the bill of materials can be submitted to dealers for bids or estimates of cost. You may realize considerable savings by obtaining two or more bids.

What Materials Are Needed for Wiring a Twelve-Circuit Farm Home?*

The wiring diagram in Fig. 141 includes twelve circuits. This, is for a typical three-bedroom farm home and is thought to be an economical and adequate wiring job. Many farm homes now have fifteen to twenty circuits.

The following bill of materials is for the total wiring job in Fig. 141.

* The drawing in Fig. 141 and the bill of materials were prepared by Oran Lewellen, Engineer, Texas Power and Light Company.

TOTAL BILL OF MATERIALS

Item	Quantity
200-ampere circuit breaker or fused switch	1
#6 solid copper ground wire	12 ft
Half-inch copper-coated steel ground rod	8 ft
Grounding connectors	2
Sill plate	1
#0 three-wire service cable	12 ft
20-ampere circuit breakers	8
30-ampere circuit breakers	6
50-ampere circuit breakers	2
#12 two-wire non-metallic sheathed cable	1,040 ft
#8 three-wire non-metallic sheathed cable	174 ft
#6 three-wire range cable entrance cable	40 ft
230-volt, single receptacle	3
230-volt, three-pole, flush-mounted range receptacle	1
Duplex receptacles	27
Flush-mounted outlet boxes	30
Flush-mounted octagon boxes	21
Single receptacle flush-mounted cover plate	3
Flush-mounted switch boxes	20
Flush-mounted toggle switches	20
Flush-mounted toggle switch plates	20
Duplex receptacle plates	27
Octagon boxes	17
Octagon box blank covers	17
Range receptacle cover plate	1
Lighting fixtures	20
Non-metallic sheathed cable connectors	177

Miscellaneous supplies: solderless connectors, plastic tape, cable straps, and a few other minor items.

Bill of Materials for Individual Circuits.

The bill of materials for circuits number 2 and 3, in Fig. 141, are presented here to illustrate the simplicity of working up the bill once the diagram has been completed. Refer to Fig. 141 again and see whether you can identify each item listed under circuits number 2 and number 3.

CIRCUIT 2: CONVENIENCE OUTLETS

Item	Quantity
20-ampere circuit breaker	1
#12 two-wire non-metallic sheathed cable	115 ft
Flush-mounted outlet boxes	9
Duplex receptacles	9
Duplex receptacle plates	9
Octagon boxes	2
Octagon box blank covers	2
Non-metallic sheathed cable connectors	23

CIRCUIT 3: LIGHTING

Item	Quantity
20-ampere circuit breaker	1
#12 two-wire non-metallic sheathed cable	310 ft
Flush-mounted octagon boxes	8
Lighting fixtures	8
Octagon boxes	4
Octagon box blank covers	4
Flush-mounted switch boxes	8
Flush toggle switches	8
Flush-mounted toggle switch plates	8
Non-metallic sheathed cable connectors	40

Summary

Before beginning a wiring job, it is important to find out whether the local code requires that a licensed electrician do the job. Local power suppliers or inspectors furnish this information.

It is a good policy to ask your electrician (if you are hiring one) whether or not he is complying with all regulations of the local code and the National Electrical Code. Wiring methods and materials are covered by both codes.

For farm use, wiring materials are classified in four ways: (1) style of wire; (2) exterior wiring materials; (3) special-purpose wire; and (4) interior wiring materials.

The styles of wire most often used on the farm include single conductor and cable; solid and stranded conductors; parallel and twisted cords; rubber, plastic, and braided covering; and plain and reinforced cord.

Exterior wiring materials for the farm include weatherproof (WP) overhead wire, service entrance cable, conduit entrance materials, and bare ground wire. Portable rubber-covered cords are used outside for operating portable electric machines and lighting.

Special-purpose wiring materials commonly used on the farm include heater cord, heavy-duty cable for welders and motors, thermostat cord, TV cord, asbestos heat-resisting cord, and acid-resistant plastic cable, which is suitable for burying directly in the soil. Many other special-purpose wiring materials are on the market although not very widely used on the farm.

The three most common types of interior wiring are (1) non-metallic sheathed cable, (2) thin-wall conduit, and (3) flexible armored cable. Non-metallic sheathed cable is the least expensive of the three types, is easiest to install, and is the most widely used type on the farm. Thin-wall conduit is the best choice for locations where the wire may be damaged; however, this type is the most expensive and is the most difficult to install. Flexible armored cable provides protection for the inside wires and is easier to install than is conduit. The cost of flexible armored cable is between the range of conduit and non-metallic sheathed cable. Flexible armored cable must not be used in wet or damp locations.

A set of electricians' tools suitable for doing farmstead wiring can be bought for around $40 and should last a lifetime if given proper care.

The four steps required in preparing a bill of materials are as follows: (1) Draw to scale a floor plan of the building to be wired; (2) sketch in the electrical system, using electrical symbols to designate outlets, switches, circuits, and the like; (3) tabulate items in each circuit; and (4) list the total bill of materials.

Questions

1. For what kind of circuit would you use type-TW wiring?
2. Why is it dangerous to use flexible armored cable in wiring barns or cellars?
3. How much would it cost to buy a set of electricians' tools for doing farmstead wiring?
4. What is a "three-pole, flush-mounted, range receptacle"?
5. Why is it necessary to have a scale drawing of a building in preparing a bill of materials?

Additional Readings

Davis, Hollis R., *Adequate Farm Wiring Systems*, Extension Bulletin 849. Ithaca, New York, Cornell University, 1956.

Henderson, G. E., *Planning the Home Wiring System*. Southern Association of Agricultural Engineering and Vocational Agriculture. Athens, Georgia, University of Georgia, 1951.

Industry Committee on Interior Wiring Design, *Farmstead Wiring Handbook*. New York, 1955.

————, *Residential Wiring Handbook*. New York, 1954.

Montgomery Ward & Co., *Modern Wiring*. Chicago, Illinois, 1955.

Richter, Herbert P., *Practical Electricity and House Wiring*. Wilmette, Illinois, Fredrick J. Drake & Co., 1952.

Sears Roebuck & Co., *Electric Wiring*. Chicago, Illinois, 1955.

Wright, Forrest B., *Electricity in the Home and on the Farm*, 3rd ed. New York, John Wiley and Sons, 1950.

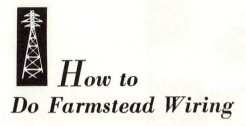

CHAPTER 8

How to Do Farmstead Wiring

The addition of a major electric appliance to the farm or farm home often requires some kind of wiring job. Because of this, farmers often put off buying equipment that is sorely needed. As a consequence, thousands of farm people are still using their backs and hands in competition with barn cleaners, silo unloaders, grain and hay elevators, wood saws, water pumps, automatic feeding and watering devices, and other electric machines. Perhaps you studied the example in Chapter 1 which shows that you earn as little as 2 to 5 cents per hour doing hand labor in competition with electric power.

Sometimes a new electric machine can be put into operation simply by installing a convenience outlet. More often, however, it is necessary to install a larger service switch and perhaps string a new feeder circuit for the new machine. As a matter of fact, there is a constant need on most farms for repairs, as well as additional branch circuits, wall switches, and so on. The farmstead wiring job is never done.

If you acquire the basic wiring skills covered in this chapter, you will have a decided advantage over many of your farm neighbors.

Should You Undertake to Do a Wiring Job Yourself?

Until you have had some experience in wiring, you should work on simple wiring jobs and not attempt to wire a major building without expert supervision. You should do a few simple wiring jobs first. An easy job for a beginner is to install a surface-type

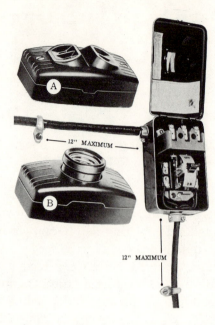

12" MAXIMUM

12" MAXIMUM

Fig. 142. Two surface-type outlets, *A* and *B*, can be installed by cutting cable and connecting the wires to the proper terminals. Outlet boxes are easily anchored to the wall by two screws.

convenience outlet in your shop or garage. As a next step you might install a two-way switch, followed by a general-purpose circuit. Then, as you learn more about wiring, you can undertake more advanced jobs.

Many farmers, farm boys, and farm women have shown by demonstration that farmstead wiring is not difficult. Proof of this can be seen in the thousands of electrification projects that are carried out each year in every section of the country. These range from small repair jobs to complete wiring of farm homes or other farmstead buildings.

The remainder of this problem-unit is devoted to instructions on *how to do* farmstead wiring. Instructions given in this section should enable you to do most of the wiring jobs on your farmstead.

How Should Wire Be Cut, Spliced, and Connected to Terminals?

The skills that are most often used in farm wiring are cutting, splicing, and connecting wire. Although these operations are rather simple, much faulty wiring can be traced to improper procedures in doing these jobs.

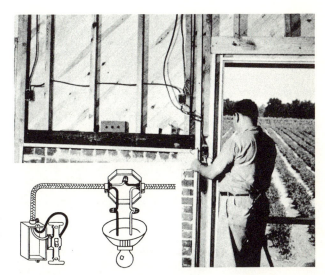

Fig. 143. A workman installing a two-way wall switch.
The diagram at left shows a
simple hookup.

How to Cut and Connect Wire to Terminals. If you are
working with cable, the first step is to remove about 8 inches of the
outer cover. For instructions on how to do this, refer to page 187.
Next, by holding your knife blade at a flat angle or by using a
stripper, remove about 1 inch of the insulation from the end of the
wire. Take care not to damage the wire, especially if you are
using a sharp knife. The traces of insulation left on the bare wire
should be scraped off with a dull knife.

Next, form a right hand loop in the end of the bare wire as
shown in Fig. 144-C (left). In Fig. 144-C (right), a wire is connected to a terminal without being cut. Notice that the insulation has been carefully trimmed at an angle.

Fig. 144. (A) Method of removing insulation with a
knife. (B) A workman pre-
paring wires for connection
to a plug-in receptacle. (C)
Two methods of forming
loops for connection to
terminals.

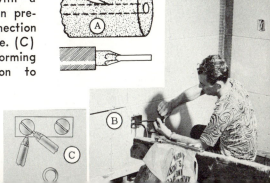

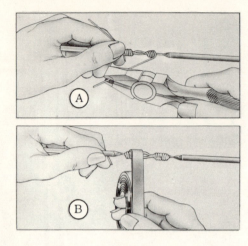

Fig. 145. (A) Method of making an end splice. (B) The completed splice, soldered and being taped.

How to Splice Wire. Remove about 3 inches of insulation from the area to be spliced. Taper the insulation cuts and scrape the bare wire clean as you did in preparing a wire for making a connection. A method of twisting the two wires together is illustrated in Fig. 145-A. This type of splice is required where it will be subjected to strains.

In Fig. 145-B, the splice has been soldered and is being wrapped with rubber tape. This will be followed with a course of friction tape. A dual-purpose plastic tape is easier to apply and can be used instead of rubber and friction tape.

The illustration at the bottom of Fig. 146 shows a rat-tail splice, which is easier to make than the line splice above. In the rat-tail splice shown, three wires have been twisted together and soldered, and are being taped. This type of splice is excellent except for the fact that it will not withstand much strain. Still another kind of splice is called a *tap splice*. In this method, the end of one wire is spliced onto an existing electrical line.

Fig. 146. (A) Rat-tail splice (three wires), soldered and being taped. (B) Tap splice.

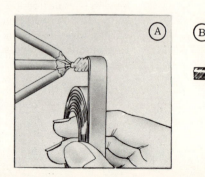

Fig. 147. The correct position of soldering iron, wire, and solder for soldering a splice.

How to Bond Electric Wires Properly. When two electric wires are twisted together, very little metal surface is in actual contact because the surfaces are round. Therefore, a splice restricts the flow of electricity unless it is bonded together with solder or by some other satisfactory method. To make matters worse, splices and connections tend to corrode with use and age. Therefore, careless splicing can create a fire hazard.

How to Solder a Splice. One of the most widely used methods of bonding electric wires is soldering. First, clean the wire surfaces that are to be soldered, then apply a paste soldering flux. Have some resin-core solder on hand along with a hot, well-tinned, soldering iron.

Fig. 147 shows the correct position of the soldering iron and wire while applying the solder. As soon as the wires become hot enough, quickly "feed" a small amount of solder into the splice and remove the soldering iron. You should barely cover the wires with solder, since too much produces a bulky joint.

Fig. 148. Steps in bonding wire with solderless connectors.

Fig. 149. At left, two solderless connectors; at right, two split-bolt connectors.

Another method of soldering splices, especially if you are doing a large job, is to briefly dip the joint, which has been cleaned and fluxed, into a pot containing molten solder. Enough solder will stick to the wires to form a good bond. Wipe off excess flux.

How to Use Wire Connectors. The use of solderless connectors is illustrated in Fig. 148. After the ends of the wires have been stripped of 1 inch of insulation and cleaned, the connector is screwed onto the ends of the bare wires. This forms a permanent bond on which tape is not needed.

In Fig. 149 the two connectors at the left are the solderless type, while the two at the right are called split-bolt connectors. The latter are used to form permanent connections that require strong attachment; for example, connecting a ground wire to a ground rod.

How Should the Exterior Distribution Equipment Be Installed?

It is essential to have the exterior distribution equipment properly installed. Generally, *the wiring of a yardpole or the installation of metering equipment at a building is done by the power supplier or by an independent electrician.* Even so, it will pay you to know the requirements of proper installation.

Metering at a Building. In Fig. 150-A, the exterior part of a service entrance, including the meter, is installed on a centrally located barn. This is a conduit installation, but service entrance (SE) cable is also widely used in installations of this type.

The main service switch and fuse panels are shown in Fig. 150-B. This part of the installation is located inside the barn.

Specifications for a standard metering service are shown in Fig. 151. You can refer to this diagram for information, knowing that it meets proper standards of farmstead wiring. Check it also to see whether or not your wiring job is being done properly.

Metering at a Yardpole. While there are many variations in the wiring of yardpoles for central metering, the two most popular types are shown in Figs. 152 and 153. By referring to the appropriate installation you can determine whether or not your wiring job is being done properly.

Kind of Pole to Use. Insist on having a durable yardpole that will last many years without danger of coming down during a storm. Creosoted timbers are usually used for yardpoles. The height

Fig. 150. Metering installation at a farm building. (A) Conduit service entrance including meter. (B) Main service switch inside building.

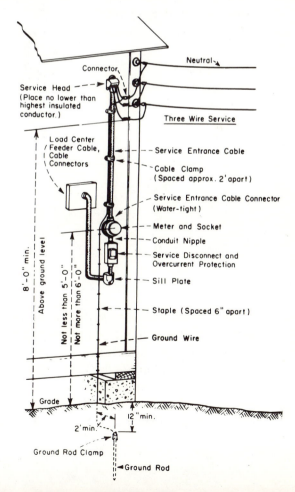

Fig. 151. Specifications for a standard service entrance using SE (cable) and a meter installed at a farm building.

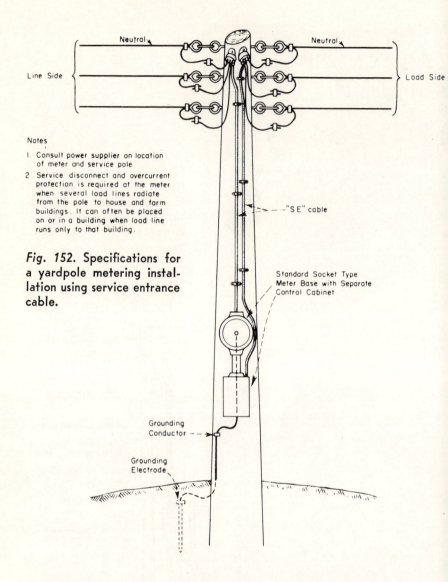

Notes

1. Consult power supplier on location of meter and service pole.
2. Service disconnect and overcurrent protection is required at the meter when several load lines radiate from the pole to house and farm buildings. It can often be placed on or in a building when load line runs only to that building.

Fig. 152. **Specifications for a yardpole metering installation using service entrance cable.**

Line Side

Load Side

Neutral

Neutral

—"S E" cable

Standard Socket Type Meter Base with Separate Control Cabinet

Grounding Conductor — —

Grounding Electrode

of the yardpole must be sufficient to maintain a 10-foot clearance of the lowest wire on the farmstead, except at driveways where at least 18 feet is required.

How to Install Feeder Circuits. Feeder circuits may lead from a yardpole to a building, from one building to another, or from one service switch to another in the same building. Feeder circuits may be three-wire, 230 volts or two-wire, 115 volts.

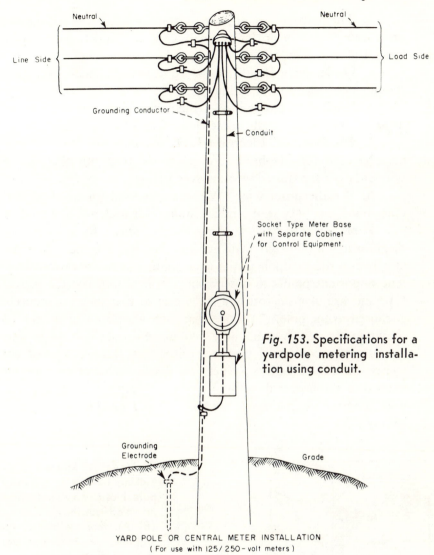

Neutral

Neutral

Line Side

Load Side

Grounding Conductor

Conduit

Socket Type Meter Base
with Separate Cabinet
for Control Equipment.

Fig. 153. Specifications for a yardpole metering installation using conduit.

Grounding
Electrode

Grade

YARD POLE OR CENTRAL METER INSTALLATION
(For use with 125/ 250- volt meters)

A farmstead will be a dangerous place if the feeders are not properly installed. The following "rules of thumb" will serve to make the service satisfactory as well as safe.

1. Feeders must touch nothing but their supporting insulators.

2. Wires should be at least 8 feet from roofs or other parts of farm buildings.

3. The lowest point of the bottom drip loop should be at least 8 feet above ground level.

4. The bottom wire of feeder circuits should have a clearance of at least 18 feet over driveways; on the remainder of the farmstead, 10 feet is acceptable.

5. Feeder wires should be spaced at least 12 inches apart and should never cross a farm building.

6. Feeders should be installed in such a way that persons and livestock will not normally come closer than 3 feet to them.

7. The National Electrical Code specifies that No. 10 wire may be used for overhead runs up to 50 feet, but that No. 8 wire or larger is required for runs over 50 feet.

8. Weatherproof wire (WP) may be used for overhead circuits, but a special type of wire is required for underground feeders.

Attachment of Feeders to the Power Source. By studying the diagram in Fig. 154 you will see that the three feeder wires are attached to the yardpole in the same manner as to the power drop. The important points to observe here are: (1) to use the proper type and size of insulators and make certain that they are securely anchored to the pole, (2) to see that each wire is correctly tied as shown in Fig. 154-A or B, and (3) to make certain that the feeders are properly connected to the service wires leading out of the switch or meter. The top (neutral) feeder is connected to the neutral of the power drop by means of a jumper wire around the pole. (NOTE: *A qualified electrician should handle the yardpole wiring job.*)

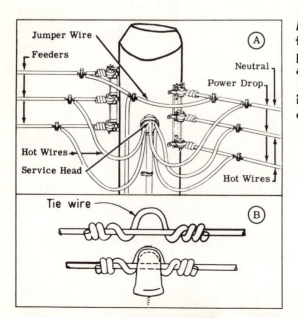

Fig. 154. **(A)** Method of attaching feeders to a power pole. Notice how the feeders are tied to the insulators. **(B)** Another method of tying, where the wire continues on to another attachment.

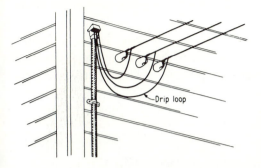

Fig. 155. Method of anchoring feeders to the side of a building. Screw-type insulators are fastened to 2-inch lumber.

Attachment of Feeders to Buildings. The diagram in Fig. 155 shows one method of attaching wires to a building. The feeders are attached to the side of the building, each wire being tied to a screw-type insulator. (See Fig. 154 for tying details.) The insulators should be anchored to 2-inch thick lumber or a double thickness of 1-inch lumber; otherwise the anchors may pull loose during storms and icing conditions. Feeder wires (and insulators) must be spaced at least 12 inches apart.

If the weather is hot when you are installing feeders, tighten each wire so that about 6 inches of sag is present in a 50-foot run,

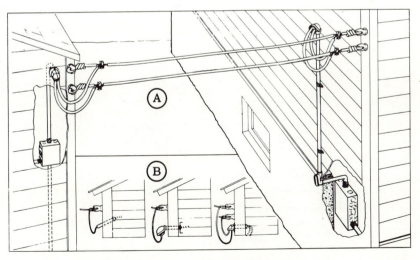

Fig. 156. (*A*) Method of wiring a two-wire feeder from the service switch at right to the building at left. (*B*) Three other methods of bringing feeder wires through a building wall.

with slightly more for a 100-foot run. In cold weather tighten about as much as you can by hand.

How to Install a Two-Wire Feeder Circuit from One Building to Another. Fig. 156-A shows a method of bringing a two-wire feeder circuit out of a service switch and stringing it to another building. The skills involved in this job are covered in the following section on installing a service entrance at a building.

Fig. 156-B shows three methods of bringing wires out of a building.

How to Wire an Underground Feeder Circuit. In Fig. 157, part of the wall sections have been removed so that you may see how an underground circuit is wired. In this installation, plastic cable is buried directly in the ground. The trench is 24 inches deep. You could use lead cable here, but this would require metal conduit in addition to the cable. The wires (either two or three) lead out of the bottom of the service switch in the building at right. Notice the length of conduit leading from the switch box and extending through the foundation wall. This tubing protects the wires from damage until they enter the ground outside the building.

The plastic cable enters the trench from the ends of tubing at both buildings. After the cable is laid and all connections have been made, the ends of the tubing are sealed with water-proof in-

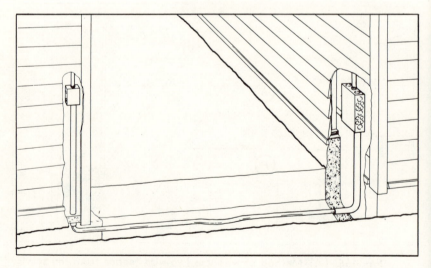

Fig. 157. Underground feeder circuit wired with acid-resistant plastic cable buried directly in the soil.

Fig. 158. The main service switch at right has a 200-ampere capacity and is fused at 150 amperes. It serves two sub-panels at left for the feed mill and the dairy barn.

sulating compound. (NOTE: For instructions on how to connect wires to a service switch, refer to the section that follows on installing a service entrance.)

In filling the trench, first lay a run of one-inch board over the plastic cable or other wiring, then cover with soil. Do not use cinders. Mark the course of the circuit with stakes or other signals.

How to Install a Service Entrance. Installing the service entrance for each farm building is one of the most important wiring jobs on the farm. You can learn to do this job by studying the diagrams and instructions that follow. Assume that a three-wire, 230-volt feeder circuit has been brought to the building and anchored to a 2-inch wall board.

Step 1: Anchor Service Switch in Place and Install Sill Plate or Conduit Ell. The service switch should be located near the point of attachment of the feeders, usually inside the building. Fig. 158 shows a service switch and two distribution panels mounted on the surface of a wall. Another type, used in a residence, is called the flush-mounted switch because it is recessed into the wall and does not protrude.

Mounting a surface switch is a simple operation of fastening the anchor screws into the wall. Installing a flush-mounted switch, however, requires sawing a proper size opening in the inside wall, then anchoring the box in place with screws or nails.

Notice the knockouts in the sides of the metal box in Fig. 159. These can be removed as needed to provide holes for wiring. Cable connectors are installed at each hole where wiring enters or leaves the box.

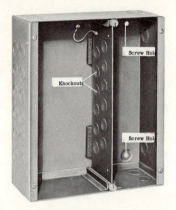

Fig. 159. Metal case in which a fuse panel is to be mounted.

Fig. 160. Fuse panel mounted in a box.

To install a sill plate or conduit ell, bore a proper size hole in the wall and insert the device. Both devices prevent the seepage of water into the wall, when properly sealed with waterproofing compound.

Step 2: Prepare Service Wires for Installation. About 10 feet of SE cable or 10 feet each of red, black, and white conduit wire is sufficient for the average service entrance. (NOTE: Refer to Chapter 5 for instructions on how to figure wire size.)

Fig. 161. (A) The cable connector fastens the cable to the switch box. (B) The sill plate makes a watertight connection for passage of the cable through the wall. (C) The conduit ell serves the same purpose as the sill plate.

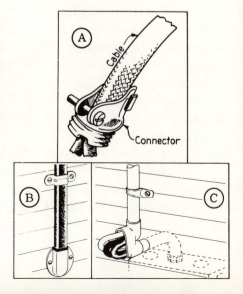

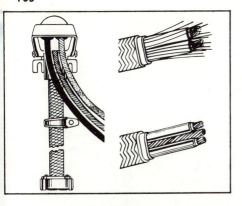

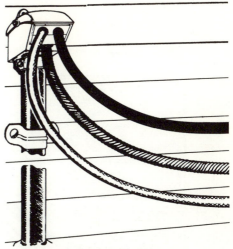

Fig. 162. Numerous small strands of wire in SE cable are twisted together to form neutral wire.

Fig. 163. Service entrance cable threaded into a service head and anchored to a wall, with one cable strap every 2 feet.

(a) In preparing SE cable for installation, remove about 3 feet of the outer covering at one end to allow for drip loops. Also remove 18 inches of the outer covering at the other end to permit connections at the switch. The neutral wire in SE cable consists of numerous strands of bare wire (Fig. 162) twisted about the two insulated wires. At both ends of the cable, these bare wires are twisted together to form the neutral. Remove 2 inches of insulation from both ends of the black and red wires and see that the bare wire is clean and ready for making connections.

(b) If conduit is used, remove 2 inches of insulation from both ends of all wires and see that the bare wire is clean and ready for making connections.

Step 3: Anchor Service Cable or Conduit to the Wall. Service cable installation is somewhat different from conduit installation.

(a) In installing SE cable, anchor the service head in place at least 10 feet above ground level. Thread the service wires into the service head. To fasten the service cable to the wall, use one cable strap every 2 feet. Push the cable through the sill plate and pull the wires into the switch box. Make certain that there is ample wire for making connections to the switch. Tighten the cable connector where the cable enters the switch box.

(b) In installing conduit, the three wires (black, red, and white) are fished through tubing and threaded into the service head

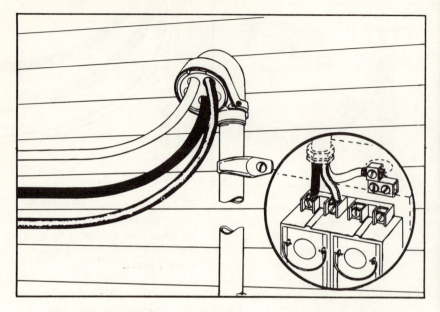

Fig. 164. Conduit wires threaded into a service head and anchored to a wall with one conduit strap every 4 feet. The inset shows the connections inside the service switch.

before the unit is anchored in place. Then fasten the conduit unit to the wall, one conduit strap every 4 feet. Push the service wires through the conduit ell, and pull them into the switch box, leaving sufficient wire to make connections to the switch. Tighten the connector where the wires enter the switch box.

Step 4: Install Grounding System. Have on hand a 12- to 15-foot length of No. 6 bare copper ground wire. Loosely anchor this wire to the wall alongside the service cable, using one staple every 6 inches. Allow about 3 feet of wire at the top for making a connection with the neutral feeder wire. Pound down the staples, taking care not to damage the ground wire.

Drive the ground rod. A ⅝-inch, copper-coated, solid steel rod, 8 feet in length, is suitable for a ground rod on the farm. Some electrical inspectors will allow ¾-inch galvanized water pipe to be used interchangeably for the ground. The rod, as indicated in Fig. 165, should be driven to a depth of at least 12 inches below ground level; in the city, the ground wire may be attached to the city water pipes by special ground clamps. (See Fig. 165.)

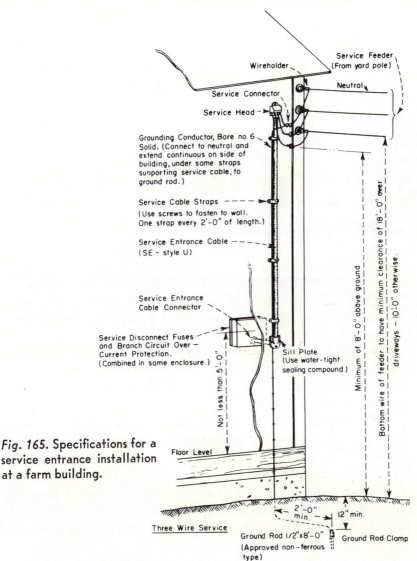

Service Feeder
(From yard pole)

Wireholder

Service Connector

Neutral

Service Head

Grounding Conductor, Bare no. 6
Solid. (Connect to neutral and
extend continuous on side of
building, under same straps
supporting service cable, to
ground rod.)

Service Cable Straps
(Use screws to fasten to wall.
One strap every 2'-0" of length.)

Service Entrance Cable
(SE - style U)

Service Entrance
Cable Connector

Service Disconnect Fuses
and Branch Circuit Over-
Current Protection.
(Combined in same enclosure.)

Not less than 5'-0"

Sill Plate
(Use water-tight
sealing compound)

Minimum of 8'-0" above ground

Bottom wire of feeder to have minimum clearance of 18'-0" over
driveways – 10'-0" otherwise

Floor Level

Fig. 165. Specifications for a
service entrance installation
at a farm building.

Three Wire Service

2'-0"
min.

12" min.

Ground Rod 1/2"x8'-0"
(Approved non-ferrous
type)

Ground Rod Clamp

Attach the ground wire to the ground rod. Using a non-rust-ing, split-bolt connector, fasten the ground wire to the ground rod or to city water pipes. Do not cover the ground rod connection until the power supplier or inspector has examined it. A faulty ground is extremely dangerous.

Step 5: Wire the Service Switch. Refer to Fig. 166 and note the order in which the service wires are connected to the upper

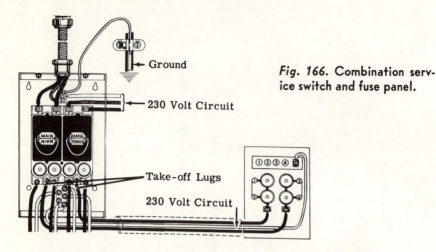

Ground

230 Volt Circuit

Take-off Lugs

230 Volt Circuit

Fig. 166. Combination serv-ice switch and fuse panel.

terminals: (1) black to the extreme left, (2) red to the terminal on the right, and (3) bare neutral (or white, if conduit) to the center. Note also that the ground wire leads from the upper center terminal to the outside ground.

Notice that a three-wire, 230-volt range circuit leads from the knock-out hole at the upper right-hand part of the switch box. This circuit is protected by a 50-ampere cartridge fuse mounted at the back of the pull-out fuse blocks.

Another three-wire, 230-volt circuit is tapped from the "take-off" lugs located underneath the row of plug fuses. This 230-volt circuit can be used to operate a dryer, air conditioner, or other high-wattage appliance, or it may be used as a feeder for another small service entrance. Four 115-volt circuits are wired from the plug-fuse panel, the wires leading from the bottom of the switch box. A modern all-electric farm home requires a larger switch than this 60-ampere size.

Step 6: Have Service Entrance Inspected and Have Service Wires Connected to Feeders. Always follow the practice of having a new wiring job inspected before turning on the current. Your power supplier will furnish this service for a nominal fee, if not free of charge.

The power supplier will furnish a lineman (or you may have to employ one) to connect your service wires to the feeders and to connect the feeders to the power drop. *Do not attempt to connect these wires yourself.* To do so is to invite death!

How Should Interior Wiring Operations Be Done?

There are some half-dozen types of wire that are suitable for use inside farm buildings. The three most popular of these are: (1) Non-metallic sheathed cable, (2) thin-wall conduit, and (3) flexible armored cable. These and other types of wire are described in detail in Chapter 7.

In this discussion, instructions are given for installing the three most common types.

How to Install Non-Metallic Sheathed Cable, or Romex. Study the illustration in Fig. 167 as you proceed. After laying out and cutting the cable into proper lengths, prepare the ends for making connections. Strip off about 8 inches of the outer covering to provide extra wire for making connections in the box, using a dull knife or wire stripper for the job. Take care not to damage the wire. After getting started, the "ripper" string inside the cable provides an easy means of removing the outer cover. Remove about 1 inch of insulation from the end of each wire that is to be connected to a terminal, leaving the bare wire exposed. Refer to page 171 for more details on making connections.

Method of Connecting Romex to Boxes. The connector in Fig. 167-D should be fastened to the outside covering of the cable

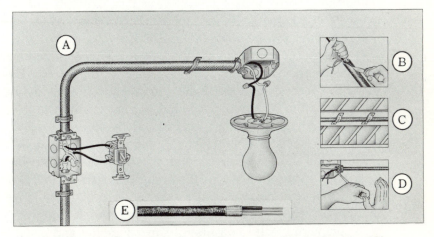

Fig. 167. (A) Sample installation of non-metallic sheathed cable: (B) method of stripping off outer jacket; (C) cable fastened to supporting board with cable strap every 3 feet; (D) method of tightening locknut with screw driver; (E) sample of 3-wire cable.

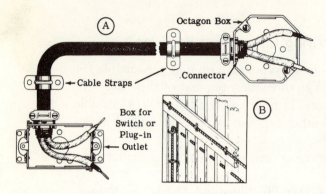

Fig. 168. (*A*) Details of connecting non-metallic sheathed cable to outlet boxes. (*B*) Method of getting cable through studs.

in the manner as shown. Next, insert the wires into the box through the knock-out hole. Finally, fasten a locknut (inside box) onto the threaded end of the connector. The inset at Fig. 167-D shows a method of tightening the locknut with a screwdriver.

Other types of boxes are equipped with built-in clamps and therefore do not require connectors and locknuts. With this type, a screw is provided for tightening the clamps.

Notice the sample of three-wire Romex in Fig. 167-E. The third wire is a bare ground wire. This extra ground is connected to the metal box and thus provides additional safety.

How to Fasten Romex to Supports. If Romex is to be exposed, as in a barn or garage, it must be fastened with a cable strap every 3 feet. It must also be supported by a stud, beam, joist, or other solid member as shown in Fig. 168-B.

In attics or other partially concealed spaces, non-metallic sheathed cable may be run across the edges of the rafters, provided that it is 7 feet or more above the attic floor. The cable should follow the contour of the roof or room and not cut across the spaces. In concealed spaces, cable straps should be spaced 4 to 4½ feet apart and 12 inches from each box. In old walls, cable may be fished through and used in these concealed runs without cable straps.

How to Install Thin-Wall Conduit. As stressed in Chapter 7, wiring that may be subjected to severe wear or possible damage should be protected by tubing. This method is referred to as "conduit wiring" and consists of a metal tubing and metal boxes connected so as to provide a grounded system. The wires used in conduit are not bound together as is true with cable, but rather are separate wires. So if you wish to run a two-wire, 115-volt circuit to a ceiling fixture, use one black and one white wire; or use two black wires to a two-way wall switch. For a three-wire, 230-volt circuit, use one black, one red, and one white wire. In short, conduit wiring provides stricter control of your colors (polarizing) than is true with Romex.

If you will study the illustrations in Figs. 169 and 170 as you proceed, you will find that it is not difficult to install conduit. You must, of course, have a few specialized tools for the job. For example, a bender, which is shown in Fig. 169-D is necessary if you are to do a very neat job of bending the tube. Directions for using this tool are furnished with it. You may be able to rent or borrow conduit tools from your wiring supply dealer or from your local department of vocational agriculture.

Step 1. Cut the conduit to proper lengths, rough in the boxes, and connect the tubing to the boxes. Since conduit is furnished in 10-foot lengths, you will have to cut shorter pieces as may be required in making runs from one box to another. Use a 32-tooth hacksaw blade to cut thin-wall conduit. The inside edges of these cuts should be smoothed with a pipe reamer or a rat-tail file so as to prevent damage to the wires.

Mount the empty conduit in place, using one conduit strap every 6 feet on exposed runs, or one every 10 feet on concealed

Fig. 169. (A) Details of a conduit lighting outlet. (B) Connection to a switch box. (C) Correctly bent tubing. (D) Conduit bender.

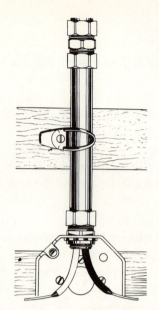

Fig. 170. Details of conduit connection to an octagon box.

runs, and connect to boxes before the wires are installed. Refer to the illustration in Fig. 170 and notice that the tubing is fitted with a connector with a threaded end. This is inserted into the box, then a locknut is tightened onto it. A screwdriver may be used to run the locknut down tight and thus give a good connection. This is important in grounding the conduit system. After all the boxes have been connected to the tubing and fastened to the wall or studs, you are ready to "fish" the wires into the conduit.

Step 2. Fish the wires into the tubing. Your wiring diagram should be followed when you insert the required number of differently colored wires for each run. The first step in fishing wires is to insert the fish tape from the outer end of a run until the hook protrudes at the inner box. Fasten wires to the hook and pull them through the tubing. Repeat this process for all runs in the wiring system, always leaving about 8 inches of excess wire for making connections at each box. You now have only to prepare the ends of your wires, connect them to the proper terminals, mount the switch, convenience outlet, or fixture, and mount the cover plates.

(NOTE: Remember to use only metal boxes with conduit, never bakelite or porcelain.)

How to Install Flexible Armored Cable (BX). In Chapter 7 it was stressed that flexible armored cable should not be used in barns, basements, or other damp locations and should never be used outside. Remember also to use only metal boxes with armored

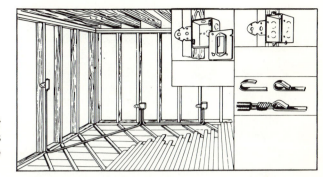

Fig. 171. Tubing and outlet boxes ready for fishing wires through. Notice the fishtape hook at right center.

cable. Bakelite or porcelain boxes with this type of wiring will destroy the "grounded" effect and result in a dangerous wiring system. The usual type of connector for fastening armored cable to boxes is shown in Fig. 172-D.

As you proceed with the job of installing armored cable, study the illustration in Fig. 172.

Step 1. Cut the armor and the wires and finish the ends of the armor. In order to get a good connection and a proper ground, it is necessary to give the cut ends of armored cable a special finish. First, after sawing through the armor with a 32-tooth hacksaw and cutting the wires, insert a fiber bushing between the insulation and the armor. This bushing is necessary to protect the insulation from damage by the sharp edges of the metal.

Fig. 172. (A) Flexible armored cable installation, including lighting outlet and duplex convenience outlet. (B) Method of sawing armor. (C) Method of inserting bushing. (D) Cable connector.

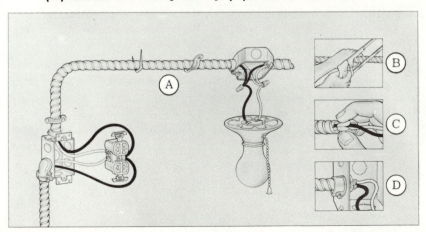

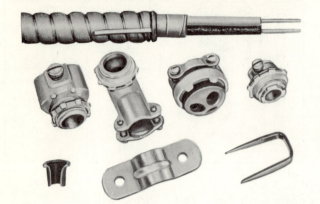

Fig. 173. Sample of flexible armored cable and fittings.

Next, cut off the bond wire, leaving about 3 inches, which is then bent back over the armor. Remove the paper covering from the wires and slip a connector (with locknut removed) onto the wires. Be sure that the fiber bushing is in contact with the connector. Tighten the set screw securely after winding the bond wire around it. This insures a sound connection between the bond wire and the metal box and thereby provides a good ground for the wiring system.

Step 2. Connect the armored cable to the boxes. Armored cable must be supported by straps or staples every 4½ feet and at a point 12 inches from each box. This support is not required in concealed runs where it is not practical to use a fastener. Insert the finished end of the armored cable into its proper box so that the threaded end of the connector protrudes into the box. Insert a locknut inside the box and tighten with the aid of a screwdriver.

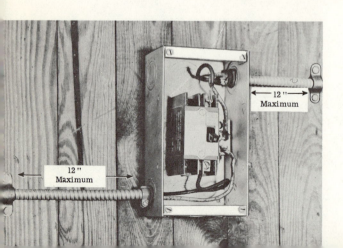

Fig. 174. Surface-type switch in a barn, wired with flexible armored cable.

The 8 inches of excess wire is ready for connection to the receptacle, switch, or other fixture that is to be installed in the box. See later sections for further information.

A surface-mounted box and switch are shown in Fig. 174. In barns, garages, and other locations where surface fixtures are not objectionable, this type of wiring is desirable because of its ease of installation.

Fig. 175. Switch or convenience outlet boxes. The screw-type box at left will hold in any wall.

How to Install Wall Switches and Convenience Outlets. The skills involved in installing wall switches and convenience outlets are very similar, except for the wiring connections.

Mark the Location of and Install Boxes. For recommendations on the number and location of switches and convenience outlets for each room and building, refer to Chapter 6. Generally, switches are placed 48 inches above the floor, and convenience outlets are placed 12 inches above floor level. In the kitchen, convenience outlets are installed at table height. Placement may vary depending upon the situations encountered.

In new construction, the installation of boxes is a simple matter of nailing or screwing each box to a stud or other strong member of the wall, after which the wall is finished out around the boxes.

In old work, where additional switches and outlets are to be installed, it is necessary to cut openings for the boxes.

How to Cut Openings for Boxes. An easy method of sawing openings for outlet boxes is shown in Fig. 176. The cardboard pattern, as shown at upper left, makes the layout job simple. After marking the area and boring four holes as indicated at upper right, you can quickly saw out the opening. A brace bit and a keyhole saw are needed for this job.

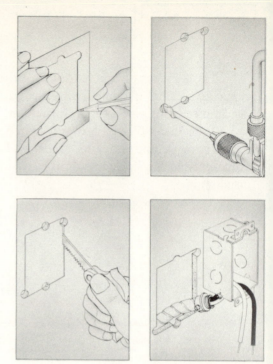

Fig. 176. Steps in installing a switch box.

At lower right, the method of connecting the cable to the box is shown. Tightening the locknut will make this box ready to anchor in place.

Caution on Cutting Plaster or Wall Paper. Before beginning to saw through wall paper, using a sharp knife, cut the paper and canvas from the area along the pattern lines. This will eliminate the danger of tearing the paper when you begin to bore or saw holes.

In cutting plaster, first locate the laths by probing into the plaster at the desired location of your box. An ice pick, in conjunction with a ⅛-inch hand drill, will help you to find the exact location of three laths.

After laying out the pattern, saw through one lath and "dap out" portions of two others, as shown in Fig. 177. In cutting plaster, support it with one hand and saw on the pulling stroke.

The final step in installing a switch or convenience outlet is to mount a cover plate. This is not done, of course, until the wiring connections have been completed and the circuit has been tested.

How to Wire Wall Switches. The next step is to wire and install the switches. Before connecting any wires, one basic principle should be reviewed; all wires connected to a switch are hot wires.

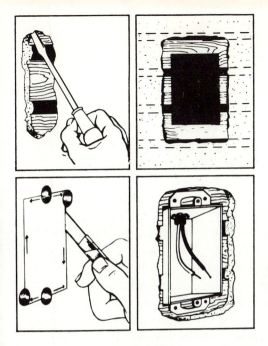

Fig. 177. Steps in installing a switch box in a plaster wall.

Therefore, in using Romex or armored cable, which contains one white wire, paint the ends of this wire black to show that it is hot; use rubber paint, not oil paint. In wiring switches with conduit, use black wires to the switch; however, it is sometimes necessary to make a white wire function as a hot wire in connecting three- or four-way switches. Again the end of the white wire should be painted black.

1. The diagram in Fig. 178 illustrates the use of a run of wire beyond a ceiling fixture to a wall switch that controls this fixture. In the junction box, the incoming black wire is connected to a black wire of the switch cable, while the other black switch wire is connected to the black fixture wire. The incoming white wire in the ceiling box is joined to the white fixture wire. The use of solderless

Fig. 178. A two-way wall switch (in conduit) beyond the lighting fixture it controls. One switch-leg wire would be white if non-metallic sheathed cable were used.

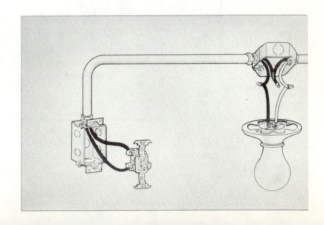

connectors eliminates the necessity of soldering. At the switch receptacle, attach the two wires to the two terminals. It doesn't matter which way, since both wires are hot. Remember that one of the switch-leg wires will be white if non-metallic sheathed cable is used; then the end of the white wire should be painted black.

2. The hookup in Fig. 179 illustrates switch control for one light fixture, with a convenience outlet on the circuit remaining hot whether the switch is on or off. For this job you will need a run of three-wire cable or three wires in conduit from the switch to the light fixture.

Proceed with connections as follows:

(a) Using solderless connectors, join the two white wires in the switch box; then, in the ceiling box, join the two white wires together and connect them to the white ceiling fixture wire. Notice that one white wire continues on to the convenience outlet, bypassing the switch.

(b) Join the two black wires in the ceiling box and connect the red wire to the black fixture wire.

(c) At the switch, connect both black wires to one terminal and connect the red wire to the other terminal.

(d) You can test your connections by using a home-made test lamp.

(e) Usually, a toggle switch or light fixture is mounted in its box by two screws. Certain types of ceiling fixtures require a dif-

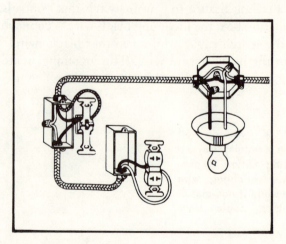

Fig. 179. This wall switch controls the ceiling fixture and leaves the convenience outlet hot.

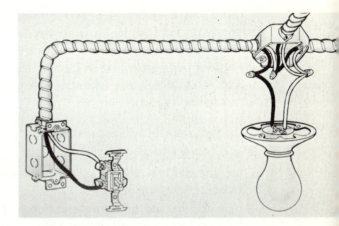

Fig. 180. The wall switch beyond the fixture is wired to
control that fixture where
circuits continue on to other
outlets.

ferent method of mounting. When the lighting fixture or switch
is being installed, first tuck the surplus wire into the box, taking
care not to damage it.

3. Fig. 180 shows a hookup for controlling a ceiling light
when the circuit continues on to other outlets.

The connections for this hookup should be made as follows:

The white wire from the source is attached to the ceiling fixture and then continues on to other outlets. The black wire from the
source is attached to the black wire leading to other outlets and
also to the white wire leading to the switch (when cable is used).
The black wire to the switch is then attached to the ceiling fixture.

The connections to the switch itself are simple. Attach each
of the wires to a terminal—it doesn't matter which way since both
are hot. The white wire that is attached to the switch box should be
painted black, using rubber paint. If conduit is used instead of cable,
use a black wire here instead of white. The manner of making the
connections depends upon the location of the switches in relation
to the fixtures and to the source of electricity.

4. Fig. 181 shows the simplest arrangement of a three-way
hookup. Notice that both three-way switches control a light fixture
that is between them. You may have several fixtures here instead of
one; for example, a large living room may require three or four
lighting outlets. Notice that the source comes through one of the
switches.

Proceed as follows in making connections. (NOTE: For this
job you will need a run of three-wire cable from one switch to the

other and to each outlet. The simple diagram in Fig. 182 will show you why two traveler wires are necessary.)

In Fig. 181, the white wire is run through the first switch box, without being attached to the switch and continues on to the light fixture. As usual, the white wire is joined to other white wires in the ceiling box and continues on to all fixtures controlled by these two switches. All wires connected to both switches are hot, as is true with all wall switch hookups. At the first switch, the black wire from the source is connected to the dark-colored terminal, sometimes referred to as the *common* terminal. All three-way switches have one of these.

At the second switch, connect the black wire to the dark-colored terminal, and connect the other end of this black wire to the black fixture wire. At this point, unused terminals remain at both switches. Finish the wiring by connecting a red wire to the lower left terminal at each switch; join the red wires together in the ceiling box.

At the first switch the remaining black wire is connected to the unused terminal there, while the other end is joined to the unused white wire in the ceiling box. At the second switch, the white wire is connected to the unused terminal there and should be painted black, using rubber paint. The two wires that run from one switch to the other are the traveler wires.

A four-way hookup is shown in Fig. 183. The connections here may appear altogether different from the previous illustration.

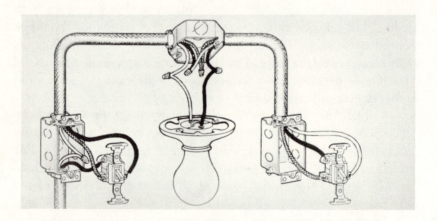

Fig. 181. Ceiling fixture controlled by two three-way switches.

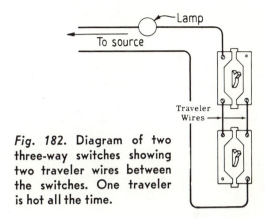

Fig. 182. Diagram of two three-way switches showing two traveler wires between the switches. One traveler is hot all the time.

Fig. 183. Three switches controlling a lighting fixture. The switch in the center is four-way, the other two are three-way.

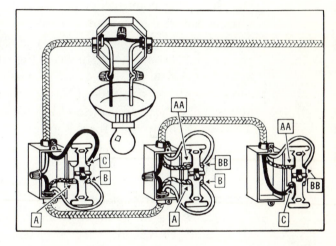

A close study of this wiring arrangement, however, will show that it is essentially the same as the previous hookup. You have two traveler wires running from one switch to the others (both hot wires) and the white wire from the source runs directly to the ceiling fixture.

How to Wire Convenience Outlets. An easy and valuable job that you can do in your spare time is to add convenience outlets, often referred to as plug-in outlets. Often, it is possible to tap several plug-ins off your present circuits. Take care, however, not to overload your wiring as one Texas farmer did. (See story on page 93).

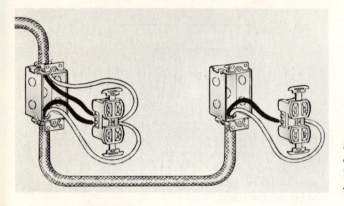

Fig. 184. A new convenience outlet is added by extending the run of the cable from the old outlet.

In wiring convenience outlets, remember that they must always be hot; that is, no switch should be wired in such a way that it can interrupt the circuit for ordinary plug-ins.

1. The arrangement shown in Fig. 184 illustrates a method of extending a run of wire from a convenience outlet to operate another outlet of this type. (NOTE: Instructions on how to install non-metallic sheathed cable and boxes can be found on page 187.) The wiring connections for this job are simple:

(a) Attach the black wire of the extension to the copper-colored terminals of both plug-in receptacles as shown in Fig. 184.

(b) Likewise, connect the white wire to the silver-colored terminals of both receptacles.

(c) Using the screws provided for this, mount each receptacle in its respective box. Then, after testing has been completed, install the cover plate.

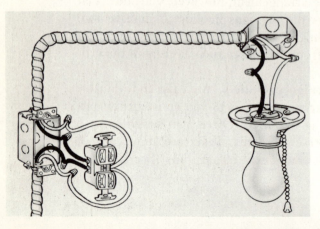

Fig. 185. A convenience outlet tapped into a circuit between an existing plug-in and a pull-chain fixture.

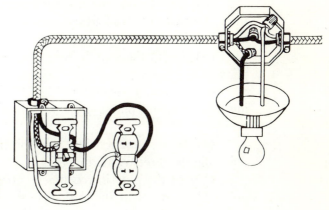

Fig. 186. A plug-in tapped off a wall switch.

2. Another practical hookup is illustrated in Fig. 185. A convenience outlet is tapped into a circuit between two outlets. These may be plug-ins, pull-chain lighting fixtures, or a combination of the two. The wiring connections, again, are very simple and can be done easily.

(a) Cut short lengths of wire, two black and two white, and connect these to the plug-in receptacle. The blacks go to the copper-colored terminals and the whites go to the silver-colored side.

(b) Using solderless connectors, join the short black wires to the incoming and outgoing blacks. Likewise, join the white wires.

(c) Mount the receptacle, test your connections, and install the cover plate as previously instructed.

3. Fig. 186 shows a method of tapping a plug-in off a wall switch. To make this outlet hot all the time you will need a run of three-wire cable from the switch to the ceiling fixture. Two-wire cable is used between the switch and plug-in.

Make connections as shown in Fig. 186.

(a) Connect the white wire of the two-wire cable to the silver-colored terminal on the plug-in receptacle. Join the white wires in the switch box and connect the other end of the white run to the ceiling fixture. (NOTE: The white wire from the source is joined at this point.)

(b) Connect the black wire to the dark-colored terminal of the plug-in receptacle and also to one terminal of the switch. The two black wires in the ceiling box are then joined.

(c) This leaves one unused terminal at the switch. Connect the red wire to this and attach the other end of the red wire to the black wire at the ceiling fixture.

(d) Install the switch in its box, test it, and install the cover plate.

4. The hookup shown in Fig. 187 illustrates a method of adding a convenience outlet and a pull chain light fixture from a junction box.

(a) In the junction box join the three black wires together. Also join the three whites together.

(b) At the plug-in receptacle, attach the incoming and outgoing black wires to the dark-colored terminal; attach the white wires to the other side of the receptacle.

(c) Connect black to black and white to white at the ceiling fixture.

(d) Install the receptacle and the fixture in the box, test, and install the cover plate.

How to Install and Wire a Light Fixture. In the preceding discussion, you observed several wiring hookups of ceiling fixtures. The connections for a particular fixture depend upon the situation there. Fixtures controlled by two-, three-, and four-way switches require special connections. Also, the location of the fixture in relation to the power source will affect the connection.

The basic principle to remember in wiring lighting fixtures is that you always have one white and one black wire attached to them. Also, the white wire runs an uninterrupted course throughout each circuit.

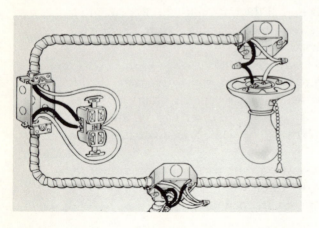

Fig. 187. A convenience outlet and pull-chain fixture added from a junction box.

Fig. 188. A ceiling box being prepared for installation of the light fixture.

How to Mount Fixture in Outlet Box. In Fig. 188 the workman is completing the installation of an outlet box. This is mounted on a metal rail, which, in turn, is anchored to the ceiling joists. (NOTE: There are several types of fixture boxes available to fit different types of fixtures.) In old work, it is necessary to fasten the box to the ceiling by means of a special hanger. Ask for this at your wiring supply house. Fig. 189 shows three methods of mounting light fixtures.

(a) In method A, the fixture is attached to a metal strap that is anchored to the ears of the box.

(b) In method B, the fixture is mounted to a metal strap that is then anchored to the box by means of a threaded center stud.

(c) In method C, the use of a hickey and a threaded stud is illustrated. By studying the illustration at right you can see how this is installed. Wall bracket fixtures can be mounted as shown in the two illustrations in Fig. 190. These are self-explanatory.

How to Connect Wires to a Ceiling Fixture. The method of wiring light fixtures is very simple. With only one or two exceptions, all that is necessary is to connect a black wire to the dark-colored terminal on the fixture and a white wire to the silver-colored terminal. If your fixture is pre-wired with one black and one white stub, you can join the source wires to the corresponding stub by use of solderless connectors. An exception is that two blacks and two whites are necessary if the fixture is equipped with a plug-in that stays hot.

For instructions on different methods of connecting wires in ceiling boxes, refer to the section on installing switches and con-

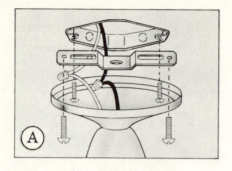

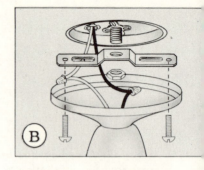

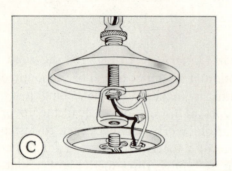

Fig. 189. Three common methods of hanging a light fixture in an outlet box.

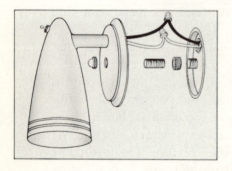

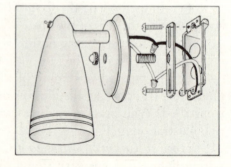

Fig. 190. Two methods of hanging a wall fixture to a box.

venience outlets. Several common wiring hookups are illustrated in those sections.

How to Wire for Three-Way Switch Control of a Yard Light. You can have three-way switch control for your yard lights by wiring them according to the diagram shown in Fig. 191. This arrangement is for overhead wiring, but an underground circuit can be substituted without changing the basic wiring connections. You

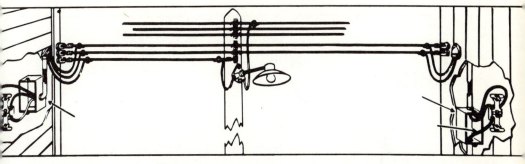

Fig. 191. Method of wiring a three-way yard light between two buildings.

can find instructions for installing overhead wiring on page 178; for underground wiring, instructions are on page 180.

Notice that three-wire cable is only required from the light fixture to one switch; a white wire to the fixture being tapped off the neutral line of the feeder circuit. The two wires that are continuous from one switch to the other serve as the travelers.

The connections at the three-way switch (at left) are made exactly as described on page 198. At the other switch, connect the black and red wires to the terminals at the top of the switch. The black wire from the source is attached to the bottom terminal, as shown. No white wire is necessary from the source since this is provided at the yardpole.

(NOTE: This method of wiring a yard light is dependent upon having a feeder circuit available as illustrated; otherwise you must run three wires from one switch to the other. In that event, both switches would have to be three-way. In the method as shown in Fig. 191, one of the switches is an ordinary two-way type.)

How to Wire 230-Volt Circuits. Throughout this book, 230-volt circuits have been referred to as having two hot wires and one neutral. Three wires are not necessary to operate certain 230-volt appliances; for example, water heaters. For motors and appliances that are handled however, it is dangerous to operate them on two hot wires without a neutral.

Range Circuit. If you will refer back to page 186, you can find a diagram for tapping a three-wire circuit off the top right position of a service switch. The wiring may be three wires in conduit or three-wire cable.

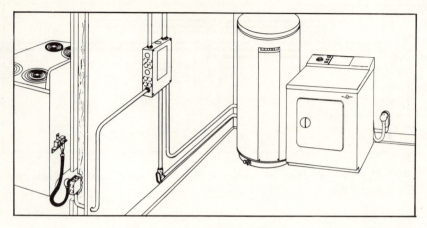

Fig. 192. Appliances wired for 230 volts.

The three wires shown leading from the switch provide both 115- and 230-volt service. The low voltage is used for low heat, high voltage for high heat. Fusing for the range circuit is also discussed on page 115.

Fig. 192 shows the circuit layout for three 230-volt appliances. At the left you can see the wiring for the range. The wire size for a high-wattage range should be No. 6; and for lower-wattage models, No. 8 is adequate.

You can see how a "pig tail" is connected to the three terminals at the back of the range, while the other end is plugged into a 230-volt receptacle. Three types of 230-volt receptacles are shown in Fig. 193. The flush-type at center is used in the installation in Fig. 193.

The blades of the male plug shown in Fig. 193 are arranged so that the neutral blade must connect with the neutral at the source. Other 230-volt appliances are equipped with the same type of plug.

Fig. 193. Three styles of 230-volt receptacles. Plug-ins at left and right are the surface-mounted type; center one is for flush mounting.

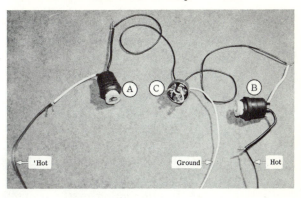

Fig. 194. Simplified method of protecting a motor wired for 230 volts. Weatherproof sockets (*A* and *B*) are wired into the two hot lines; two Fusetrons (totaling motor amperage) are inserted in the sockets. A three-prong plug (*C*) automatically polarizes the circuit.

Many 115-volt portable machines are being adapted to a three-wire hookup for added safety.

Water Heater. Only two wires (both hot) are run to the 4,000w water heater shown in Fig. 192. No. 12 wire is satisfactory for this installation, but you should use a larger wire for a run over 40 feet. The two hot wires are tapped off the bottom of the service switch and are protected by a 20-ampere cartridge fuse. These two hot wires are connected to the two terminals of the heater with each wire connected to a terminal.

(Note: The method of wiring your water heater may be governed by your power supplier; for example, if you are on an off-peak rate, you may have to use a separate meter or other special wiring.)

Clothes Dryer. Your clothes dryer, like your range, must have a three-wire circuit. The hookup for this is the same as for a range. The frame of the clothes dryer must be grounded. Ordinarily, No. 10 wire is sufficient for this installation. A "pig tail" plug may be used, as is customary with a range. Sometimes, however, a clothes dryer is connected permanently.

Other 230-volt circuits may be installed for air conditioners and similar high-wattage appliances. Use two hot wires and one neutral, tapped off the service switch and fused according to the wattage of the appliance.

How to Protect an Electric Motor Circuit. The wiring necessary to install a Fustat or Fusetron for motor protection is very simple: (see Fig. 194).

(a) Cut the hot wire of the two-wire, 115-volt circuit serving the motor. Prepare the ends of the wire for splicing.

(b) Using solderless connectors or solder, join the two legs of a weatherproof socket to the two loose ends of the wire, either leg to either end of the cut wire.. Anchor the wiring, including the socket, to a support.

(c) Insert a Fusetron of the proper size.

(d) For a three-wire, 230-volt motor circuit, install two weatherproof sockets and fuse both hot wires; divide the rated motor amperage by two and insert Fusetrons of that size, one in each socket. Fustats can be used for motor protection but they require a special adapter base.

(e) In connecting motor protectors (magnetic breakers, and the like) for large motors, follow the wiring diagram furnished with the device.

How to Construct a 115-Volt 230-Volt Test Lamp. To construct the inexpensive test lamp shown in Fig. 195, obtain two weatherproof sockets and prepare the ends of the four wires for splicing. Splice two legs together, and finish by soldering and taping in the usual manner.

Prepare two sharp pointed probes (nails will do) and solder one to each unused leg of the socket assembly. Finish by taping the soldered joints, leaving 1 inch of the nails exposed. Insert two 15w bulbs and you are ready to test circuits and electrical devices of all types.

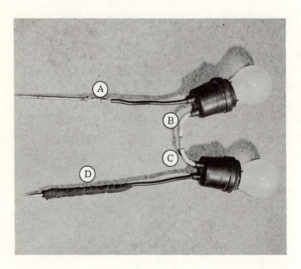

Fig. 195. A test lamp for 115- and 230-volt circuits can be made from two weatherproof sockets. Splice and solder *B* and *C*. Solder pointed probes to the two unused wires. *D* shows taped probe with 1 inch exposed. Tape *A* and *BC* before using.

To use this tester, touch one prong to the hot side of a circuit, fuse panel, motor, or other electrical item to be tested. Touch the other prong to the neutral side. If the circuit or device is hot, the bulbs will glow dimly on 115 volts, brightly on 230 volts.

If the bulbs fail to come on, the circuit or device being tested is dead. A little experience with this test lamp will enable you to trace and locate troubles in your electrical system in a few minutes.

Summary

Thousands of farm people throughout the United States are doing all types of wiring, from simple jobs to the complete wiring of a farm home.

In learning to do wiring skills, the simplest jobs should be tried first. These should include splicing wire, repairing lamp cords, and, perhaps, installing convenience outlets. Afterwards, the wiring of two- and three-way switches and lighting fixtures will be in order. Following that, the installation of a small service entrance and branch circuits for a farm building will be a reasonable undertaking.

The first rule in wiring is to obtain a wiring diagram and instructions and follow these carefully.

Exterior wiring involves wiring a meter pole or service entrance at a building. The essentials here include securing the wires firmly to the pole or building so that there will be no danger of their coming loose. Insulators must, of course, be used at the points of attachment.

A good ground rod (or proper connection to city water pipes) is necessary for a safe electrical system. An improper ground may result in injury or even death.

The holes through which wires enter a building should be properly sealed, either by a sill plate or by sealing compound (for underground circuits).

In some areas the service entrance must be a conduit installation; in others, service entrance cable (type SE) is allowed.

Another essential of exterior wiring is the proper installation of feeder circuits. A feeder that runs too close to a building, a tree, or other object may cause a fire or an accident.

The essentials of interior wiring are good splices and connections, as well as properly polarized wires. A poor splice (one not soldered or otherwise bonded) may eventually cause a fire or other trouble. After soldering, a splice must be taped to provide insulation.

In making connections, all white wires should run an uninterrupted course throughout the system. That is, when a white wire runs to a fixture, it must be spliced so that a main white wire continues on to all other fixtures in the system.

A neutral wire is never attached to a switch. Sometimes a white wire is allowed to function as a hot wire in certain switch connections. Where this is so, the white wire must be painted black to show that it is hot.

Between two three-way switches there will usually be three wires. One of these is called a traveler wire.

With the exception of wiring for heating devices, all 230-volt circuits should have three wires. Usually one of the two hot wires will be black and the other red. If a neutral wire is not used in a 230-volt circuit, a dangerous (ungrounded) situation will be present. Thus, it is especially important to ground a washing machine and all other high-wattage appliances that are handled.

Questions

1. How does a solderless connector form a permanent bond in splicing wires?
2. Why is it important to drive a ground rod at least 8 feet into the earth?
3. Can you explain the principle that all wires connected to two- and three-way wall switches are hot wires?
4. Why must plug-in receptacles and lighting outlets be connected to both hot and neutral wires?
5. Why is a traveler wire necessary in three-way wall switches?
6. Why is it necessary always to use metal boxes when wiring with thin-wall conduit or flexible armored cable?
7. Why is it important that the bond wire in flexible armored cable be properly fastened to the metal casing?
8. Why must a washing machine always be grounded?
9. Why does a range "pig tail" have three wires?

Additional Readings

Brown, R. H., *Farm Electrification*. New York, McGraw-Hill, 1956.

Davis, Hollis R., *Adequate Farm Wiring Systems*, Extension Bulletin 849. Ithaca, New York, Cornell University, 1956.

Farm Wiring Subcommittee, *Specifications for Farmstead Wiring*. Farm Electrification Bureau, New York, (no date).

Henderson, G. E., *Maintaining the Farm Wiring and Lighting System*. Southern Association of Agricultural Engineering and Vocational Agriculture. Athens, Georgia, University of Georgia, 1952.

Montgomery Ward & Co., *Modern Wiring*. Chicago, Illinois, 1955.

Richter, Herbert P., *Practical Electricity and House Wiring*. Wilmette, Illinois, Fredrick J. Drake & Co., 1952.

Sears Roebuck & Co., *Electric Wiring*. Chicago, Illinois, 1955.

Suggested Projects for Problem-Unit Three

1. **Easy-to-Make Trouble Lamp.** You can reduce expense and gain experience by constructing your own trouble lamp. Parts are listed in the diagram in Fig. 196. Details for installing the plug are shown in four steps in Fig. 196-B.

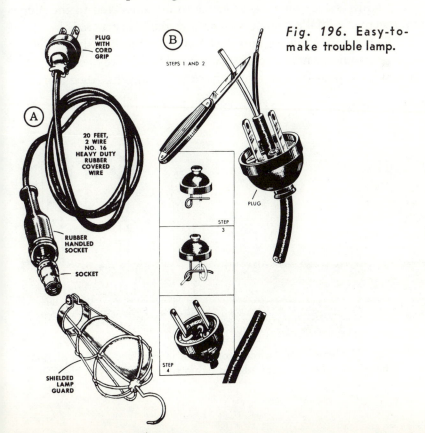

PLUG WITH CORD GRIP

B

STEPS 1 AND 2

Fig. 196. Easy-to-make trouble lamp.

A

20 FEET, 2 WIRE NO. 16 HEAVY DUTY RUBBER COVERED WIRE

PLUG

STEP 3

RUBBER HANDLED SOCKET

SOCKET

STEP 4

SHIELDED LAMP GUARD

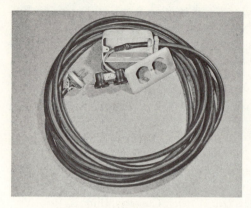

Fig. 197. Heavy-duty extension cord for the farm shop. The plug-in consists of a metal outlet box, a duplex receptacle, a metal cover plate, and a cable clamp. The receptacle mounts in the box and is held in place by two screws. Note the durable male plug also equipped with a cable clamp. Wire is No. 12 gauge, rubber-covered heavy portable cable.

2. Heavy-Duty Extension Cord. A dependable extension cord for operating portable electric machines is shown in Fig. 197. Parts needed include a metal outlet box (surface type) and cover, a duplex receptacle, and 50 (or more) feet of No. 10 reinforced portable rubber cord.

Lightly solder the ends of wires to be connected to the plug and receptacle. Make connections as previously instructed.

3. Outdoor Plug-ins and Post Lantern. Fig. 198 shows a layout for an underground circuit (using plastic cable) to operate a post lantern, post plug-in, and two outside wall plug-ins. Make certain

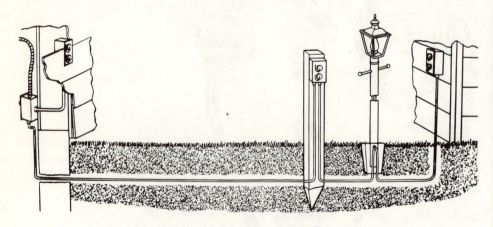

Fig. 198. Underground circuit for a post lantern and outside plug-ins. The wire is acid-resistant plastic cable buried directly in the soil.

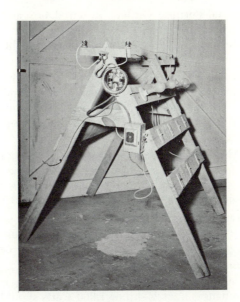

Fig. 199. Wiring demonstration panel constructed by a student in Mississippi.

that boxes and receptacles are of the outside type. Plastic cable is wired to the source in the building at left and leads to (1) a box on building wall, (2) a post-mounted plug-in, (3) a post lantern, and (4) a surface-type plug-in at the other building. Instructions for installing plastic cable for an underground circuit are given on page 180.

    4. Wiring Demonstration Board. The board shown in Fig. 199 was constructed by a student in Mississippi. It involved most of the basic wiring skills, including the installation of a meter, a service switch, two-, three-, and four-way switches, circuits, convenience outlets, and lighting outlets.

Glossary for Problem-Unit Three:

Lighting Outlet   A wired box to which various types of lighting fixtures may be fastened and supplied with electricity.

Convenience Outlet   A wired box and plug-in receptacle supplying electricity for operating appliances. Receptacle outlets should be duplex type (two plug-in positions) except as otherwise specified by codes. Plug-ins for a dairy barn may be mounted on a heavy-duty cord suspended from the ceiling.

Special-Purpose Outlet A wired box and receptacle supplying electricity for a particular appliance; for example, a range or water heater. A special-purpose outlet may be a plug-in receptacle, or it may be an outlet to which equipment is permanently connected.

Service Entrance Includes the service head, the entrance cable, the main switch, the distribution panel, and all accessories such as the sill plate and the cable straps. The ground wire, the ground rod, and the connections are considered a part of the service entrance.

Feeder Wires extending from a distribution panel in one building to the service entrance of another building, or from a distribution panel to a branch circuit panel in the same building. Also, conductors which connect a meter-pole installation to the service-entrance conductors of the various buildings served from the meter pole.

Branch Circuit, General Purpose That portion of the wiring system extending from the final fuse or circuit breaker to the outlets for general use; for example, lighting and convenience outlets.

Branch Circuit, Individual Equipment A circuit that is intended for supplying a single motor or appliance. In general, all stationary appliances over $\frac{1}{2}$-hp or 1,000 watts should be permanently connected to an individual circuit.

Appliance Circuit A 115-volt circuit consisting of one hot and one neutral wire designed to supply electricity to appliances in the kitchen, dining room, laundry, and outdoors. Appliance circuits should be wired with No. 12 wire (up to 40 feet) and protected by a 20-ampere fuse.

Voltages In this book, two-wire circuits are treated as supplying 115 volts; three-wire circuits, 230 volts.

Usable Wall Space All portions of a wall, except that occupied by a door opening or a fireplace opening. Window width is considered usable wall space. The minimum usable wall space requiring a convenience outlet is three feet in length at the floor line.

Floor Area Refers to area computed from the outside dimensions of the building and the number of floors. In computing the floor area of a farm home, open porches, garages, and unfinished spaces in the basement and attic are not included, unless adaptable for future use.

Closed Circuit A circuit that is carrying current is a closed circuit. It is sometimes referred to as a live or hot circuit.

Open Circuit A circuit that has been disconnected by a switch, fuse, or circuit breaker. An open circuit is sometimes referred to as being dead or cold.

Short Circuit An improper or accidental contact between two or more electric wires, or between one wire and a path to the ground.

Switch A device for controlling the flow of electricity. A switch opens or interrupts the circuit to stop the current.

Entrance (Service) Switch   A wiring device for breaking the connection between the farmstead wiring system and the wires leading from the power company's lines, or for interrupting current to a building or separate service.

Ground   A safety precaution consisting of an electrically sound connection to moist earth. A ground conducts into the earth currents and short circuits that sometimes develop in the wiring system.

Fuse   A ribbon of soft wire or metal mounted in a container connected to an electric circuit. A fuse limits the amount of current in a circuit. When the circuit is overloaded, the ribbon of wire melts or blows, thereby disconnecting the circuit.

Circuit Breaker   A device for protecting the wiring and appliances against too much current (overload). A circuit breaker may be used instead of a fuse. A breaker operates on the principle of tripping by spring tension when an overload occurs.

(NOTE: This glossary was adapted in part from a publication issued by the Tennessee Valley Authority. Now out of print.)

(NOTE: Wiring instructions in Problem-Unit 3 were drawn in part from the booklets by Sears Roebuck & Co. and Montgomery Ward & Co. listed on page 211.)

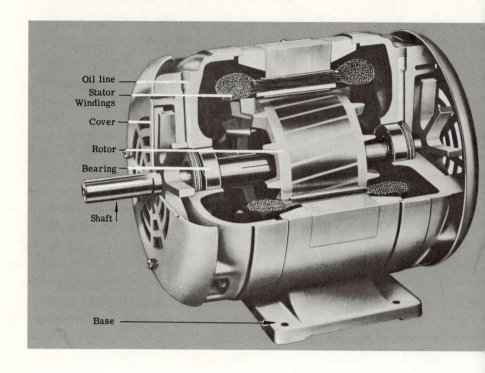

Oil line
Stator
Windings
Cover
Rotor
Bearing
Shaft
Base

Fig. 200. Electric power from this motor can do the work of a grown man for less than 15 cents a day.

PROBLEM-UNIT **IV**

How to
Select and Care for
Electric Motors

About 90 per cent of all stationary farm power jobs in the United States are done by electric motors. The popularity of electric power is mainly due to its convenience and low cost.

In Chapter 1, it was shown that a homemade elevator powered by a ¼-hp motor could be used in some situations to replace a hired hand. The total cost of electricity and depreciation on this equipment would be less than 60 cents per eight-hour day.

Studies have shown that you can earn the following amounts in competition with electric power:

1. Milking cows by hand, 1 cent per 100 pounds of milk.
2. Handling grain with a hand scoop, 2 or 3 cents per hour.
3. Pumping water by hand, 5 cents per 1,000 gallons.
4. Cleaning a barn and moving manure by hand scoop and cart, 3 cents per hour.
5. Grinding and mixing feed by hand mill, 35 cents per ton.

In addition to providing low-cost power for the farm, electric motors offer other advantages: up to 90 per cent efficiency in comparison with 25 to 50 per cent for engines; ease of starting in cold weather; quiet operation with no fumes; adaptation to automatic operation; long life with very little upkeep; less danger of fire with no inflammable fuel used; and little or no supervision necessary, permitting operation by unskilled help.

Fig. 201. An Illinois dairyman lets electric power handle the silage feeding chore while he does more profitable work elsewhere.

CHAPTER 9

How to Select
Electric Motors and Motor Drives
for the Farm

Most electric appliances come from the factory equipped with the proper type and size of motor. However, you may need to convert a hand-operated or engine-powered machine to electric power. Or, you may need to exchange the motor on a machine for a different type or size. If so, you must make a selection from a number of different types and sizes on the market.

The first electric motor to operate entirely by electric current was made by Thomas Davenport in 1837. He used it for drilling and other light work in his blacksmith shop. By 1850, Davenport's motor had been improved and was being used to do a greater variety of jobs. The one serious flaw in these early motors was the fact that they were operated by batteries and were therefore too expensive to be practical.

In 1886, an alternating-current system was installed at New Barrington, Massachusetts. This made available a plentiful supply of economical electricity so that when Nikola Tesla produced the first workable a-c motor in 1888, it met with almost immediate success.

How to Identify the Parts of Your Motor. Today, the farm motor is a vastly superior machine in comparison with the early models. Yet the operating principle is practically the same as that used in 1888. Moreover, the parts of a modern electric motor are quite similar to those in Tesla's first a-c motor.

The cutaway section of the motor in Fig. 202 shows the following parts: a stationary set of windings called a stator; a rotating

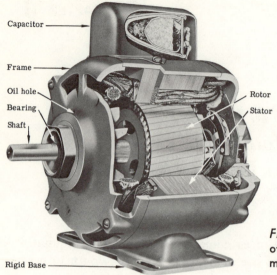

Capacitor

Frame

Oil hole

Bearing

Shaft

Rotor

Stator

Rigid Base

Fig. 202. Cutaway section of 1/2-hp motor with the major parts labeled.

unit of insulated metal sections called a rotor; a set of bearings; a capacitor (condenser) for giving greater starting torque; and a lubrication system. This motor also contains a wiring box with electric leads for connection to an extension cord. The motor shown has a drip-proof cover and solid metal base.

Before going farther, you should refer to page 55 and review the explanation of how an electric motor runs.

What Points Should Be Considered in Selecting Electric Motors?

The things that you will be most concerned about in selecting a motor are the size in horsepower, the motor type, the starting torque, the type of motor enclosure, and the type of bearings.

In getting the most from your motor you will also need to select a suitable drive. This job involves figuring the types and sizes of pulleys as well as the types and sizes of belts needed.

The first cost of a motor is of less importance than the necessity of getting the right motor for the job. A cheap motor often turns out to be the most expensive by burning out in a short time.

You can find the speed and horsepower rating of a motor by checking its nameplate. Other information appearing on this plate includes cycles, voltage, phase, and allowable heat rise. All these facts should be carefully noted before you purchase a motor.

How to Determine Size of Motor Needed. Motor sizes in the range of ⅛ through ¾ hp are referred to as fractional-horse-power motors. Sizes from 1 hp up are called integral-horsepower motors.

The largest motor normally permitted on a single-phase line is 7½ hp, but 10-hp motors are allowed in some areas. There is no limit to the size of a motor that can be operated on three-phase service, provided, of course, the wire size is adequate. Where irrigation equipment is operated on three-phase service, it is common to find motors up to 50 hp and larger. There may be a rather heavy demand charge for electric service of this type. Make certain that you understand your contract thoroughly before investing in three-phase electric irrigation equipment.

How Motor Power Is Related to Time and Speed. What is 1 horsepower? A motor that would lift 33,000 pounds 1 foot high in 1 minute or any equivalent of this would be doing work at the rate of 1 hp. This should require 746 watts of electricity. Due to losses caused by friction, heat, and wind resistance, however, it takes about 1,200 to 1,400 watts to produce 1 horsepower. Motors

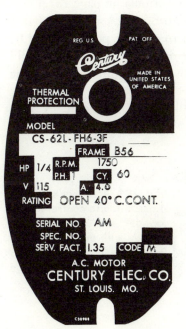

Fig. 203. The nameplate of an electric motor specifies important information about the motor—hp rating, speed in rpm, amperes, volts, whether 115- or 230-volt service, and the like.

in the larger sizes usually give higher efficiency than do the fractional-horsepower sizes. Thus, a 5-hp motor may draw only 4,500w, whereas ten ½-hp motors together would draw from 7,000 to 8,000 watts.

A ¼-hp motor can be used to replace a 1-hp motor provided the smaller motor is given four times as long to do the same amount of work. It would be necessary, of course, to give the ¼-hp motor a 4 to 1 mechanical advantage over the larger size; otherwise the smaller motor could not pull the load. This can be done by using a 4 to 1 pulley ratio. See page 233 for instructions on figuring pulley size.

There is an important principle involved here. For example, farmers have found that a 5-hp motor will operate a combination hammer mill and feed-handling system just as well as a 10-hp motor will. The 5-hp unit simply runs twice as many hours to do the same amount of work. Since the system can be controlled by a time switch, it makes no difference how many hours are required to grind the daily feed supply so long as it can be done in 24 hours or less. The advantage is obvious. The original cost of wiring, motor, and equipment is much less for the 5-hp system.

(NOTE: Using a smaller motor and a slower speed for a water pump is not recommended. Stick to the formula on page 285.)

Common Rules of Thumb on Motor Size. A machine that is being converted from hand operation to electric power should be operated at its original speed. If this is done, a ¼-hp motor should be adequate. A faster speed requires a larger motor for the same load.

A ¾-hp electric motor will replace a 1-hp engine. A 3-hp motor should be adequate to replace a 5-hp engine.

Fig. 204. A farmer setting a time switch to control a feed grinder and conveyors. The switch will cut the motors off at the proper time, thus allowing the farmer to go about other tasks.

(CAUTION: If a motor becomes too hot to handle with your bare hands, you will know that it is either too small for the job or is being operated improperly. Sometimes an overloaded motor will operate properly if its speed is reduced.)

If a motor is to be replaced, the new one should be the same size unless the load on the machine is to be increased or the speed of the machine is to be increased.

If a motor overheats because of low voltage, a change to 220-volt service may correct the trouble.

What Type of Motor Should You Choose?

The large majority of farm motors are built to operate on single-phase, 60-cycle current. Nearly all motors ½ hp and larger can and should be operated on 230 volts.

There are six types of single-phase motors adaptable to the farm: (1) split-phase, (2) capacitor-start, (3) capacitor-start capacitor-run, (4) repulsion-start, (5) repulsion-start induction-run, and (6) repulsion-start capacitor-run.

Since three-phase service is now being made available in many localities, three-phase motors are certain to become more popular in the future. The two types of three-phase motors that are adaptable to the farm are the three-phase, general-purpose motor and the high starting torque motor.

Why Starting Torque of Motors Varies. Torque refers to the thrust that is produced by a motor or an engine. The major weakness of electric motors is their low starting torque. Once a motor gets up to three-quarter speed it has very high efficiency. The problem is to get it up to that speed. The starting problem may be especially serious when a motor must start under a heavy load.

In general, three "extras" are found in electric motors to give them greater starting torque. An extra winding is added in the split-phase motor; other types are equipped with brushes and special windings; still others are equipped with capacitors (condensers) that give additional starting power.

Several combinations of these "extras" are recommended for various jobs, according to the difficulty of starting and running. The three windings of the three-phase motor give it greater natural starting torque.

Fig. 205. This 1/3-hp split-phase motor is the least expensive farm type on the market.

You will likely find that farm jobs for electric motors fall into three classes according to difficulty of starting: (1) easy starting loads, (2) moderate starting loads, and (3) heavy starting loads.

As you would perhaps expect, motors that are built for heavy starting loads have extra equipment on them and, therefore, cost more than motors having low starting torque.

Types of Motors for Light Starting Loads. If you need a motor for operating fans, power saws, small grinders, portable concrete mixers, or other easy-to-start machines, you should choose the *split-phase motor.* This type is the least expensive, simplest in construction, and easiest to maintain of any electric motor. Its weakness is its low starting torque. Then too, it is not available in sizes larger than ⅓ hp.

The split-phase motor gets its name from the two windings in the stator. The starter winding in this motor gives added torque to the rotor until it attains about 75 per cent full speed, at which point a centrifugal switch disconnects the starter winding. The motor then runs on the running winding only.

Split-phase motors are available in fractional horsepower of ⅙ to ⅓ hp. This type of motor uses six to eight times the normal running amperage while it is starting. Such heavy draft of current makes it impractical to use large split-phase motors on rural lines.

The split-phase motor operates on 115 volts and will burn out if plugged into a 230-volt circuit for more than a few seconds. Its direction of rotation can be reversed, and it will operate at a uniform speed up to full load.

For light starting loads up to ⅓ hp, you can save money by selecting a split-phase motor.

Types of Motors for Moderate Starting Loads. For starting a pump jack, a corn sheller, a large shop grinder, a milker, a feed mixer, an air compressor, or other moderate starting loads, you should choose a capacitor-start motor or a three-phase, general-purpose motor (if three-phase service is available).

1. *The Capacitor-Start Motor.* This type differs from a split-phase motor in that it is equipped with a capacitor and has more starting windings and larger wire size. A capacitor is a condenser that has the ability to store electricity for a few seconds and use it when the motor needs an added charge of power for starting. This gives the capacitor motors about three times greater starting ability than split-phase motors.

A capacitor motor can be operated on either 115 or 230 volts. Its speed will be uniform up to full load and its direction of rotation can be changed by a simple adjustment.

The amount of current for starting a capacitor motor will be about four to six times the requirement for running. Sizes vary from ⅙ to 5 hp, and the cost is about 20 per cent more than the same size split-phase motor. Due to the higher cost, you should not

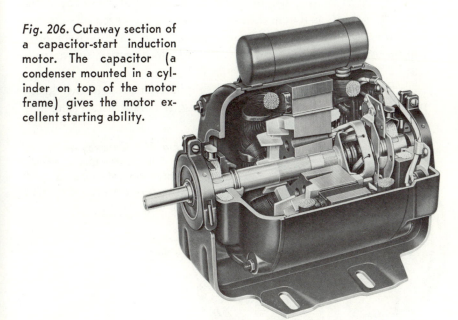

Fig. 206. Cutaway section of a capacitor-start induction motor. The capacitor (a condenser mounted in a cylinder on top of the motor frame) gives the motor excellent starting ability.

choose a capacitor-start motor where a split-phase type can be used. But, for moderate starting loads, a capacitor-start motor is desirable.

Although capacitor-start motors are made in 3- to 7.5-hp sizes, the cost of this type is about one-third greater than that of an equal size motor of the three-phase, general-purpose type. Therefore, you will probably choose a three-phase motor in preference to a capacitor type if you have three-phase electric service available.

2. *The Three-Phase, General-Purpose Motor.* This type motor is also for moderate starting loads. It differs from the split-phase and capacitor-start types principally in construction. The name "three-phase" comes from the three windings in the motor instead of the one that is usual for single-phase motors. Each of these is fed by a "separate" current from a three-phase high line. These three windings produce a rotating magnetic field, giving the motor a natural high starting torque. This type of motor draws about three to four times the normal running current while starting, which is about one half the starting draft of split-phase motors. The three-phase, general-purpose motor is available in sizes from one-third to several hundred hp. In comparison with the same size capacitor-start motor, the three-phase, general-purpose type costs about two thirds as much. The cost of wiring for three-phase service, however, will be considerably more. The three-phase motor can be operated on 115 or 230 volts and the direction of rotation can be reversed.

Because of its ruggedness and simplicity of design, the three-phase, general-purpose motor gives long, trouble-free service; and there are not many parts to maintain.

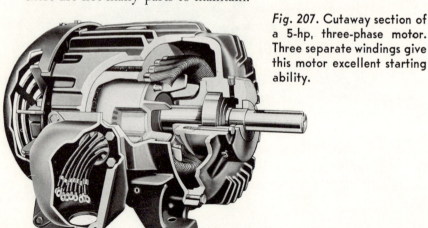

Fig. 207. Cutaway section of a 5-hp, three-phase motor. Three separate windings give this motor excellent starting ability.

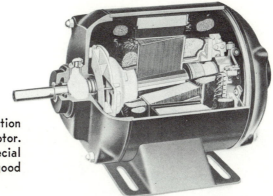

Fig. 208. Cutaway section of a repulsion-start motor. Brushes and other special parts give this motor good starting ability.

If three-phase service is available, the best choice of a motor for medium-starting loads (1 hp and above) is the three-phase, general-purpose motor.

Types of Motors for Heavy Starting Loads. If you need a motor to operate a hammer mill, a heavy-duty compressor, a silage cutter, a grain elevator, a hay hoist, or other heavy-starting loads, you will need a *repulsion-start motor*, a *repulsion-induction motor*, a *capacitor-start capacitor-run motor*, a *three-phase, high starting torque motor*, or a *repulsion-capacitor motor*.

1. *The Repulsion-Start Motor.* For heavy starting loads with single-phase current, the *repulsion-start* motor is satisfactory. It has high starting torque with a minimum amount of current. Its direction of rotation can be changed, and the motor will operate on 115 or 230 volts. It has brushes and other parts that will require regular servicing.

Repulsion-start motors are made in sizes ranging from ⅙ to 10 hp. The smaller sizes cost about 10 to 15·per cent more than the same size in a capacitor-start type. Larger sizes cost about the same for these two types.

2. *The Capacitor-Start Capacitor-Run Motor.* This type has good starting ability and runs on single-phase power. In addition to its capacitor for extra starting power, this motor has a second capacitor which operates in both starting and running.

This type of motor comes in 5- to 10-hp sizes and costs about the same as the repulsion-start motor. It draws three to five times the normal running current for starting. This type motor requires

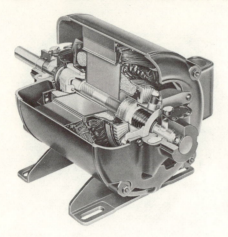

Fig. 209. Cutaway section of a repulsion-induction motor. This type has excellent starting ability and a low draft of current while running.

less maintenance than the repulsion-start type. Capacitors are more likely to need repairs than the other parts of the motor. The direction of rotation can be changed.

3. *The Repulsion-Induction Motor.* When heavy starting loads are encountered and operating loads vary, the repulsion-induction type is needed. This motor is also equipped with brushes. Voltage can be 115 or 230. In addition to having good starting power, this type of motor draws a minimum of current while running. It has the advantage of being less complicated in construction and of requiring less maintenance than repulsion-start motors. The cost is about the same as for other high starting-torque loads. The repulsion-induction motor draws only 15 per cent more current for starting than for running. The direction of rotation is easy to change in this motor.

4. *The Repulsion-Capacitor Motor.* This type motor is a newcomer to the field. It is highly efficient while running. It com-

Fig. 210. Cutaway section of a repulsion-capacitor motor, featuring excellent starting ability, low running current, and high efficiency.

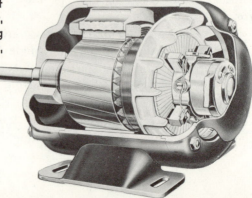

bines the repulsion-start feature, which gives high starting torque, with the capacitor feature for running. The capacitor provides more efficiency in use of current after the motor has attained full speed.

This motor was developed as a general-purpose power unit for the farm; that is, a 3- to 10-hp motor for operating grain or hay dryers, which require heavy running loads in the summer. The motor can then be transferred to a barn cleaner, a feed mill, or a silo unloader, which require high starting torque and also heavy running loads.

The principal advantages of the repulsion-capacitor motor are: (1) high starting torque, (2) low starting current, (3) efficiency, and (4) excellent construction features. Original cost runs about 10 per cent more than a capacitor-start capacitor-run motor.

How Will the Type of Electric Service
Influence Motor Selection?

The type of electric service available varies from one community to another. It is necessary, therefore, to check with the power supplier before buying and installing large motors. For instance, if you have a 115-volt service drop to your farm, you cannot use a 230-volt motor until a three-wire service drop is provided. The same holds true for three-phase current, which requires three hot wires and one neutral. If three-phase service is available, it will probably pay you to use three-phase motors for heavy work. Also, check the cycle specifications of a motor before buying.

Proper size service entrance must be provided for large motors. For example, if you have a 30-ampere switch now, you would probably need to install a larger service entrance to take care of an additional 5- to 10-hp motor.

What Motor Accessories Should You Select?

When choosing a type and size of motor, you should consider the accessories that will make your motor give satisfactory service over a long period of time. You should consider the type of bearings and the kind of motor enclosure needed.

Type of Bearings to Choose. Electric motors are equipped with two types of bearings: (1) sleeve bearings and (2) ball bear-

TABLE 16

Comparison of Farm Motors

Name	Horsepower Size	Electric Service (volts & phase)	Starting Current %*	Starting Ability	Maintenance Cost	Relative Cost
Split-Phase	1/20 to 1/3	Usually 115, Single-phase	600 to 800	Poor	Low	Low
Capacitor-Start	1/3 to 7 1/2	115-230, Single-phase	300 to 600	Good	Moderate	Moderate
Repulsion-Start	1/6 to 10	115-230, Single-phase	200 to 300	Excellent	High	Moderate
Capacitor-Start Capacitor-Run	5 to 10	115-230, Single-phase	300 to 400	Excellent	Moderate	Moderate
Repulsion-Induction	1 to 15	115-230	150 to 200	Excellent	Moderate	Moderate
Three-Phase, General-Purpose	1/3 and up	115-230, Three-phase	200 to 400	Good to Excellent	Low	Low
High Starting Torque, Three-Phase	1/3 and up	115-230, Three-phase	100 to 200	Excellent	Low	High
Repulsion-Capacitor	3 to 10	230, Single-phase	150 to 300	Good to Excellent	Moderate	Moderate

* Starting current based on normal running current.

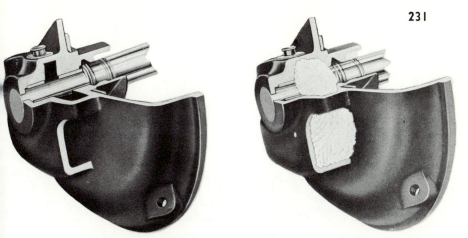

Fig. 211. Sleeve-type bearings, showing the oil reservoir. Yarn is sometimes packed into the housing to help distribute the oil.

ings. Small motors are often equipped with sleeve bearings and usually cost less than ball-bearing motors. Motors larger than 1 hp usually come equipped with ball bearings. Also, totally enclosed motors are of the ball-bearing type. Motors having ball bearings operate with less friction and may be mounted in any position. With one or two exceptions, sleeve-bearing motors must always be mounted with the motor shaft parallel to the floor. Otherwise, the shaft and bearings would soon wear out for lack of lubrication. Examples of the need for vertical mounting are lawn mowers or power drills.

Sleeve bearings require regular oil lubrication, whereas ball bearings, which are lubricated with grease, may be operated for

Fig. 212. At right, cutaway section of a ball-bearing motor; at left, enlarged cutaway section of a ball bearing and bearing race.

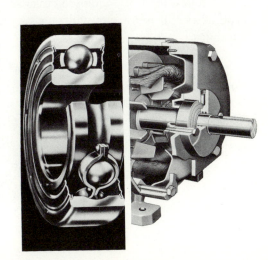

Fig. 213. Farm motor with an open drip-proof cover. Not for use in wet or dusty locations.

long periods of time before new lubrication is required. Some ball bearings are sealed for life.

Excessive belt tension will wear out your motor bearings. See page 250 for further information on this.

Type of Motor Enclosure Needed. The housings or covers for electric motors are designed to meet a variety of needs. Three types are adaptable to the farm. These are (1) the open, drip-proof (2) the splash-proof, and (3) the totally enclosed.

If your motor is to be operated where the surrounding air is clean and dry, choose a drip-proof enclosure since this is the most economical kind.

Choose the splash-proof cover if liquids may splash against the motor from the sides; this kind costs more but the cover protects the motor windings.

Choose the fully enclosed cover if excess dust is present. This type costs still more but will save on bearings, shafts, and motor windings.

Fig. 214. A splash-proof cover makes this motor suitable for use in locations where liquids may splash against the sides.

Fig. 215. This totally enclosed cover is required in very wet or dusty locations. Note the amount of dust in the inset at lower left.

What Type and Size of Motor Drive Should You Have?

The most common method of transmitting electric motor power is by V-pulleys and V-belts. A few farm jobs require a flat drive or a combination flat and V-belt drive. For hookups where the motor is mounted directly on the machine, a flexible coupling should be used. For low-power applications in the farm shop, a flexible shaft is a valuable piece of equipment since it gives portable power in any position.

How to Determine the Size of a Pulley. Pulley problems will be easy for you if you think of them as a simple ratio. First, you will already know the speed of your motor (see label), and you will need to know the correct speed of the machine involved. In the case of a feed grinder, assuming the common speed 1,750 rpm for the motor and 350 rpm for the grinder, a 5 to 1 ratio is obtained. Next, select a pair of pulleys that are likewise in the proportion of 5 to 1. Example, if a 3-inch pulley is used on the motor, then a 15-inch pulley would be needed on the feed grinder. The motor shaft will then turn over five times to each one revolution of the feed grinder. Remember that the machine will operate

234

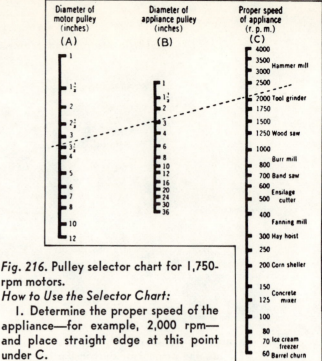

Fig. 216. Pulley selector chart for 1,750-rpm motors.

How to Use the Selector Chart:

1. Determine the proper speed of the appliance—for example, 2,000 rpm—and place straight edge at this point under C.

2. Determine the diameter of the motor pulley—for example 3½ inches—and place the straight edge at this point under A.

3. Read the proper pulley size for the appliance where the straight edge crosses the chartline under B. Answer: the appliance pulley should be 3 inches.

NOTE: If C and B are known, A can be determined in the same manner.

at the same speed as the motor if both pulleys are the same size, provided there is no slippage.

The easiest method of determining the proper size pulley is to use the chart in Fig. 216. Simply lay a straight edge along the two columns and the correct size pulley will be shown.

Types of Pulleys for the Farm. Pulleys are made of cast iron, steel, or aluminum alloy. The larger, three-groove types are usually made of cast iron. Aluminum-alloy pulleys are used with smaller motors and for light loads.

The V-pulley is the most common type used with electric motors and the machines they operate. V-pulleys may be purchased in several styles; namely, A-section, B-section, C-section, two-groove, three-groove, four-step cone, and variable-speed pul-

Fig. 217. Two styles of V-pulleys. At left, a B-section groove pulley fitted with an interchangeable arbor unit. At right, an A-section groove pulley with a 3/4-inch arbor.

leys. The standard V-pulley, single groove, is usually found on motors up to 2 hp unless the load is unusually heavy. For motors larger than 2 hp, a two-groove V-pulley with B-belts may be needed. The C-section type is for still heavier power transmission.

TABLE 17

Number and Type of V-Belts Needed for 1,750-RPM Motors*

Diameter of Pulley in Inches	Motor H.P.							
	½ or smaller	¾	1	1½	2	3	5	7½
2	FHP**	FHP**	..	..	..	..	..	..
2½	FHP**	FHP**	..	..	..	..	..	..
3	1-A	1-A	1-A	2-A	2-A	3-A	5-A	8-A
3½	1-A	1-A	1-A	2-A	2-A	3-A	4-A	7-A
4	1-A	1-A	1-A	1-A	2-A	2-A	3-A	5-A
4½	1-A	1-A	1-A	1-A	1-A	2-A	3-A	5-A
5	1-A	1-A	1-A	1-A	1-A	2-A	3-A	4-A
5½	1-A	1-A	1-A	1-A	1-A	1-B	2-B	3-B
6	1-A	1-A	1-A	1-A	1-A	1-B	2-B	2-B
7	1-A	1-A	1-A	1-A	1-A	1-B	2-B***	2-B
8	1-A	1-A	1-A	1-A	1-A	1-B***	1-B	2-B

    * Adapted from *Electricity on the Farm Magazine* (New York, The Reuben H. Donnelley Corp., April, 1956), p. 18.
    ** FHP (Fractional horsepower) refers to a V-belt that is designed for small motors using small pulleys. Available in ⅜-, ½-, and ⅝-inch widths.
    *** The same number of A-section belts could be used instead of B-section.
    (NOTE: 2- or 2½-inch pulleys should not be used on motors larger than 1 hp.)

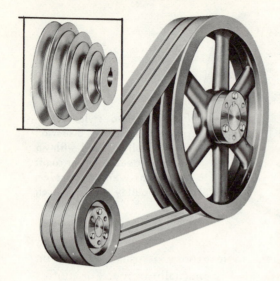

Fig. 218. The four-step cone pulley at upper left gives four different speeds of machine. The B-section, three-groove V-pulleys and belts at right are for extra heavy duty.

By referring to Table 17, you can find the type and number of V-belts required for various combinations of pulley sizes and horsepower. You will note that pulley size as well as horsepower influences the number and size of belts required.

Four-Step Cone Pulleys. Because of the four different speeds you can get, the four-step cone pulley works well with a portable motor that is used for operating more than one kind of machine. It is valuable for use with a drill and with other machines that operate at several different speeds.

How to Select the Proper Type of V-Belt. V-belts are usually made of rubber and fibrous materials. Some contain metal fibers also. The size of a V-belt refers to two dimensions; namely, its cross section and its length. For farm use, four cross sectional sizes of V-belts are available: (1) the A-section, which is ⅜ inch wide at the top; (2) the B-section, ½ inch at the top; (3) the C-section, ⅞ inch at the top (actually ²¹⁄₃₂ inch); and the FHP-type for motors under ¾ hp in size. The larger cross sections are used for

Fig. 219. Cross-sectional sizes of V-belts for farm use.

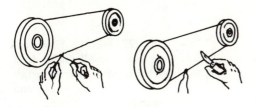

Fig. 220. Farmer's method of measuring the length of a V-belt.

transmitting heavy loads; however, these larger, thicker belts will not bend to as small a pulley as will the ⅜-inch size or the FHP-type. Fig. 219 shows cross sections of the major farm types.

How to Determine the Length of Belt Needed. If your motor can be installed in any location it is best to locate it at a distance from the machine as determined by the following:

> Four times the diameter of the largest pulley plus 1.6 times the diameter of the motor pulley plus 1.6 times the diameter of the machine pulley equals length of belt for correct distance between motor and machine. Buy the standard size nearest to this figure.

In measuring the length of belt for a machine and pulley already installed, the best procedure is to take the old belt to the supplier and have it matched. If this is not possible, tie a string.

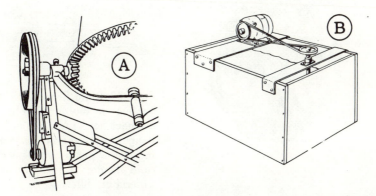

Fig. 221. (A) The drive unit consists of a V-pulley on the motor and a flat pulley on the machine. The large flat pulley costs less than the same size V-pulley yet does the same job. (B) The quarter-turn drive is valuable for operating machines in a vertical position where the motor must be mounted horizontally.

Fig. 222. Flexible hose connecting a small motor to a water pump is easy to install and easy on the motor and machine.

around both pulleys where the belt normally runs. Cut the string and measure with a tape or ruler and get this size. Most motors are mounted so that some adjustment in length can be made. This may make it possible to use a size above or below the old belt size.

Some jobs require a flat pulley on the machine and a V-drive on the motor. The size of a flat pulley is figured on the diameter at the largest point. V-belts are used to operate this combination.

In a few instances, it may be satisfactory to use a flat pulley on the motor as well as the machine. A flat leather belt with the ends secured together with steel lacing can be used for flat drives; rubber fibrous belts are also satisfactory for flat drives.

Types of Positive and Direct Drives for the Farm. Some jobs require that a motor be connected directly to its load. For this you may use a flexible hose, a rigid flange, or a flexible shaft.

Fig. 223. Rigid flanges for connecting a motor directly to a machine: (*A*) chain-drive flange; (*B*) a motor connected to a water pump by means of a rigid flange; (*C*) rigid flange with rubber filler.

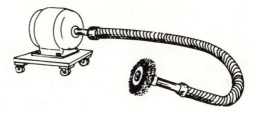

Fig. 224. A flexible shaft makes it possible to use power equipment in all positions.

1. A piece of flexible hose can be used for driving light loads, usually ⅓ hp or less. Hose will soon come apart if it is coupled to loads heavier than this. For light work, however, a piece of hose makes an inexpensive, convenient, and easily installed drive.

2. A rigid flange is sometimes needed where pulleys and gears are not feasible. Such a coupling eliminates all slippage. Usually one half of the flange is bolted to the motor and the other half is fastened to the machine. The two parts are secured together with pins. Rubber or leather fillers are used in the space between the two parts of the flange to serve as shock absorbers. This protects the motor bearings against damage from vibration. With the exception of fans, motors should not be attached directly to a machine without a proper flange. Fans produce little or no shock and therefore may be attached directly to the shaft of the motor.

3. A flexible shaft is excellent for operating a grinder, a buffer, a sander, and other similar equipment. Almost every farm shop should have this piece of equipment for use with a ⅓- to ½-hp motor. This type of drive can be bought for motors up to 2 hp. The advantage is apparent. You can operate the equipment in any position and it can be moved about while in operation. The cost varies from $15 up.

Summary

In all situations where electric motors can be used to do farm work, savings on power costs can be effected. Electric motors, on the average, are almost twice as efficient as engines. Also, motors that are given proper care should last up to 30 years with very little repair and upkeep.

The two main parts or units of an electric motor are (1) a rotor, or rotating part, and (2) a stator, or stationary part. All other parts act as accessories to these two main units. These other parts include bearings, lead wires, and covers. Some types of motors have capacitors and brushes, which are used for giving the motor added starting torque.

A rotor, when turning, is a spinning magnet. The current flowing through the stator coils creates a magnetic field and a current flowing through the rotor conductors also magnetizes the rotor. Magnetic forces in the stator, acting upon the magnets in the rotor cause it to turn.

The common size of single-phase motors for farm use ranges from ⅛ hp to 7½ hp. In some areas, up to 15-hp sizes are allowed. Three-phase motors are available in sizes up to a 100 hp or more. Most farm motors have a speed of 1,725 rpm; some operate at 3,450 rpm.

Single-phase motors for farm use come in six types: (1) split-phase, (2) capacitor-start, (3) capacitor-start capacitor-run, (4) repulsion-start, (5) repulsion-induction, and (6) repulsion-capacitor. Three-phase motors come in two farm types: (1) general-purpose, and (2) high starting torque.

For easy starting loads, the split-phase motor (up to ⅓ hp) is satisfactory and is the least expensive. For moderate starting loads, the capacitor types or the three-phase, general-purpose motors should be used. For heavy starting loads, the repulsion-start types are best. Also, the three-phase, high starting torque motor is excellent for heavy loads, where it can be used.

If a motor must be operated in dusty or wet surroundings, a totally enclosed cover should be used. This type of cover is accompanied by sealed ball bearings. Sleeve bearings are less costly but are not suitable for operation out of level. Also, sleeve bearings must be lubricated periodically.

The most widely used drive for electric motors is the V-belt and V-pulley. These come in a variety of sizes and types suitable for most farm needs. Also, the flat belt, rigid flange, flexible hose, and flexible shaft are useful drives for a variety of needs on the farm.

Questions

1. Why do electric motors have such high running efficiency in comparison with engines?
2. Why do electric motors have low starting torque? How can starting torque be increased?

3. Why does a 1-hp motor draw more than 746 watts (1 hp)? What happens to the extra 400 to 600 watts (total draft 1,400 watts) that are normally used by a 1-hp motor?
4. Why is it economical to buy the proper type of motor, even if it costs more?
5. For what special combinations of farm jobs is the new repulsion-capacitor motor adapted?
6. What effects will excess tension in a belt have on the motor?

Additional Readings

Brown, R. H., *Farm Electrification.* New York, McGraw-Hill, 1956.

Henderson, G. E., *Selecting Farm Electric Motors, Controls, and Drives.* Southern Association of Agricultural Engineering and Vocational Agriculture. Athens, Georgia, University of Georgia, 1953.

Schaenzer, J. P., *Rural Electrification,* 5th rev. ed. Milwaukee, Wisconsin, Bruce Publishing Co., 1955.

South Dakota Rural Electric Association, *Electrical Textbook for Vocational Agriculture Students.* Huron, South Dakota, 1956.

University of Illinois, Vocational Agriculture Service, *Electric Motors for Farm Use.* Urbana, Illinois, College of Agriculture (no date).

U.S. Department of Agriculture, *Electric Motors for the Farm.* Farmers' Bulletin No. 1858. Washington, D.C., 1940.

Wright, Forrest B., *Electricity in the Home and on the Farm,* 3rd ed. New York, John Wiley and Sons, 1950.

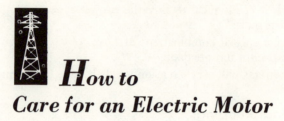

CHAPTER 10

How to Care for an Electric Motor

Despite the fact that an electric motor is built to last thirty years or longer, some motors have been known to burn out in a few minutes after installation. It is possible to select the proper type and size of motor and still get short life and unsatisfactory service from it. Whether or not your motors give good service and last as long as they should will depend upon the way you install and care for them.

Authorities claim that most motor failures result from one or more of the following abuses: (1) Overloading; for example, calling on a ¼-hp motor to do the work of a ½-hp size; (2) improper wiring and low voltage; (3) overfusing, which results in heating; (4) using the wrong type of motor for the job; (5) improper lubrication; (6) improper installation; (7) too tight belts, and (8) allowing excess dust, water, oil, or fumes to enter the motor.

A suggested remedy for most motor troubles can be found in Table 18.

How Can You Protect Your Motors from Overloading?

Several things can cause overloading even though you have the proper size and type of motor. For example, a foreign object can get into a machine and cause it to become locked. When this happens, the current continues to flow through the locked rotor and, within seconds, enough heat is generated to burn the insulation off the windings unless the motor circuit is properly protected. Therefore, it is essential to provide the proper kind of fuses

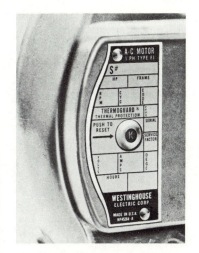

Fig. 225. Built-in protector. When overload causes the motor to cut out, wait two minutes, then reset the switch by pressing the button.

and other protection so as to avoid burn outs from overloads. Motor protectors are of two general types, built-in and manual reset.

Motors With Built-in Protection. Fig. 225 shows a ⅓-hp motor which came from the factory equipped with a built-in protector. This device breaks the circuit when excess heat causes a metallic strip to expand. This expansion has the same effect as a switch. When the metal strip cools sufficiently, it comes back into position and thus reconnects the circuit. Built-in protectors may be manual or automatic.

Manual Switch Protection. A manual reset control is the type of protector suitable for shop machines and other electric devices that are handled. Why is this so? It would be dangerous to have an automatic reset control for a bench saw or jointer because the automatic reset could reestablish the current while you are working on the machine and thus cause a serious injury. Therefore the automatic control is adapted to refrigeration, water pumping, and other continuous processes, not shop machinery. The protection device (sometimes called a relay) may be connected to the motor itself or it may be mounted in a separate unit.

Electric motors of ½ to 3 hp in size may come from the dealer without built-in protection. If so, install the proper-size manual-start switch or magnetic switch:

Manual-Start Switch. This type of switch is suitable for use on ½- to 3-hp motors. It operates on the principle of excess heat

244

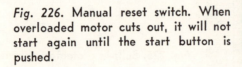

Fig. 226. Manual reset switch. When overloaded motor cuts out, it will not start again until the start button is pushed.

breaking the circuit. The circuit is broken when a metal strip in the protector expands a certain amount and thus breaks the circuit. Another type of switch operates by spring tension and still another breaks the circuit when a ribbon of solder melts. To re-establish the circuit, reset the switch by hand.

Magnetic Switch With Built-in Protection. This type of protector is used for 5-hp motors and up. The cost is excessive for small motors. The protection principle is the same as in other types previously discussed. An additional feature of the magnetic switch, however, is that a magnetic relay protects the motor against both

Fig. 227. A magnetic switch (left) affords protection for low voltage as well as overloads. The diagram (right) illustrates the result of low voltage when the motor is unprotected.

heating and low voltage. If the voltage drops below a safe operating level, the magnetic switch opens the circuit, thus preventing damage to the motor from overheating.

Protection by Time-Delay Fuses. On page 118 you will find a detailed explanation of a time-delay fuse. This type of fuse allows a motor to draw up to six or eight times its normal running current while it is starting. If the motor continues to draw this much current for more than 20 to 30 seconds however, the fuse will blow. The common trade names of this type fuse are Fusetrons and Fustats. The amperage rating must not exceed the motor current rating over 25%, and no other appliance may be operated on the same circuit.

Protection by Special Starter. For 5-, 7½-, or 10-hp motors it may be necessary to use a *current-limiting* starter, sometimes called a resistor starter. This device controls the amount of current while the motor is getting up to full speed. A current adjustment arm can be moved so as to increase the current from starting position up to full speed.

The value of such control is to prevent excess dimming of lights while a large motor gets started.

How Should an Electric Motor Be Installed?

Many good motors are ruined every year because of improper installation. It is essential that several steps be properly followed in the installation of a motor.

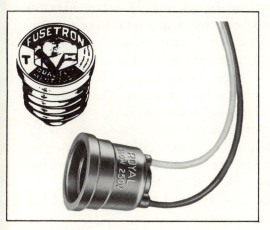

Fig. 228. One easy way to provide motor protection is to install a weather-proof socket in the hot line(s) of the motor circuit and insert the proper size Fusetron.

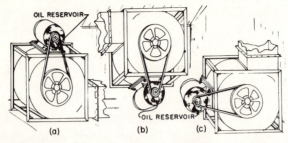

Fig. 229. The motors in *A, B,* and *C* have sleeve bearings and therefore must be mounted in a horizontal position. The oil cups must be positioned up by rotating the end bell of the motor. The ball-bearing motor in *D* may be operated in a vertical position.

Install the Motor in the Correct Operating Position. It is essential that sleeve-bearing motors be mounted in a horizontal position unless they are manufactured especially for vertical installation. A motor that is tilted as much as 15 degrees is considered as being in a vertical position. Ball-bearing motors may be mounted in a vertical position.

The Motor Should Be Mounted Securely. It is important to have your motor mounted securely. A concrete base will provide a substantial mount and result in a quiet running motor. Fig. 230 shows an inexpensive method of mounting a farm shop grinder. This machine will operate without vibration. Materials needed for building this project include a discarded oil drum, ½ yard of gravel or other ballast, and ¼ yard of concrete.

For heavier motors which require a secure and adjustable anchor, you need an adjustable metal frame similar to that in Fig. 231. This type may come with a heavy-duty motor or it may be purchased separately. The adjustable frame is convenient for tightening or loosening belts. If you are handy with the farm welder, you can construct one using angle iron for the main rails.

The motor frame should be fastened to a substantial base, perhaps concrete or heavy floor boards.

Fig. 230. A 1-hp grinder mounted on a concrete base. The oil drum is partially filled with crushed stone then topped with 12 inches of concrete. The anchor bolts were set when the concrete was poured.

Due to vibration, motor mounts, pulleys, and other parts often tend to work loose. Therefore, it is necessary to tighten all anchor bolts and pulley screws occasionally. Loose motor parts will result in excessive wear.

When to Use a Rigid Shaft. A rigid shaft makes it possible to operate several machines with one motor. It is important that the shaft be located out of the way, or, better still, have it enclosed. An exposed shaft is dangerous to those working around it. To operate successfully, a rigid shaft should be installed level with the floor. It should be equipped with good bearings which can be reached for ease of lubrication. Transmission of power from the shaft to a machine may be by V-pulley and V-belts or by gears.

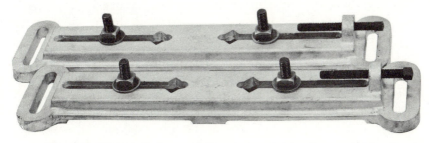

Fig. 231. Slide rails for mounting heavy-duty motors provide about 2½ inches of horizontal adjustment. Anchor the rails to a solid foundation.

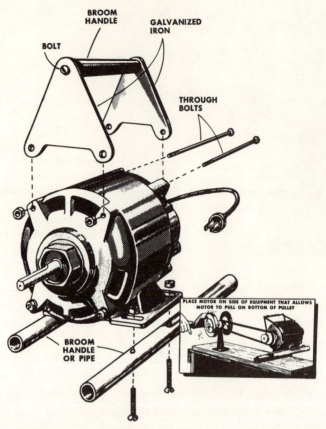

Fig. 232. Exploded view of a portable motor. One motor can thus be used to operate several machines. Install one four-step cone pulley on the motor and one on the machine.

Make certain that the pulleys and belts or the gears are properly aligned and not too tight.

How to Make a Small Motor Portable. A ½- to ¾-hp motor can be mounted on a portable frame, as illustrated in Fig. 232, and used to operate several different machines on the farm. This arrangement is especially adapted for use in the farm shop. Study the diagram in Fig. 232 to see how you can construct one of these projects.

How to Mount a Large Motor on a Portable Cart. Another convenient arrangement for portable farm power is a large motor on a cart. This type of project makes it possible to operate a feed

MAGNETIC SWITCH

PUSH-
BUTTON
STARTER

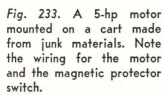

Fig. 233. A 5-hp motor mounted on a cart made from junk materials. Note the wiring for the motor and the magnetic protector switch.

grinder, a barn cleaner, a silo unloader, and other machines with a single large motor.

Whatever type of mount you use, the motor should be properly aligned with the machine it is to operate. The motor shaft should be parallel with the machine shaft so that no "twisting" action is present. The motor pulley should be in line with the machine pulley, since misalignment causes excessive wear and friction and also reduces efficiency.

The most desirable position of the motor is level with the machine shaft, but this may not be possible. Your motor will operate above or below the machine-shaft level but with less efficiency.

How Should You Care for Your Pulleys and Belts?

Good transmission of power and long life of motors and belts will depend on a few common-sense practices. It will pay you to follow these.

How to Anchor a Pulley to a Shaft. Light-load pulleys may have a single setscrew for anchoring to the shaft. It is sometimes necessary to drill and tap another hole in the pulley collar to prevent slippage. The second setscrew should be installed one quarter of the way around the pulley collar, not on the side opposite the original setscrew.

Pulleys that are designed to do heavy work usually have a keyway corresponding to a keyway on the shaft of the motor or the machine to be operated. A setscrew holds the key in place and anchors the pulley so that it cannot slip. In buying a new pulley that requires keying to the shaft, it is necessary to state the dimensions of the keyway—$\frac{3}{16}$ x $\frac{1}{4}$ inches, for example. The diameter of the pulley bore must be stated also.

1/4 - inch
Keyway

1/4 - inch
Key

Fig. 234. The key in the motor shaft must fit keyway in the pulley arbor of a rigid flange.

The larger, heavy-duty, two- and three-groove pulleys usually have an inner cone which is universal for a given line of pulleys. The outer part of these pulleys may be interchanged for any desired size and can then be mounted on the universal cone.

How to Care for Pulleys and Belts. Rubber-base belts should never be oiled, as oil causes rubber to rot. Special compounds are available for use on flat belts to reduce slippage.

Care should be taken not to adjust a belt too tightly. Correct tension for a V-belt is determined as follows:

Fig. 235. (A) These belts are too loose as indicated by flapping. *(B)* Correct and incorrect alignment of belts. See that motor and machine shafts are parallel.

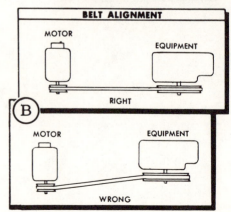

BELT ALIGNMENT

MOTOR

EQUIPMENT

RIGHT

MOTOR

EQUIPMENT

WRONG

1. Grasp both sides of the belt and force together with the hand.

2. The belt should have enough slack to allow for closing in by one fourth of the distance between them.

Too much tension will cause the bearings in your motor and machine to wear out, and the belt may be ruined also.

In installing a belt, see that the pulleys are lined up to make the belt run true and not bind in any way. Always loosen your motor sufficiently to allow for installing the belts without undue stretching. Never use a stick or crow bar to force a belt onto pulleys.

The best operating position of a motor is to have its shaft horizontal to the machine shaft. Other operating positions, however, are possible and the loss in efficiency is not excessive even when mounted directly overhead.

Pulleys should be removed from the motor shaft by using a puller. Pounding on the rim of a pulley may ruin it. Do not scar the pulley opening or the end of the shaft, since this will interfere with removal of the pulley. If you are attempting to remove a pulley from a battered shaft, you may have to file off the metal burr.

What Routine Maintenance Jobs Should You Do?

1. Replace worn brushes as soon as you notice sparks between the brushes and the armature. The armature will require truing up in a lathe if it becomes out-of-round or acquires high spots.

2. A motor should not be installed in a location where the surrounding air gets above 104 degrees F.

3. A motor shaft should turn freely. A slight misalignment of the shaft with relation to the bearings will cause heating and ruin the motor if it is operated in this condition. This can be checked by removing the belt from the drive pulley and spinning the shaft by hand.

4. Avoid excessive belt tension, as this causes motor bearings to wear too fast.

5. Never blow out a motor with compressed air as this forces dust into the windings and bearings. To clean a motor, first disassemble it, then brush out all dust and other foreign matter. Bearings should be washed in solvent or kerosene.

How Should You Lubricate Your Electric Motors?

The lubrication of electric motors varies according to the type of bearings the motor has. As stated before, improper lubrication is one of the main causes of motor failures. Always use the kind of lubricant recommended by your service manual and follow instructions in applying it.

How to Lubricate a Sleeve-Bearing Motor. Since sleeve-bearing motors ordinarily come from the factory with the oil wells dry, the bearings must be oiled before the motor is operated. Fig. 236 shows how wool yarn is used to assure continuous lubrication of the bearings in motors up to 2 or 3 hp.

A good grade of SAE-10 cylinder oil is satisfactory for lubricating sleeve bearings. Heavier oil will not give proper lubrication. For average farm use, fill oil wells twice a year.

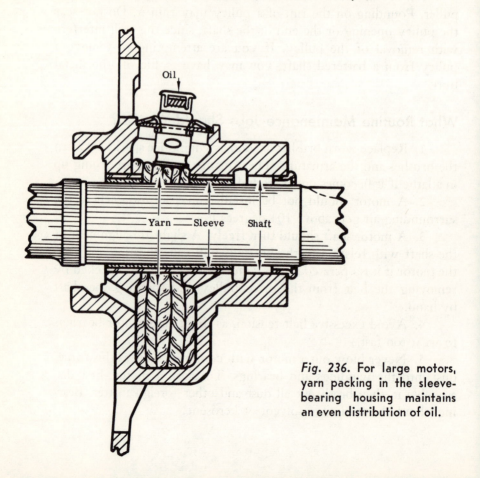

Fig. 236. For large motors, yarn packing in the sleeve-bearing housing maintains an even distribution of oil.

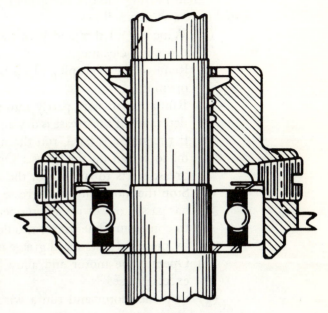

Fig. 237. Cross-sectional view of ball bearings, shaft, and bearing race. Note the space for ball-bearing grease.

(NOTE: Sleeve-bearing motors can be mounted on side walls or ceiling. However, the end plates must be removed and rotated so that the oil wells will always be up, otherwise the oil will drain out.)

How to Lubricate a Ball-Bearing Motor. The type of grease used for lubricating a ball-bearing motor will affect the life of the motor and the quality of service it will give. Special ball-bearing grease recommended by the manufacturer should always be used. Ordinary cup grease or pressure grease is not satisfactory. You must have a lubricant that will not melt and drip out of the bearings.

The following steps are essential in getting the long life you expect from your ball-bearing motor:*

1. A new motor should be inspected when installed, and lubricated if necessary.

2. Ball-bearing motors should be lubricated approximately once a year. Certain ball-bearing motors should be lubricated at shorter intervals if the original instruction has indicated that additional attention will be required.

* Wagner Electric Corp., *To Grease or Not to Grease*, St. Louis, Missouri (no date).

3. Ball-bearing motors for general farm use should be lubricated once a year as follows:

(a) Wipe off all dirt and give the exterior of the motor a thorough cleaning.

(b) Remove the pipe plug from both lubrication and drain openings.

(c) Run a rod or wire partly into the lubrication opening to determine if the grease is dry and hard.

(d) If the grease is hard, run the motor while adding a little oil to soften up the grease. Operate the motor until the grease starts to run out of the drain opening.

(e) Stop the motor and add grease until the old black grease has passed out of the drain opening and new grease starts to come out. The grease should be added to the housing by means of a standard grease cup.

(f) Operate the motor and allow the bearing to force out excess grease.

(g) Stop the motor and run a wire into the lubrication and drain openings to force out a quantity of the grease. This allows for grease expansion after the motor warms up.

(h) Replace both pipe plugs.

TABLE 18*
Trouble-Shooting Chart for Electric Motors

Probable Cause	Test and Remedy
I. Motor Will Not Start	
1. Blown fuse or tripped protector device	Test motor bearings to see if they are in good condition and well lubricated. Machine and motor should turn freely without binding. Test voltage at motor terminals against line voltage. See if protection devices are open or fuse blown. Replace motor fuse with Buss Fusetron (time-delay) fuse of the proper amperage (see nameplate of motor). After replacing fuse or resetting relay, allow motor to operate for awhile to see if it goes off again. If so, check further before using the motor.
2. No voltage or low voltage	Test voltage at motor terminals with switch closed. It should not be more than 10 per cent lower than the voltage called for on the nameplate.

* The Wagner Electric Corp., *Servicing Wagner Single-Phase Motors,* St. Louis, Missouri (no date). (Slightly condensed and re-arranged.) (Note: Codes for motor types, Repulsion-Induction—RA; Split-Phase—RB; Capacitor-Start-RK.)

TABLE 18 (Continued)

Trouble-Shooting Chart for Electric Motors

Probable Cause	*Test and Remedy*
3. Improper current, wrong voltage, or wrong frequency	Single-phase current will not operate three-phase motors and three-phase current will not operate single-phase motors without a converter. Some power companies do not recommend converters. When purchasing an electric motor, check current, voltage, and frequency against your power supply.
4. Improper line connections	Check your motor connections with the diagram which is sent with the motor. Wiring connections for 115 volts are different than for 230 volts. Motor connections must match the voltage on your line.
5. Open circuited field (types RB & RK)	Motor hums when switch is on. Examine for broken wires, loose connections, faulty switch, or open protector.
6. Open circuited field or armature (type RA)	Excessive sparking appears on starting. Motor may refuse to start altogether at certain positions of the rotor, or motor may hum when switch is on. See if protector is tripped, check for loose wires, or see if there are burned segments in the commutator. Check commutator for foreign metallic substance which might short-circuit it.
7. Condenser short-circuited	See item 1 above.
8. Worn or sticking brushes	Poor contact of brushes with commutator will result in slow or weak starting. Brushes may be worn or may stick in holders. Brush springs may be weak, or commutator may be dirty. Clean commutator with piece of fine sandpaper, not emery cloth. Do not oil or grease commutator.
9. Improper brush setting	Brush holder or rocker arm should be opposite index and locked in position. If new armature has been installed, this may vary a little.
10. Excessive load	If items 1 through 9 are all right, motor should start with load on it. If it fails to do so, test by starting without load. If it will start idle, and refuses to start loaded, motor is overloaded. Have an electric motor shop to test for starting torque.

TABLE 18 (Continued)

Trouble-Shooting Chart for Electric Motors

Probable Cause	*Test and Remedy*
	II. MOTOR RUNS HOT
1. Bearing trouble	See section on "Excessive Bearing Wear."
2. Stator coils are short-circuited	Short-circuited coil will be much hotter than others.
3. Rotor rubbing against stator	Check bearings for excessive wear and see if foreign substance is present between stator and rotor.
4. Excessive loads	Check pulley ratios to determine whether machine is turning too fast (faster speed requires more horsepower). Check current with ammeter. Amperes should not exceed amount stated on nameplate.
5. Low voltage	Check voltage at motor terminals. It should not exceed 10% of stated voltage on nameplate.
6. High voltage	Same test as item 5.
7. Incorrect connections to motor leads	Check motor connections with the diagram sent with the motor. Be sure that connections match voltage on your lines.
	III. NOISY MOTOR
1. Unbalanced rotor	Run motor without load, holding the palm of your hand on the case. If shaft is bent or rotor is unbalanced, you can feel the vibration. This is a repair job for a motor shop.
2. Worn bearings	Worn bearings will result in "side play" in the shaft. Replace with new bearings (have this done at a motor shop) and check for cause of bearing wear. (See also section on "Excessive Bearing Wear.")
3. Switch rattles	Install new switch hub and felt washer.
4. Rough commutator or improperly seated brushes	Noise occurs only during starting but should be corrected to avoid further trouble.
5. Excessive end play	End play should be kept at or near zero. Bearings should not bind, however, in making this adjustment. Use washers furnished by the factory and be sure rotor turns freely.
6. Improper alignment of motor and driven machine	Line up pulleys and correct all other misalignments.

TABLE 18 (Continued)

Trouble-Shooting Chart for Electric Motors

Probable Cause	*Test and Remedy*
7. Loosely mounted motor	Tighten up all connections. Check motor base to see if it fits the floor or table on which it is mounted. A loose motor will vibrate.
8. Loose motor accessories	Tighten up capacitor box, switch box, pulleys and other parts. Excessive noise and vibration will result from loose accessories.
9. Amplified motor noise	Use rubber mounts to reduce motor roar.

IV. Burned-Out Motor

1. Frozen bearings	Check section on "Excessive Bearing Wear."
2. Prolonged and excessive overload	Before replacing the burned-out motor, locate and correct the cause of overloading. The driven machine may be at fault as a result of worn bearings, lack of lubrication, bent wheel shafts, and so on. Figure the present work being done by the machine as compared with its original capacity. Check pulley ratios; an oversize pulley on the motor would cause overloading of the motor.

V. Excessive Bearing Wear

1. Belt tension too great; misalignment of motor and machine; improper meshing of gears	Flat or V-belts should have only sufficient tension to provide power without slippage. At midpoint between the motor and machine pulleys, you should be able to compress the two sides of the belt about one fourth the distance between them. A flat belt will require slightly greater tension. Slippage of belts will cause squeaking noise and make the pulley heat. If machine operation requires that the belt be too tight, replace with heavier belt or use two-groove or three-groove pulleys. Check for correct distance from motor to driven machine. (See also section on "How To Select Motor Drive.")
2. Too much, too little, or wrong kind of lubricant	Follow manufacturer's instructions for proper lubrication. Use oil and/or grease recommended for the motor being lubricated. (See page 252.)

TABLE 18 (Continued)
Trouble-Shooting Chart for Electric Motors

Probable Cause	*Test and Remedy*
3. Dirty bearings	Disassemble motor and wash bearings with solvent. Dry with clean cloth and reassemble after lubricating with proper oil or grease. Excessive dirt or dust in bearings indicates that a dust-proof motor enclosure may be needed.

VI. Excessive Brush Wear

1. Dirty commutator	Clean with piece of fine sandpaper.
2. Brushes make poor contact with commutator	Brushes may have worn off too short to reach commutator. Replace short brushes with a new set. See that brushes move freely in their slots; springs should hold brushes firmly against commutator without excessive pressure.
3. Excessive load	If brush wear is due to excessive load, you can tell this by timing the starting cycle. Brushes should lift within five seconds.
4. Brushes fail to lift and stay off during running	Check conditions under "Motor Runs Hot."
5. High mica	Glazed appearance of surface of commutator. Take motor to shop and have a light cut taken off surface of commutator.
6. Rough commutator	See preceding item.

VII. Motor Operates Without Releasing Brushes

1. Dirty commutator	Clean with fine sandpaper.
2. Governor mechanism or brushes sticking; brushes worn too short for contact	Replace worn brushes with new set. Check governor mechanism to see whether it works freely by hand. Faulty governor must be replaced with new one. See that brushes work freely in slots.
3. Frequency of current not correct for motor	If motor varies more than 10% from speed on nameplate while running idle, this indicates that motor does not match the frequency cycle of your current. Ordinarily, rural electric power lines carry single-phase, 60-cycle current. In some sections, three-phase current may be available also. Motor must match the current you have available.
4. Low voltage	See that voltage is within 10% of nameplate voltage with the switch closed.

TABLE 18 (Continued)

Trouble-Shooting Chart for Electric Motors

Probable Cause	*Test and Remedy*
5. Line connections not correct and not making good contact	Tighten up all terminal connections, solder any loose wires which appear to be corroding (after cleaning), and check wiring diagram furnished with the motor.
6. Incorrect brush setting	See that rocker arm setting corresponds with index mark.
7. Incorrect adjustment of governor spring	Governor should throw off brushes at about 75% of speed on nameplate. If it does this at less than 65% or over 85% of nameplate speed, the governor must be repaired or replaced.
8. Excessive load	Motor may start a heavy load but fail to attain sufficient speed to throw off brushes. Check motor bearings for tightness and correct lubrication. Or, motor may throw off brushes for a time but they come back on commutator. Reduce load on motor or replace with larger motor.
9. Shorted stator	See "Motor Runs Hot."

Summary

Electric motors may burn out or be ruined in other ways if not properly protected and correctly installed.

The first essential in caring for a motor is to see that it is properly fused or has some other type of protection. For a water pump or refrigerator motor, an automatic reset protector is best. But for a farm shop machine, a manual reset protector should always be used—never an automatic type.

A separate circuit for an electric motor can be fused with a Fusetron and thus provide protection against overloads. To restore interrupted service, it is necessary to put in a new fuse each time.

Ball-bearing motors may be installed in a vertical position, but sleeve-bearing motors must be operated level or very nearly so.

TABLE 19*

Wire and Fuse Size for Electric Motor Circuits, Single-Phase,
Two-Phase, and Three-Phase, 60-Cycle Current

Motor H.P.	Volts	14	12	10	8	6	4	2	Fuse Size for Motor Circuit
				Maximum Length of Span in Feet					

FOR SINGLE PHASE

Motor H.P.	Volts	14	12	10	8	6	4	2	Fuse
¼	115	80	130	210	280	520			15
¼	230	360	520	840	1,160				10
⅓	115	70	105	215	245	435			20
⅓	230	280	420	860	980				15
½	115	60	95	150	235	375	600		25
½	230	240	380	600	940	1,400			15
¾	115	40	65	105	165	260	420	670	30
¾	230	160	260	420	660	1,040			20
1	115	35	60	95	150	240	375	610	35
1	230	140	240	380	600	960	1,500		20
1½	115			65	105	165	260	415	45
1½	230			260	420	660	1,040		25
2	115			50	85	130	210	335	60
2	230			200	340	520	840	1,340	30
3	115			35	55	85	140	225	90
3	230			140	220	340	560	900	45
5	115			20	35	55	90	145	150
5	220			80	140	220	360	580	80

FOR TWO OR THREE PHASE

Motor H.P.	Volts	14	12	10	8	6	4	2	Fuse
½	220	150	225	300					15
½	440	600	900	1,200					15
¾	220	150	225	300	450				15
¾	440	600	900	1,200	1,800				15
1	220	150	225	300	450				15
1	440	600	900	1,200	1,800				15
1½	220			300	450				15
1½	440			1,200	1,800				15
2	220			250	400				20
2	440			1,000	1,600				15
3	220			150	250				30
3	440			600	1,000				15
5	220			100	175	300	500		45
5	440			400	700	1,200	2,000		25

* The Deming Pump Co., *Deming Pump Catalog C-57* (Salem, Ohio, 1957), p. 71. (NOTE: Data based on National Electrical Manufacturers' Association rating for a maximum of 2 per cent voltage drop with allowance of 25 per cent for heavy starting loads. Table slightly re-arranged.)

Fifteen degrees out-of-level is considered vertical because the lubricating oil will drain out.

Special installations include rigid shafts and portable mounts. A large motor mounted on a cart provides power for several different jobs. The same is true with a rigid shaft. A small portable motor is handy around the farm shop for operating several different machines.

V-belts are easily ruined by operating when improperly adjusted. A belt that is too tight will wear rapidly and may ruin the motor bearings as well. If too loose, a belt will tend to tear and frazzle at the edges and will overheat.

In lubricating motors, the manufacturer's instructions should be carefully followed. It is essential that the proper lubricant be used.

Most motor troubles can be detected before they become serious. The trouble-shooting chart in this chapter describes clues to possible future difficulties. In general, excessive noise, heat, vibration, or the presence of smoke is an indication of trouble.

Questions

1. What is meant by protection against overloading? How does it affect electric motors?
2. Why is it necessary to use a manual-start protector on a table saw instead of an automatic restart protector?
3. Why will a sleeve-bearing motor be ruined if operated at 15 degrees or more out of horizontal (level) position shaft-wise?
4. Why does a motor repairman never pound on a pulley or motor shaft?
5. Why is it necessary to use special grease in lubricating a ball-bearing motor.
6. What would cause a motor to become too hot to touch with your hand?

Additional Readings

Brown, R. H., *Farm Electrification*. New York, McGraw-Hill, 1956.

Henderson, G. E., *Selecting Farm Electric Motors, Controls, and Drives*. Southern Association of Agricultural Engineering and Vocational Agriculture. Athens, Georgia, University of Georgia, 1953.

University of Illinois, Vocational Agriculture Service, *Electric Motors for Farm Use.* Urbana, Illinois, College of Agriculture (no date).

U.S. Department of Agriculture, *Electric Motors for the Farm.* Farmers' Bulletin No. 1858. Washington, D.C., 1940.

Suggested Projects for Problem-Unit Four

Several illustrations used in Chapter 9 and 10 will make excellent projects:

1. Provide Fusetron protection for motor circuits. (See Fig. 194.)

2. Construct permanent mount for grinder. (See Fig. 230.)

3. Make ½-hp motor into portable style. (See Fig. 232.)

4. Construct cart and mount heavy-duty motor on it. (See Fig. 233.)

5. Reverse direction of capacitor or split-phase motor. Interchange leads 1 and 2 as shown in Fig. 238; motor will run in opposite direction.

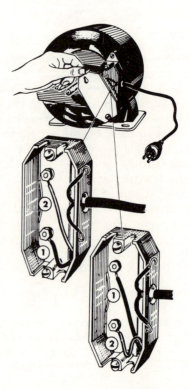

Fig. 238. By interchanging leads number I and 2, as illustrated, the direction of split-phase and capacitor motors can be reversed.

Glossary for Problem-Unit Four:

Rotor   The rotating part of a motor or generator.

Stator   The stationary part of a motor or generator. In most small motors, the stator contains the field windings. In larger motors and generators, the rotor may contain the field poles.

Pole   That part of the motor magnetic circuit around which the field windings are wound. The purpose is to confine the magnetic flux to given locations within the motor since iron will support many times as much magnetism as the same volume of air. The pole in the alternating-current motor is made of laminated iron.

Commutator   A device which changes the direction of the flow of electricity through the rotating part. It consists of narrow copper bars insulated from each other by layers of mica. The ends of the rotor windings are soldered to the commutator bars or segments.

Brushes   Small carbon blocks which make contact with the commutator of an electric motor. These are used to carry electricity from the stationary to the rotating parts of the motor.

Condenser   An electric device in which an electric charge may be stored temporarily. It consists of two or more electric conductors or plates separated by a thin insulating material.

Time-Delay Fuse   A fuse which has the ability to carry overload currents of short duration without melting. The heavier the overload, the less is the time required for the fuse to blow. In motor circuits, where the starting currents are high, a time-delay fuse or other special device is necessary to permit the motor to be started. When properly selected and installed so as to carry only the current of a single motor, such fuses can also be used to provide motor running (overload) protection. Like the common fuse, the time-delay fuse is also made in plug and cartridge types.

Torque   The measure of the tendency of a force to rotate the body upon which it acts. (EXAMPLE: A pull on the spoke of a wheel.) A pull of 1 pound at 1 foot from the center of rotation equals 1 foot-pound of torque.

(NOTE: The organization of Problem-Unit 4 is based in part on the booklet by the Southern Association of Agricultural Engineering and Vocational Agriculture listed on page 261.)

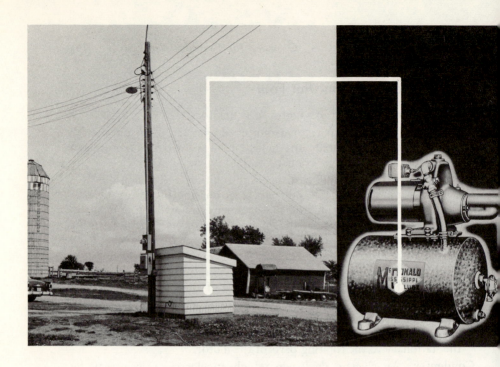

Fig. 239. The water pump at the right is necessary in the operation of this modern farm.

PROBLEM-UNIT **V**

*F*armstead
Lighting and Water Systems

Good light and plenty of water are necessary for successful farming and comfortable living. In fact, you might say that almost every phase of farming and farm life depends, to some extent, upon these two essentials.

As farms become larger and more specialized, the need for water and lighting is likely to increase. So, in planning your water and lighting systems, take the future into account. Many farmers buy and install electric equipment two or three times before they get adequate systems.

In this problem-unit, you will find suggestions on how to select and care for water systems and lighting equipment. The lighting section presents many scenes of proper lighting arrangements including the kinds of equipment needed for special purposes. The chapter on water systems includes basic principles to consider in selecting the proper types and sizes of pumps and pump motors for the farmstead.

Some principles of irrigation and suggestions on how to select irrigation equipment are presented in the latter section of Chapter 11. When all the factors are favorable, irrigation holds great promise for good profits. Many things, however, can cause complete failure.

How to Select and Care for Electric Water Pumps and Related Equipment

Running water has not always been so commonplace on the American farm. In fact, it was considered a luxury before rural electric power became plentiful. Most of the few farms that had running water in those days used engines or windmills for power.

Rural electrification has changed this situation. A recent census publication shows that approximately 60 per cent of all non-dilapidated farm homes had access to running water. This figure includes water inside the residence as well as on the farm grounds.*

A plentiful supply of water for the farm home, although essential, is no more important than water for farm production. In fact, it would be almost impossible to operate a modern dairy or a large laying-hen unit without running water. Many other farming operations are at least partially dependent upon an adequate water supply.

In selecting and caring for farmstead water systems or irrigation equipment, it is necessary to understand and be able to do the following things: (1) select the location and type of well; (2) determine the size of pump needed; (3) select the type of pump needed; (4) determine the size of water pipes required; (5) determine the size of the motor required; (6) identify and correct pump troubles; (7) select pumps and accessories for irrigation; and (8) select and care for irrigation equipment.

* United States Bureau of the Census, *Statistical Abstract of the United States*, 77th ed., Washington, D.C., p. 783.

What Should You Consider in Choosing the Location and Type of Well for the Farmstead?

By selecting a safe location for your well, you can help to insure the health of your family. Outbreaks of typhoid fever and other diseases have been traced to contaminated water supplies. Very often, the cause of contamination is the improper placement of a well.

The diagram in Fig. 240 shows three wells that are safe because they are located on a slope above the level of the farm buildings where there is no danger of seepage. On the other hand, the three wells to the right of and below the buildings are all unsafe. Why? Because of seepage from a septic tank, a barnyard, and an open pool. The water from any one of these wells would be unsafe to use.

Type of Well. The diagram in Fig. 241 shows five types of wells. Dug wells are suitable for shallow depths in soils that do not cave in. A dug well must have a wall of some kind. This can be stone, concrete, wood, or other durable material.

A driven well is the easiest and least expensive to put down; that is, in soils where it is practical to use this type. Notice the sharp "drive point" at the bottom of the casing. This point is necessary in driving the casing down to the water supply. A special cap is installed on top of the well casing, then driving force is applied to the cap. A tractor driving unit may be used for this, or a com-

Fig. 240. Safe and unsafe locations for water wells.

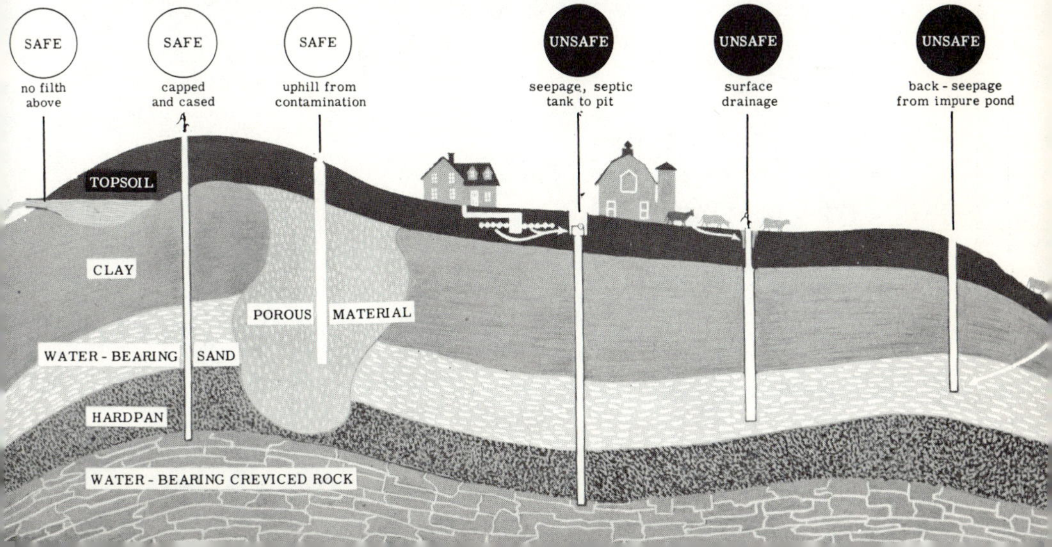

SAFE — no filth above
SAFE — capped and cased
SAFE — uphill from contamination
UNSAFE — seepage, septic tank to pit
UNSAFE — surface drainage
UNSAFE — back-seepage from impure pond

TOPSOIL

CLAY

POROUS MATERIAL

WATER-BEARING SAND

HARDPAN

WATER-BEARING CREVICED ROCK

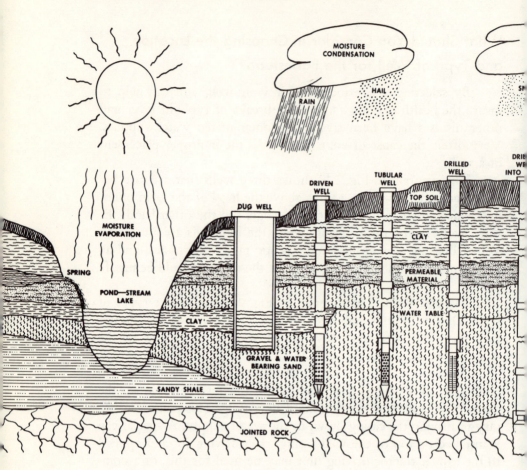

Fig. 241. Five types of wells for the farmstead.

mercial well driller will have proper driving equipment. Where casing is to be driven, the soil must be of a permeable nature and must be free of large stones.

The other illustrations show tubular and drilled wells—the types most often used in deep-well construction and in hard soils where driving is not practical. The diameter of drilled wells varies from 2 inches up. A 2-inch casing, however, is too small to provide an adequate supply of water for the average farm. It will pay you to make the well large enough during the first drilling—at least 4 inches.

How to Protect Your Well from Pollution. Your water supply can become contaminated even though its location is ideal. The following precautions should be observed.

1. Take the necessary steps to direct surface drainage away from the well.

2. See that the septic tank, the cesspool, or the disposal field is located at least 150 feet from the well.

3. Have a sample of water tested at least once a year.

What Size Pump Should You Have?

The capacity of farmstead water pumps is rated in *gallons per hour* or *gallons per minute*. This is stated as *gph* or *gpm* throughout this chapter. A 250gph pump costs less than a 720gph size. No doubt this is why some farmers buy pumps that are too small.

One farmer got into the following difficulties when he bought a pump that was not large enough:

1. During peak-use periods there was a shortage of water, and this prevented the needed expansion of the dairy.

2. After two years the farmer finally decided to install a larger pump, whereupon he found that he needed a larger well.

3. In addition to the cost of the new equipment, the farmer had to pay for removing the old pump as well as installing the new one.

Didn't this farmer have an expensive water system?

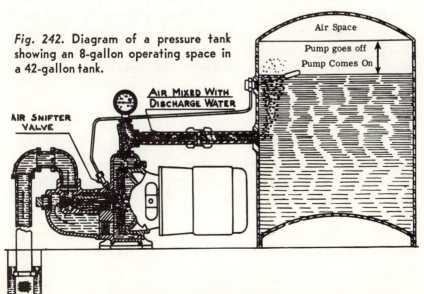

Fig. 242. Diagram of a pressure tank showing an 8-gallon operating space in a 42-gallon tank.

Air Space

Pump goes off
Pump Comes On

AIR MIXED WITH
DISCHARGE WATER

AIR SNIFTER
VALVE

How to Determine the Number of Faucets Needed. In determining pump size, disregard the amount of water in a pressure tank because the few gallons it holds are not of any real help to a pump. To illustrate, only 8 gallons of water can be drained from a 42-gallon tank before the pump takes over. Refer to the diagram of a pump and pressure tank in Fig. 242 and notice how small the space for water is. After the pump starts, you can get only the amount of water that the pump delivers and no more.

Since the pump must meet the requirements of the farm and farm home during peak periods, the most accurate way to figure pump size is to determine the amount of water required during peak-use periods. You will find it convenient to use the following formula for determining the size of pump needed by a particular farm.

1. Identify the peak period use.
2. Count the number of faucets that will be running continuously (1½ minutes or longer).
3. Figure at the rate of 3gpm for each ½-inch faucet counted.
4. Convert to gph (gpm x 60) and buy this size.

PROBLEM: Assume that you have ½-inch faucets in the following locations: 20-cow dairy barn, milk house, holding area for cows, pasture or holding area for young stock, farm home, vegetable garden and lawn, tenant house, and farm shop. List the number of faucets as shown in Table 20.

The situation in Table 20 is based on a peak-use period occurring early in the morning during the milking chore. Water is used at both kitchens, and in the milking barn; however, the only faucets to be counted as *continuous* are one for a bathtub in the farm home, two for filling stock watering tanks, and one for garden or lawn watering.

The result is:

Four ½-inch faucets $\times$ 3gpm $=$ 12gpm
12gpm $\times$ 60 (minutes) $=$ 720gph

ANSWER: A 720gph pump is needed to furnish water during the peak period. By watering the garden or lawn in the evening, a three-faucet setup would be adequate. This would take a 540gph pump.

Watch Out for Fire. Protection of farm buildings against fire requires a pump of at least 500gph capacity. Moreover, your sav-

TABLE 20

Total Number of Faucets and Number That Will Count as Continuous During Peak-Use Period for Farm and Two Residences

Location of Faucet	*Total Number of Faucets* Hot	*Total Number of Faucets* Cold	*Number To Count**	*Number Continuous*
Kitchen sink, farm home	1	1	1	0
Bath tub or shower, farm home	1	1	1	1
Lavatory in bathroom, farm home	1	1	1	0
Tenant house	1	1	1	0
Dairy barn, milking room	1	1	1	0
Milk house	1	1	1	0
Holding or lounging area (tank)		1	1	1
Young stock area (tank)		1	1	1
Farm shop		1	1	0
Vegetable garden and lawn		1	1	1
Totals	6	10	10	4

* Each pair of faucets, one hot and one cold, counts as *one* faucet only.

ings on insurance rates with an adequate pump may pay the additional cost of a larger size. Remember that friction loss in long runs of pipe results in low pressure and less water, unless the pipe size is adequate. For further information, see the section on selection of pipe size.

Well Capacity Must Equal or Exceed Pump Capacity. Before buying a pump, make certain that your well has an output equal to or greater than the capacity of the pump you plan to buy. If your well has a limited capacity—say 400gph—the 720gph pump could not be used since it would pump the well dry in a little over 30 minutes. Emptying a well completely stirs up the water and may cause trouble in the pump.

If your well does not have sufficient output to supply the various needs at the proper time, you may need to install a large reservoir or overhead tank. A smaller pump could then be used to fill the reservoir over a longer period of the day. One precaution to remember is that if a pumping period longer than 3 to 4 hours in each 24 hours is required, it may be necessary to have a special type of motor; that is, one that will operate continuously.

Larger Motors Require Larger Pressure Tanks. If the pumping load requires a motor larger than ½ hp, a larger pressure tank should be used. This will allow the necessary time between pumping intervals for the larger motor to cool. It is recommended that an 82-gallon tank be used for motors from ½ to 1 hp. One hundred and twenty-gallon, or larger, tanks should be used for motors larger than 1 hp. Pressure tanks range in size from 12 to 525 gallons capacity.

What Kind of Pump Should You Choose?

For a well that is less than 25 feet deep, you can use a *shallow-well* pump, and it will cost less than a *deep-well* pump of equal capacity. For well depths greater than 25 feet, however, it

Fig. 243. (A) Diagram of factors involved in figuring pump size. (B) Shallow and deep wells.

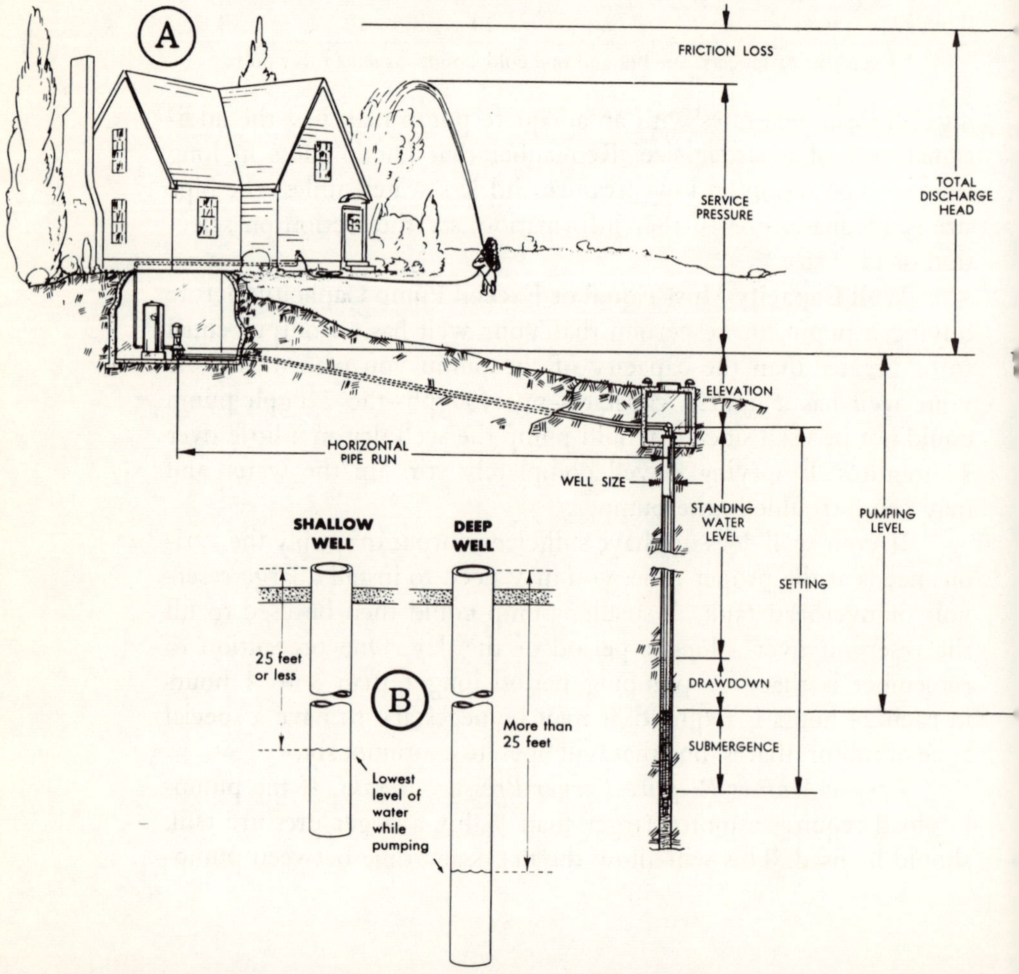

is necessary to use deep-well pumps. Both types are discussed in detail a little later.

How to Determine Whether a Deep-Well Pump Will Be Required. The normal (standing water) level in a well is not the true depth load for a pump. Other factors include (1) the amount of drop or "drawdown" that occurs during pumping, (2) the elevation of the pump above ground level, and (3) the amount of power lost to friction in the suction pipes.

Therefore, in deciding whether or not a deep-well pump will be required, the following factors must be considered: Normal or standing water level plus drawdown plus pump elevation plus friction loss. If the total is greater than 25 feet, choose a deep-well pump; if less than 25 feet, select a shallow-well pump. The water level and pump elevation can be measured, but the amount of friction loss must be figured for each well, and this will vary according to the size of the suction pipe and rate of flow.

How to Figure Friction Loss. In this problem, you will be interested only in the friction loss on the suction side of the pump load. This includes the water lines and fittings leading from the pump into the well. Both horizontal and vertical runs of water pipes are included in computing friction losses of the suction side. Horizontal runs are not counted in well depth, of course, only the friction loss in these runs.

TABLE 21

Friction Head Loss in Feet Per 100 Feet of Pipe for Various Rates of Flow*

Gallons per Hour	Minute	½-inch pipe	¾-inch pipe	1-inch pipe	1¼-inch pipe	1½-inch pipe	2-inch pipe	2½-inch pipe	3-inch pipe
240	4	27.0	7.0	2.1	.6				
300	5	41.0	10.5	3.25	.84	.39			
360	6		17.17	4.55	1.20	.56	.20		
480	8		25.0	7.8	2.03	.95	.33	.11	
600	10		38.0	11.7	3.05	1.43	.50	.17	
720	12			16.4	4.3	2.01	.70	.24	
900	15			25.0	6.5	3.0	1.09	.36	.15
1200	20			42.0	11.10	5.2	1.82	.61	.25
1500	25			64.0	16.6	7.8	2.73	.92	.38

* Based on William and Hazen Formula for ordinary iron water pipe.

TABLE 22

Friction Loss for Various Size Fittings*
(Stated As "Feet" of Loss)

Size of Fitting	Elbows			Valves		
	90°	45°	Tees	Gate	Globe	Angle
½	2.0	1.2	3	.4	15	8
¾	2.4	1.5	4	.5	20	12
1	2.9	1.7	5	.6	25	15
1¼	3.7	2.3	6	.8	35	18
1½	4.9	3.0	7	1.0	45	22
2	7.0	4.0	10	1.3	55	28
2½	8.0	5.0	12	1.6	65	34
3	10.0	6.0	15	2.0	80	40

* Add these values to the total lift and other loads on the pump.

Tests have been conducted to determine the exact amount of friction loss incurred in different sizes of pipes at different rates of flow. These data are presented in Table 21. First, locate the size of pipe you will use; assume ½-inch. Second, locate the rate of flow; assume 300gph, or 5gpm. Third, read along this line until you find the figure directly under the pipe size. The answer is 41.0 feet.

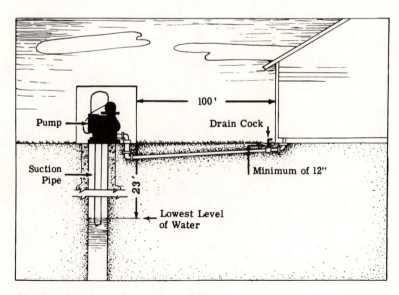

Fig. 244. Diagram of a pump problem.

This simply means that in 100 feet of ½-inch pipe (at 5gpm) friction would have the effect of adding 41 feet of pipe. In short, friction would "steal" about 40 per cent of the horsepower required in pumping 5gpm through ½-inch pipe. Friction loss would be less in ¾-inch pipe at the same rate (5gpm).

(NOTE: Friction loss is measured in pounds pressure but is easily converted to feet by the formula: pounds pressure × 2.3 = feet. This gets all the suction load into feet and the total is expressed as *feet of head*. The data in Table 21 have already been converted into feet. To convert feet of head to pounds pressure, divide feet by 2.3.)

PROBLEM: Keeping the four preceding points in mind, work out the problem as shown in the diagram in Fig. 244 and decide whether or not you could use a shallow-well pump equipped with 1-inch suction pipe. Use the 720gph pump (or 12gpm) from a previous example.

SOLUTION 1:

1. Measure the standing water level	20.00 feet
2. Determine the drawdown during pumping	3.00 feet
3. Measure the pump elevation	0.00 feet
4. Figure the friction loss in 23 feet of 1-inch pipe (See Table 21)	3.77 feet
Total suction head	26.77 feet

CONCLUSION 1: Since the total suction head of 26.77 exceeds the 25-foot maximum suction lift of a shallow-well pump, a shallow-well type could *not* be used with 1-inch suction pipe.

SOLUTION 2: Substitute 1¼-inch suction pipe and refigure the problem as follows:

1. Total pumping level, as determined in solution 1	23 feet
2. Friction loss in 23 feet of 1¼-inch pipe (See Table 21)	.99 feet
Total suction head	23.99 feet

CONCLUSION 2: By using 1¼-inch suction pipe, a shallow-well pump would work successfully since the total suction load is less than 25 feet.

(NOTE: Figures in Table 21 are for 100 feet of pipe. Therefore the friction in 23 feet of suction pipe in the preceding example is found by taking .23 of the appropriate figure in Table 21.)

CAUTION: If your farm is located at a high altitude, the amount of suction lift of shallow-well pumps will be reduced. See Table 23 for further information.

TABLE 23
Suction Lift of Pumps at Different Altitudes

Altitude	*Maximum Suction in Feet*
Sea level	25
¼ mile (1,320 feet) above sea level	23
½ mile (2,640 feet) above sea level	22
¾ mile (3,960 feet) above sea level	21
1 mile (5,280 feet) above sea level	20
1¼ miles (6,600 feet) above sea level	19
1½ miles (7,920 feet) above sea level	18
2 miles (10,560 feet) above sea level	16

Things to Consider in Choosing a Shallow-Well Pump. There are two types of shallow-well pumps commonly used on the farm. Each has certain advantages (as well as disadvantages) depending upon the situation. These types are the centrifugal pump and the piston pump.

Fig. 245. (*A*) Diagram of a centrifugal pump. (*B*) Cutaway section of a vertical-type centrifugal pump.

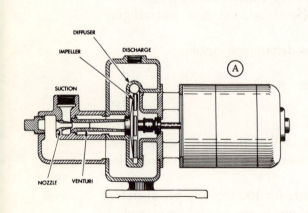
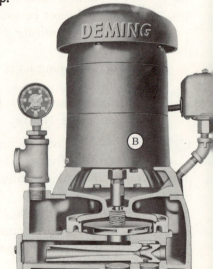

Fig. 246. (A) Cutaway section of a single-piston pump. (B) Cutaway section of a duplex- (2-) piston pump.

When to Choose a Centrifugal Pump. The centrifugal pump is the simplest in design of any type. It contains only one moving part called the *impeller*. Fig. 245-A shows a diagram of this type of pump, with the main parts labeled. This impeller has slots in the disk which rotates at high speed inside a chamber.

Notice that the impeller is mounted on a shaft that is connected to the motor shaft. As the impeller turns, it creates a suction that pulls water into the impeller chamber. At the same time, water is forced from the opening at the top.

The centrifugal pump is quite efficient up to a total lift of about 18 feet. Above that, the efficiency drops. Then you get less pressure and less output of water.

This type of pump is quiet running and costs little to maintain. When repairs are necessary, the pump is easy to dismantle and put back together again.

Another popular style of centrifugal pump is shown in Fig. 245-B. The motor and pump in this style are mounted in a vertical position.

When to Choose a Shallow-Well Piston Pump. If your water table is between 18 and 25 feet deep, a piston pump may give better service than a centrifugal type. The piston pump shown in

Fig. 246-A produces positive action and will maintain high pressure in long lines and against high working heads. The pump shown here is a single piston, double-acting type.

Unlike the centrifugal pump, the piston pump puts out a constant volume of water regardless of lift; that is, as long as the pistons make the same number of strokes. The pressure drops in the centrifugal pump as well depth increases.

A "duplex" piston pump is shown in Fig. 246-B. This style has two pistons which are both double acting. You can get up to 125 pounds pressure with this piston pump. It is advocated for supplying long runs of pipe.

The main disadvantage of the piston pump is that there are many moving parts; therefore, repair jobs are required more frequently than in centrifugal or jet pumps. Piston pumps are also noisier than centrifugal types.

Things to Consider in Selecting a Deep-Well Pump. If the vertical lift of water in your well is 25 feet or more, you will need a deep-well pump. There are five major types of deep-well

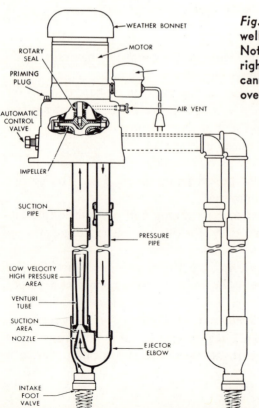

Fig. 247. Diagram of a deep-well jet-pump installation. Notice the alternate offset at right for use where the pump cannot be located directly over the well.

pumps on the market and three of these are widely used for farmstead water systems. The three are: (1) the deep-well jet or ejector pump; (2) the plunger or cylinder-type pump; and (3) the submersible pump. The other two deep-well types, which are less used for farmstead water systems, are the rotary pump and the turbine.

There are several variations in these types. For example, the jet pump can be bought in a horizontal or vertical style; the same holds true with the cylinder pump. Some models of the jet pump are made so that they can be converted from shallow to deep-well operation. Another variation in pump types is the incorporation of several "stages" (impellers). This pump is called the multi-stage jet. It will develop higher pressures than will the single-stage jet.

When to Choose a Deep-Well Jet Pump. The centrifugal jet, as shown in Fig. 247, is practically the same as a shallow-well jet with the exception that the pumping mechanism is equipped with an ejector. This is located down in the well instead of being in the pump. Pumps of this type are satisfactory for depths up to 80 feet. They will operate at depths greater than this but with less efficiency. The same advantages apply to deep-well jets as to shallow-well jets; that is, quiet and economical operation. Where high pressures are required, several sets of impellers (stages) are used. Notice the alternate offset suction pipes at right, showing that the pump can be located somewhere away from the well.

When to Choose a Deep-Well Plunger Pump. The plunger-type pump, as illustrated in Fig. 248, will work successfully at depths to 850 feet. A plunger (sucker rod) operates a piston, which is down in the well under water. Each stroke of the piston forces water up through the casing and into the tank. Again, this type of pump is noisier than jets and may require periodic repairs. The working head must be set directly over the well. The plunger pump develops good pressure so long as the cylinder and piston are in good condition.

When to Choose a Submersible Pump. The submersible pump, which is illustrated in diagram form in Fig. 249, is becoming popular for well depths to 400 feet. The pump and motor are located down in the well under water. Being located down in the water, a submersible pump "pushes" the water out of the well. This type has no sucker rod or other moving parts between the pump

Fig. 248. Cutaway section of a plunger-type deep-well pump.

and the tank. The pumping mechanism consists of several stages of turbines for building up pressure. The electric cable to the motor is insulated with waterproof plastic. The pump and motor parts are permanently lubricated and sealed to give long and trouble-free service. The well casing for a submersible pump must be four inches in diameter or larger. The special-built motor for this type of pump is shaped to fit into this small diameter.

A word of warning is in order here. *The submersible pump will not hold up in sandy conditions.* If your well contains loose, fine sand, a submersible pump will not be satisfactory.

The advantages of the submersible-type pump are (1) long, trouble-free service, (2) little or no noise, (3) no priming, and (4) the tank and controls may be placed at any convenient location—at a distance or nearby, whichever is most practicable.

Two other types of pumps are available, though these are not as widely used as are the preceding five types. These are the rotary and the turbine.

When to Choose a Rotary Pump. The rotary pump is simple in construction. It consists of two or more close-fitting gears mounted inside a housing. The gear teeth "trap" a certain amount of water as they turn, forcing it out of the opening with considerable pressure. The rotary pump delivers water at a constant volume without pulsation, but the gears will wear out quickly if there is any sand in the water. This type of pump is most often used for moving oils and other heavy liquids.

When to Choose a Turbine Pump. The turbine pump consists of a bronze disk mounted on a shaft and fitted inside a case with very little clearance. As the disk or impeller turns, it forces water through the opening that leads to the water tank. For deep wells and large volumes of water, several impellers (stages) may be used to build up pressure and increase volume.

If you need help with your water problems, call on a representative of any well-known pump manufacturer. Ordinarily, you must know three things about your water problem before these agents can help you pick the right pump. You must determine (1) the number of "continuous" faucets for the farm and home, (2) the total head of your system, and (3) the total length and elevation of water pipes from the tank to the supply points. You should also know the approximate capacity of your well.

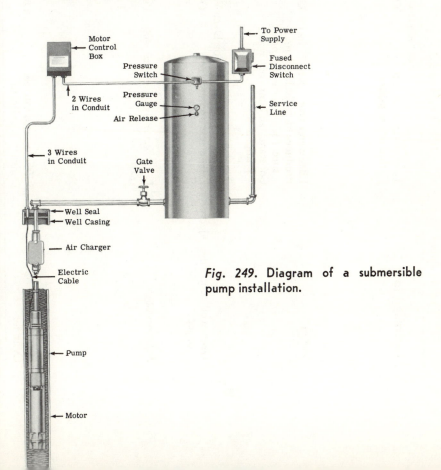

Fig. 249. Diagram of a submersible pump installation.

TABLE 24

Characteristics of Major Types of Pumps

Type of Pump	Type of Service for Which Best Suited	Practical Location	Other Considerations
For Shallow Wells			
Centrifugal Jet	Lifts water to 18 feet Rather low pressure	Over the well or off the well	Quiet operation Low first cost No moving parts in well May require priming Few repairs Can be converted for deep well service
Piston	Lifts water from 18 to 25 feet Produces high discharge pressure for long water pipes Constant amount of water pumped	Over the well or off the well	No moving parts in well May be noisy Can be converted for deep well service Requires more service than jet pump
For Deep Wells			
Deep-well centrifugal ejector or jet	Lifts water up to 80 feet	Over the well or off the well	One moving part Adaptable to wells having 2- or 3-inch casing Quiet operation
Submersible	Lifts water from 60 to 400 feet	Pump and motor are mounted in the well under water Tank and controls may be installed wherever most convenient	Self priming pump No oiling or greasing Quiet operation Easy to install Motor is cooled by well water Long life Original cost may be more than other types
Plunger or Cylinder	Lifts water to 850 feet Delivery is uniform	Over the well	Noisy May vibrate

What Size Water Pipe Will You Need?

When you worked a problem to determine the amount of water needed for a farm and two residences, you allowed 3gpm for each ½-inch faucet. For a ¾-inch faucet you should allow 5gpm. These figures are based on a pressure range of 20 to 40 pounds for a farmstead water system.

In long runs of pipe—say 400-500 feet beyond the tank—you will have the problem of low pressure due to friction loss. Since it is not practical to operate a farm pump at pressures higher than 40 or 50 pounds, the only way to maintain pressure in long lines is to use larger pipe.

How large should a long run of water pipe be? This will depend on the amount of water delivered and on the length of run. Fig. 250 contains data that will enable you to select the correct-size pipe for any farm water problem up to 650gph and up to 1,000 feet of pipe. Study the following example and see how easy it is to use the chart in Fig. 250.

PROBLEM: Determine the pipe size needed to supply the two ½-inch faucets which you counted as "continuous" in an earlier problem. Allow 3gpm each (or 6gpm total) and figure the length of run to the two stock watering tanks at 400 feet.

SOLUTION:

1. Convert 6gpm to gph as follows, 6gpm × 60 minutes = 360gph.

2. Refer to Fig. 250. Reading downward under heading "Capacity of Pump in Gallons Per Hour," find 360, which is the amount of water needed to operate two ½-inch faucets. The nearest figures to this are 350 or 375.

3. Reading along either of these lines to the right, locate the block directly under the column "400 Feet."

4. This falls in the 1¼-inch zone.

CONCLUSION: To keep two ½-inch faucets going full force at the stock watering tanks, 400 feet from the pressure tank, 1¼-inch pipe is required. Notice that 1¼-inch pipe is also satisfactory for operating the two faucets up to 700 or 800 feet from the pressure tank.

You can use the data in Fig. 250 to determine pipe size for any average farm water problem.

What Size and Type of Motor Will You Need?

Usually, a water pump comes from the factory equipped with the correct size and type of motor. Sometimes, however, the pumping load on a motor increases after it is installed. For example, the water table in your well may drop, or you may have to move your tank to a higher elevation. These or other changes in your water system may require a larger and perhaps different type of motor. Therefore, you may need to know how to figure the size and type of motor needed for a water system.

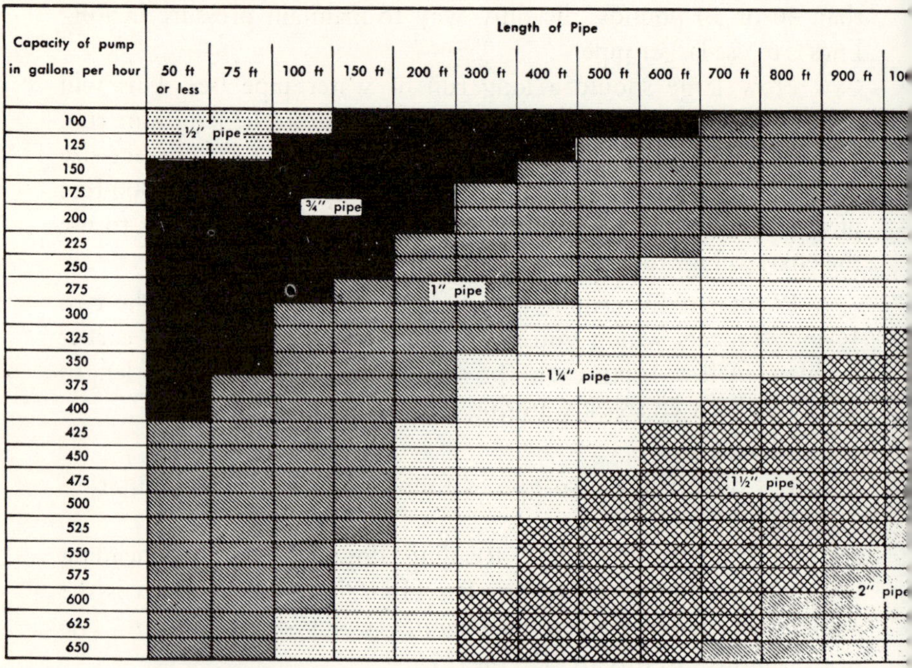

Fig. 250. Pipe size selector chart.

The motor required for a water system is determined by (1) the capacity of the pump and (2) the total working head (or load) that is on the motor. Once you know these two factors, you can easily apply the horsepower formula.

How to Determine Pump Capacity. Earlier in this chapter you observed an example in which a farm with two residences required four "continuous" faucets during the peak-use period. A

720gph pump was selected to keep these four ½-inch faucets running. The 720gph size is used in the problem that follows later.

How to Determine the Total Working Head of a Water System. The *total head* refers to the total load that a pump must work against, and therefore represents the load that the pump motor must pull. The total head is divided into two parts: (1) the *suction head*, or the total load on the suction side of the pump; and (2) the *discharge head*, or the total load on the discharge side of the pump.

Suction Head. The method of computing the suction head is presented on page 275. By referring to that topic, you will see that the total suction head consists of the depth to the normal standing water level plus the amount of drawdown during pumping plus the elevation of the pump above ground level plus the friction loss in the suction lines and fittings. Total suction head is expressed as *feet of head.*

Discharge Head. All of the load on the discharge side of the pump is referred to as discharge head or pressure head. It consists of the tank pressure plus the elevation of the tank above the well plus the friction loss in the discharge pipes and fittings. Tank pressure is converted to feet before being added. See the example that follows for more details.

How to Apply the Formula for Water Horsepower. From previous experience you should know that work is force or weight moving through distance, and horsepower is the rate at which work is done. One horsepower equals 33,000 foot-pounds of work in 1 minute or any equivalent of this. Therefore, one simple formula for computing horsepower is:

$$hp = \frac{ft\ lb\ per\ min}{33,000}$$

The corrected formula for water horsepower is:

$$hp = \frac{gpm \times lbs\ per\ gal \times total\ head}{33,000 \times pump\ efficiency}$$

This formula is exactly the same as the former with the exception that pump efficiency has been included. This may be taken as 50 per cent for farmstead pumps. Since water weighs 8.3 pounds per gallon, you can further reduce the formula to the following form:

$$hp = \frac{gpm \times 8.3 \times total\ head\ (feet)}{33,000 \times 50\%}$$

and this will reduce to approximately the following:

$$hp = \frac{gpm \times total\ head}{2,000}$$

This latter formula is used in the following example.

PROBLEM: 1. Your pump capacity is 720gph, or 12gpm. The suction and discharge pipe is 1¼-inch. Your tank operates on a range of 20 to 40 pounds pressure.

2. The drawdown water level in your well is 42 feet and the elevation of your tank is 3 feet above ground level. Allow for three 90 degree elbows in the two lines. What size motor will you need?

SOLUTION: 1. Determine pump capacity   12   gpm
2. Determine working head
    (a) Vertical lift, drawdown level   42   feet
    (b) Additional elevation of tank   3   feet

        Total amount of lift   45   feet
    (c) Friction loss in 45 feet of 1¼-
       inch suction pipe at 12gpm* =
       .45 × 4.3 (see Table 21)   1.9 feet
    (d) Friction loss in three 90 degree
       elbows** = 3 elbows × 3.7
       (see Table 22)   11.1 feet
    (e) Convert tank pressure to feet,
       or 40 pounds × 2.3***   92   feet

        Total working head   150   feet

Substituting these values in the formula, you can solve for hp:

$$hp = \frac{12gpm \times 150\ feet\ head}{2,000} = 9/10\ or\ .9hp$$

* Table 21 shows that friction loss in 100 feet of 1¼-inch pipe at 12gpm is 4.3 feet.
** Table 22 shows that friction loss in one 90 degree elbow (1¼-inch) is 3.7 feet.
*** To convert pounds pressure to feet, multiply by 2.3.

CONCLUSION: Your water system would require a .9-hp motor, but you would have to buy a 1-hp size.

By applying the method demonstrated in the preceding example, you can determine the size of the motor needed for any given size pump and depth of well.

Type of Motor Needed. For detailed information on types of motors, refer to Chapter 9. Generally, pumps requiring up to a ¾-hp motor come from the factory equipped with a capacitor-start motor. The next range in size—1 to 5 hp—usually is of the capacitor-start or the repulsion-induction type for pumps. The 5- to 7½-hp size may be of the newer repulsion-capacitor type. This new type of motor is well adapted to the farm since it draws less starting current than other types of single-phase motors.

If three-phase service is available, in all likelihood you would choose a three-phase, general-purpose motor for any load above ¾ hp.

What Kind of Pump House Should You Have?

The farmstead water system deserves a good house for protection against weather and pollution. The footings and floor slab of a pump house should prevent surface water from seeping into

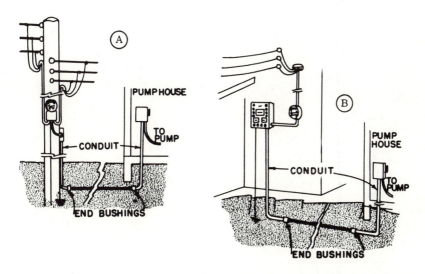

Fig. 251. Underground wiring for a pump motor: (*A*) wiring from a pole meter; (*B*) wiring from a meter located on a farm building.

the well, and proper construction should protect the system from frost. Blueprints and plans for pump houses to fit weather conditions in different sections of the country can be obtained from the nearest land-grant college.

How Should the Pump Motor Be Wired?

Information on all phases of wiring can be found in Problem-Unit Three. For detailed instructions on selecting and installing wiring materials, refer to the appropriate section.

The trend in wiring pump houses is toward an *underground feeder circuit* that is wired ahead of the main disconnect switch. As previously discussed, this arrangement provides the best fire protection possible, and the wiring is safe from storm damage.

What Care Should Be Given to
the Farmstead Water System?

The best insurance for long, trouble-free service from your water system is to follow the operator's manual in every detail. Fig. 252 shows a farmer greasing his pump according to instructions in the operator's manual. It pays to follow directions like this farmer.

Fig. 252. A farmer greasing a pump in accordance with the operator's manual.

TABLE 25*

Trouble-Shooting Chart

Trouble	*Cause*
Motor runs, no water delivered	1. Pump needs priming 2. Air volume control lines leaking 3. Check valve stuck 4. Water level in well too low 5. Water suction pipes plugged 6. Working head too great for pump 7. Pump or motor speed too slow 8. Wrong direction of rotation 9. Air pocket in suction line
Motor runs, not enough water delivered	1. Leaky suction pipes 2. Water level too low 3. Low line voltage, motor not running up to full speed 4. Strainer or suction pipes partially blocked 5. Pumping mechanism worn 6. Suction pipe or valve too small 7. Working head too great for pump or motor
Low pressure in the system	1. Speed too slow 2. Air in water 3. Pumping mechanism worn 4. Foreign matter under valves
Pump starts too often	1. Tank water-logged; drain and refill with air 2. Tank, valves, or pipes leaking 3. Pressure switch out of adjustment
Pump is noisy	1. Too much working head, pump overloaded 2. Bent or misaligned shaft 3. Parts binding or too loose 4. Worn pump or motor bearing 5. Driving unit not properly aligned with pump
Too much power required	1. Speed too high 2. Pressure set too high 3. Misaligned or bent shaft 4. Pump parts binding 5. Pump and driving unit not properly aligned
Pump leaks	1. Packing worn or improperly lubricated 2. Packing improperly inserted 3. Wrong kind of packing 4. Shaft scored

* This chart applies to several common types of pumps; therefore, some items listed will not fit every pump.

Trouble Shooting. You may save yourself a lot of inconvenience and expense by knowing how to take care of ordinary pump and motor troubles. The pump troubles listed in Table 25 are the ones most often encountered in keeping up a farmstead water system. With a little experience and study, you should be able to handle most of your pump troubles yourself.

Again, use your operator's manual, if it covers the particular trouble, in preference to this chart.

What Electric Equipment Is Needed for Irrigation?

In recent years farmers and experiment stations have reported many exciting results from irrigation. Some crop yields have been increased as much as 500 per cent; in years of extreme drought, crops have been saved outright; strawberries, as well as other tender crops, have been saved from killing frost by sprinkler irrigation.

Despite these results, however, irrigation is not a guarantee of large farm profits. If irrigation is to pay, it must be used in conjunction with appropriate crops and correct farming practices, and the soil must be adaptable to irrigation. The location of the water supply is another very important factor in irrigation.

Electric Power Supply. In localities where only single-phase service is available, the largest motor permitted will likely be 5, 7½, or 10 hp. Where this is so, irrigation by electric power is limited to small areas.

Where three-phase service is available and large electric motors can be used, they are considered one of the best sources of power for irrigation.

Things Involved in Planning an Irrigation System. The planning of an irrigation system is a job for a specialist. However, you should be prepared to discuss several important things about your situation when the specialist arrives. The following are among the most important points.

Water Supply and Crops to Be Grown. If the source of your water is a well, you can figure about 10gpm capacity per acre; that is, a 500gpm well will furnish water for about 50 acres of crops.

If your water source is a lake or pond, figure 2 to 3 acre-feet per acre of crops to be irrigated. (NOTE: 1 foot of water over 1 acre equals 1 acre-foot.) Also, allow for evaporation of approximately 1½ acre-feet per acre of water during a growing season. For

Fig. 253. Supplemental (overhead) irrigation in a sweet potato field.

example, a 30-acre lake, averaging 4 feet in depth, would be adequate for 30 to 40 acres of crops.

If there is any question about excess minerals in your water, have it tested before going ahead. Much acreage has been ruined by excess salts in the water.

The total amount of water required, as well as the rate of application, will vary for different crops. For example, a heavy crop of corn uses at the rate of .2 inches of water per day during the peak season of growth; strawberries use about .15 inches per day; and alfalfa uses about .3 inches. These amounts will vary somewhat, depending upon local temperatures. You can apply water faster to alfalfa and other close-growing crops than to clean cultivated crops.

Fig. 254. Underground irrigation pipe ready for lowering into a ditch.

A selection of crops that mature at different times allows for greater use of an irrigation system. Remember, however, that vegetables, fruits, and similar intensive-type crops offer the greatest returns. For example, results of irrigation of tomatoes, beans, and sweet potatoes in Mississippi resulted in increases of yields by 100 to 300 per cent.[*]

Topography and Types of Soil. The lay of your land will be a large factor in determining whether or not you can use the furrow or flooding method. On other than flat land or gentle slopes, irrigation is limited to the overhead or sprinkler method.

The type of soil to be irrigated will determine the rate of application of water. A loamy soil will absorb water at a much faster rate than will a tight clay. Therefore, a clay soil requires a longer setting of the equipment than does sandy loam. Sandy soils, on the other hand, have a lower water-holding capacity and therefore require more frequent applications.

Labor Available. Considerable labor is required in operating all irrigation systems. The moving and setting up of sprinkler equipment, for example, is quite time consuming. This should be remembered in planning your farm irrigation system.

In sprinkler irrigation the trend is toward smaller diameter pipe of shorter lengths to enable one man to move the setting. Also, you can have your designer plan a sprinkler system that can be moved between 6 and 7 a.m. and again between 6 and 7 p.m. In this way, the moving of water lines will cause a minimum of interference with the regular work day.

[*] Mississippi Agricultural Experiment Station, *Irrigation for Truck Crops,* Circular 163 (1951), and Irrigation for Vegetable Crops, Circular 182 (1953). State College, Mississippi State University.

Fig. 255. Considerable labor is required in moving sprinkler irrigation equipment.

Fig. 256. Three-phase service makes it possible to use a 50-hp motor (or larger if needed).

Amount of Power Required. The amount of power required to pump a given amount of water against a given head in a given period of time is a simple horsepower computation. In fact, the same hp formula used in figuring motor size for the farmstead system can be used: hp = gpm × total head ÷ 2,000.

(NOTE: This formula is based on a pump, motor, and system that is rated at 50 per cent efficiency. Some irrigation pumps and motors may have higher efficiency. Check this with your dealer.)

PROBLEM: Assume that you wish to put 1½ inches of water on 30 acres of corn. Your well is 150 feet deep and you will operate your pump at 40 pounds pressure for eight hours a day. You wish to complete this job in 5 days (40 hours). What size motor will be required?

SOLUTION: 1. Determine the gpm rate required. Apply the rule that 453gpm pumping for 1 hour = 1 inch on 1 acre. Then the rate required to pump 1½ acre-inches per hour would be 453 × 1.5 = 679.5gpm.

Therefore, the rate required to pump 1½ inches on 30 acres in 1 hour would be 679.5 × 30 = 20,385gpm. Since this rate is for 1 hour, you can determine the rate required to do this job in 40 hours by dividing by 40; thus: 20,385 ÷ 40 = 509.6gpm.

COARSE-SANDY SOIL

Dig down to main root system. Take a handful of soil and "ball" it in your hands. If it looks like this, it's time to start irrigating.

Tends to ball under pressure —but won't hold together when bounced in hand.

HAND TEST FOR MOISTURE

Here's how the soil looks when it's down to 50 per cent or less of moisture-holding capacity. Here you have waited too long.

When squeezed, soil appears dry, won't form a ball under pressure.

Fig. 257. When to start irrigating.

Rounding this off, you see that a rate of 510gpm would be necessary to put 1½ inches of water on 30 acres in 40 hours.

2. Total head:

(a) 40 pounds pressure × 2.3 =   92.0 feet
(b) 20% friction loss in laterals = 8 pounds,
        then 8 × 2.3 =   18.4 feet
(c) 20% friction loss in mains =   18.4 feet
(d) Total elevation (well depth + field ele-
        vation) =   150.0 feet

Total head   278.8 feet

Also, round this figure off to 279 feet.

(NOTE: One pound pressure equals 2.3 feet of head. Friction loss of 20 per cent (on 40 pounds pressure) is the maximum amount that is usually designed into the system.)

MEDIUM TEXTURE   **FINE-CLAY**

Forms ball — is somewhat
plastic — sticks together
slightly with pressure.

Forms ball, ribbons out between thumb and forefinger,
has slick feeling.

Soil is somewhat crumbly
but it will hold together in
ball from pressure.

This soil is somewhat pliable,
and will form a ball under
pressure.

3. Apply formula: hp = gpm × total head ÷ 2,000.

Substituting values found in 1 and 2, you get $510 \times 279 \div 2,000 = 71.1$hp.

ANSWER: You would buy a 75-hp engine. Take note that a 60-hp, three-phase electric motor would do as much work as the larger engine. Moreover, you could get by with a 20-hp electric motor by increasing the 8-hour day to 24 hours.

Cost of Irrigation. Studies in various parts of the country show that the total investment in irrigation varies from a low of $65.00 per acre, where a natural source of water is available, to $200 per acre for deep-well systems. The average investment is around $100 to $110 per acre.

The overall cost of irrigation ranges from $4.50 to $7.50 per acre-inch of water applied. Therefore, the cost of 1½ inches of water on the 30 acres of corn in the preceding problem ranges from about $200 to $300, or a maximum of $10 per acre per application of 1½ inches.

A rule of thumb on well cost is to figure $1.25 per inch of diameter per foot of depth. On this basis a 6-inch well should cost around $7.50 per foot of depth. Add $20 to $40 per foot of screen needed at the bottom of the well, depending on size. In the irrigated sections of the country, well size goes up to 24 inches or so.

Aluminum pipe for a sprinkler system costs from 80 to 90 cents a foot for 4-inch size in 20-foot lengths. Longer lengths are less costly per foot but are more difficult to handle.

Operation. The most general rule about starting to irrigate is to start your pump when the soil water capacity is down to 60 or 75 per cent. For best results 50 per cent is considered too late. After irrigation has been started, the top 12 inches of soil should be kept in a good moist condition until the crop is matured. Fig. 257 shows a practical hand test for determining when to irrigate.*

Engines will last from 3 to 10 years depending on the type and upon the care received. Electric motors should last 10 to 30 years with proper lubrication and correct wiring.

Summary

The first essential in getting a pure water supply is to select a well site that is safe from pollution. If a well is located on a slope below a barnyard, cesspool, or other unclean spot, contaminated water may find its way underground into the well. Typhoid fever and other diseases may be spread in this manner.

Well depths under 25 feet are considered shallow wells; depths over 25 feet are considered deep wells. This is the basis of determining whether a shallow or a deep-well pump is required.

Pump size is determined by counting the number of continuous faucets that operate during the peak-use period for the farmstead. A continuous faucet is one that runs continuously for 1½ minutes or more. For each ½-inch continuous faucet, 3gpm is allowed; for each ¾-inch faucet, 5gpm. Example, a 12gpm peak rate requires a 720gph pump (60 min × 12gpm = 720gph).

Two types of shallow-well pumps are common to the farm: (1) the centrifugal pump and (2) the piston pump. The centrifugal

---

* "When and How Much to Irrigate," *Successful Farming* (May, 1957), pp. 146-148.

pump is suitable for depths to 18 feet. The piston pump is better adapted to well depths of 18 to 25 feet and gives higher, more uniform pressure at these depths than the centrifugal pump. Quieter operation and fewer repairs are the main advantages of the centrifugal pump.

The three most common types of deep-well pumps are (1) the jet or ejector, (2) the plunger, and (3) the submersible. The deep-well jet pump is suitable to well depths to 80 feet. By using several stages of jets, greater pressure can be developed. The jet type can be located some distance from the well. The plunger pump is suitable for well depths to 850 feet. The working head of this type of pump must be located directly over the well. The submersible pump is so called because the pump and motor are located in the well under water. This type pump is suitable for wells of 400 feet in depth, but the water must be free of sand since the pump turbines will quickly wear out when sand gets into them. The submersible type is one of the most dependable on the market where pumping conditions are favorable for it.

Due to friction loss, long runs of pipe result in a drop in water pressure. Where it is necessary to use long runs, larger pipe must be used in order to maintain the proper volume of water. The proper-size pipe can be chosen from data in Fig. 250.

The size of a motor required for a given pump and situation can be determined by the formula hp = gpm $\times$ total head $\div$ 2,000. Total head refers to the total load on the pump, both suction and pressure.

In areas where frost may damage water pipes, an insulated, heated pump house is necessary. The house should also have means of preventing surface water from seeping in around the footings.

Most pump troubles can be identified by referring to the trouble-shooting chart on page 289. A maintenance program, based on the operator's manual is the best insurance against pump troubles.

Irrigation may result in as much as 400 to 500 per cent increase in crop yields. On the other hand, it may not pay at all. The first requirement for irrigation is to have an adequate water supply. A widely used rule of thumb is to figure 10gpm well capacity for each acre of crops. Allow 3 to 4 acre-feet in lake capacity for each acre of crops. This figure includes an allowance for loss by evaporation of 1 to 1½ feet of water per acre.

The type of soil, type of crop to be grown, lay of the land, labor supply, and amount of power are important factors that enter into the design of a system. Because of the large number of factors to consider, it is best to have an expert design the irrigation system. A good many farmers have been ruined financially by investing in an irrigation system that did not fit their situations.

The cost of irrigation ranges from about $4.50 to $7.50 per acre-inch of water applied, and total investment ranges from $65 to $200 per acre. The lesser amount here applies to farms having a natural water supply (lake, pond, or stream) and other favorable factors. The top figure applies to drilled wells, which often run to $7.50 per foot of depth (6-inch well).

Questions

1. Why is a deep-well pump required for depths over 25 feet?
2. Why must friction loss be added to well depth in computing the total depth load?
3. Why is larger pipe required for longer runs of water lines?
4. Why will sand ruin a submersible pump?
5. How does a pump and motor react to a water-logged tank?
6. How can you determine the number of acres a well will irrigate?
7. When should irrigation be started for a given crop?
8. Why is it necessary to have an irrigation specialist design the irrigation system?

Additional Readings

Brown, R. H., *Farm Electrification*. New York, McGraw-Hill, 1956.

Henderson, G. E., *Planning Farm Water Systems*. Southern Association of Agricultural Engineering and Vocational Agriculture. Athens, Georgia, University of Georgia, 1955.

Schaenzer, J. P., *Rural Electrification*, 5th rev. ed. Milwaukee, Wisconsin, Bruce Publishing Co., 1955.

Wright, Forrest B., *Rural Water Supply and Sanitation*. New York, John Wiley & Sons, 1939.

CHAPTER 12

How to Provide Good Light for Farm Homes, Farm Grounds, and Farm Service Buildings

A replica of Edison's first incandescent light bulb, which he perfected in 1879, is shown in Fig. 258. Ever since that memorable date, the American farmer and his family have used electric light more than any other form of electricity. Indeed, for many years after the beginning of rural electrification, lighting was regarded as the major use of "high-line" electric power.

Fig. 258. Replica of Edison's first successful incandescent lamp.

Fig. 259. A well-lighted farmstead includes good light in the buildings as well as on the farm grounds.

Only recently has electricity been used to any extent in doing farm work. Despite the fact that it has largely replaced human labor on many farms, a large number continue to use it mainly for lighting.

A recent United States census publication showed that 87 per cent of all non-dilapidated farm residences in the country were lighted with electricity.* This does not mean that all were well lighted. Only a small percentage of them, in fact, could have been classified as having *good light*.

Plenty of good light seems to be so essential to the production and efficiency of the farm and to the health and safety of farm people that the lack of proper lighting appears to be one of the major farm problems in this country today.

What Is Good Light?

Light is considered good light only when there is the *right amount of the right kind in the right place*. The need for light at different places on the farm and in the farm home varies in both kind and amount.

Amount of Light. Amount of light refers to the *brightness* of light at a given spot. To illustrate, a 100w bulb will produce more light than a 50w bulb, provided they are the same type and are located at an equal distance from the lighted spot.

The overall problem of how to provide the right amount of light for a given need involves three smaller problems: (1) deter-

* United States Bureau of the Census, *Statistical Abstract of the United States.* 77th ed. (Washington, D.C.), p. 784.

mining the amount of light needed for different areas on the farm and in the farm home, (2) choosing the proper color schemes for interior walls and ceilings, (3) placing lamps and fixtures to get the proper amount of light from a given size bulb or tube.

Amount of Light Needed for Different Locations and Different Jobs. The standard measure of light is the *foot-candle—the amount of light falling on a surface 1 foot away from a standard candle.* The only accurate method of measuring light is to use a *light meter* as shown in Fig. 260.

The inexpensive meter in Fig. 260 is used to check light in residences, schools, and other similar places. Perhaps you can borrow one to use at home. Ask your local agriculture teacher, club agent, or power representative about this.

The foot-candle meter is easy to read. You can measure and record the amount of light you have in the different localities at your farm and farm home in a few minutes. These figures will tell you whether or not the amount at each spot is adequate. Simply check your readings against those listed in Table 26. If your readings show too little light at any given spot, the size of bulbs or tubes should be increased. This may require some new circuits as well as new fixtures. Sometimes, a change to a lighter color scheme will solve the lighting problem.

How to Choose the Proper Color Schemes for Interiors. If walls and ceilings are dark blue, only 5 per cent of the light from a

Fig. 260. A meter that measures footcandles of light.

TABLE 26

Amount of Light Needed for Farm Homes, Farm Grounds, and Farm Buildings

Lighting Task	Foot-candles
GENERAL OR "FILL IN" LIGHT	
Kitchen	10
All other rooms and areas in the farm home	5 – 10
Farm grounds	2 – 5
Interior of barns and poultry houses	3 – 5
Farm shop and pump house	5
LOCAL OR CONCENTRATED LIGHT	
Fine sewing on dark fabrics	150
Fine sewing on light fabrics	100
Medium sewing and machine sewing	40
Prolonged reading, studying, writing, shaving, handicraft	40
Close work in kitchen	30 – 40
Casual reading, of good type on white paper, facial make-up, coarse sewing, reading music, table tennis, card playing, laundry work	20
Milk house	30 – 50
Milking room, at milking station	20
Egg handling	10 – 15
Vegetable grading	30 – 40
Farm shop	
Close work	20 – 40
General work	15 – 20
Tobacco grading	100
Feed handling	10
Pump house, pump repairing	20
Animal grooming	10 – 15
Seed cleaning	20
Poultry slaughter	40 – 50

lamp will be reflected. This is why it is hard to get adequate light in dark-colored interiors. Therefore, if your light-meter readings are low, you should check the color schemes of your interiors. In addition, check the sizes and types of light bulbs being used.

The reflective powers of 15 different basic colors are listed in Table 27. Mixing two or three of these colors will result in a reflection that is an average for the colors mixed.

If you plan to buy new lighting fixtures, the cost can be reduced by using light colors on your interior walls and ceilings. This will allow you to use smaller, less costly fixtures.

TABLE 27

Per Cent of Light Reflected by Fifteen Basic Colors

Color	Approximate Per Cent Reflectance
White	85
Ivory	75
Lemon peel	72
Baby blue	71
Pink	65
Yellow	65
Tan	60
Medium gray	60
Light blue	60
Light green	55
Apricot	50
Cardinal red	20
Dark brown	10
Olive green	10
Dark blue	5

Rules of Thumb on Interior Colors. Pick color schemes for your ceilings that will reflect 60 to 90 per cent of the light; for the side walls, 35 to 60 per cent; for the floors, 15 to 35 per cent.

Take meter readings again after the painting is completed. They should be higher if your interiors were dark colored before. An extra-high ceiling will also reduce the amount of light reflected by a given size bulb.

How to Place a Lamp to Get Proper Light From It. A light fixture that is mounted too high will not cast as much light on the work area as it should. An example of this is a light fixture mounted in the top of a high-ceiling hay mow. For this type of interior, a reflector lamp or a reflector-type bulb should be used.

An ordinary light bulb (inside frosted) in an open fixture without a reflector will waste light when mounted in an open area. This fact is illustrated by the smoke-box pattern in Fig. 261-A. Notice the amount of light falling on the ceiling. This light would be lost if the fixture is located outdoors; it would be lost on the inside of buildings if the ceiling is high or has very little reflective power. Compare the patterns of light produced by reflector-type bulbs as shown in Fig. 261-B, C, and D. From two and one-half to four times more light is directed onto the work area by a reflector-

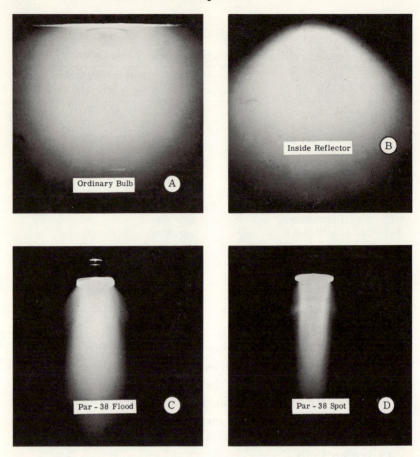

Ordinary Bulb   A

Inside Reflector   B

Par - 38 Flood   C

Par - 38 Spot   D

Fig. 261. Smoke-box light patterns of four different types of light bulbs.

type bulb. White porcelain reflectors used with ordinary bulbs have a similar reflective power.

These tests show that some kind of reflector or reflector bulb is necessary for large buildings with high ceilings and for outdoor lighting. Otherwise light (and electricity) will be wasted.

On the other hand, a yard light can be too low. The result is an excess amount of light directly under the lamp and not enough spread. A yard light that is too low will also produce a blinding effect.

The diagrams in Fig. 262-A and B illustrate the point here. A low yard light causes a long shadow to be cast. Be sure to place your outside lights at least 15 feet high. This height will require at least a 200w bulb.

Sizes of Bulbs, Tubes, and Circlines for the Farm and Farm Home. For ordinary farmstead use, incandescent bulbs are made in sizes ranging from 10w to 300w. Fluorescent tubes and Circlines come in sizes from 15w to 60w.

For a lighting arrangement that calls for 250w or 300w, it is a common practice to use a fixture carrying three to seven small bulbs instead of a single large one. Better diffusion of light can be produced this way because of the greater bulb area.

Important Things to Know About Kind of Light. Kind of light has reference to quality and light source, which may be incandescent or fluorescent.

How to Provide Good Quality Light. In lighting, *quality* refers to an even distribution of light so that there is no glare or shadow present. A contrast between bright and dark spots in a room can cause eyestrain.

The human eye has a lens to control the amount of light that may enter it. When you look at a bright spot these lenses will contract. Then, if you quickly look at a dark area, they will expand again. "Spotty" light in a room where you read or work may

Fig. 262. (A) The lamp is too low—note the large shadow. (B) The lamp is mounted at the correct height (15 feet). Compare the shadow with the one in A.

TYPES OF LIGHTING

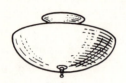

Indirect lighting: 90-100% of light upward, 10-0% downward; the ceiling is the light source; little glare and shadows practically eliminated.

Semi-indirect lighting: 60-90% of light upward, 40-10% downward; ceiling is main light source; more glare and shadow than indirect.

General diffuse lighting: 40-60% of light upward, 60-40% downward; major portion of light directly on working surface.

Direct lighting: 0-10% of light upward, 100-90% downward; all the light is directed toward the work surface; excessive contrast of light and shadow with reflected glare.

Semi-direct lighting: 10-40% of light upward, 90-60% downward; most of the light directly on work surface; glare and shadows.

Fig. 263. Five types of lighting according to direction and diffusion of the light.

damage your vision. This can result from eyestrain brought on by too much contracting and expanding. Your vision is too valuable to take chances with poor quality lighting.

Getting quality light is closely related to the selection and placement of types and sizes of fixtures and lamps. Generally, the larger the diffuser or bowl, the better the quality of light. A large diffuser distributes light over a wider area, yet does not reduce the amount of light produced. The glass bowl of a lamp fixture serves as a type of diffuser too. The white finish on a light bulb also acts as a diffuser.

The manner of directing or reflecting light into a room or on a particular spot has a strong influence on quality. According to the method of directing the light, lamps and fixtures are classified into five groups. These are illustrated and described in Fig. 263.

For reading, sewing, preparing food, and other close work in your farm home, choose *indirect lighting. Semi-indirect* lighting can be used for a few special needs in the residence.

For outside lights and for most farm work, other types of lighting can be used and will be less expensive.

Important Things to Know About Light Sources. The two light sources common to the farm and farm home are *incandescent* and *fluorescent.* Both types have advantages as well as disadvantages. No doubt you will find a need for both in your farmstead lighting system. Moreover, you may find a need for heat lamps and other special sources of light.

Incandescent Bulbs. The light bulb invented by Edison (Fig. 258) was of the incandescent type. This is still the most widely used on the farm or in the farm home. However, there has been a trend in recent years toward the use of more fluorescent lighting.

Notice the details of the bulb shown by diagram in Fig. 264. The globe is filled with certain inactive gases. A current flows through the metal base and on through the metal filament. In the presence of the inactive gases, the electric current causes the filament to become white hot and to give off light.

An ordinary household light bulb is built to last from 700 to 1,000 hours. The wrong voltage may reduce this life span however.

Fluorescent Tubes and Circlines. The soft, daylight appearance of fluorescent light is almost ideal for the milk room and for

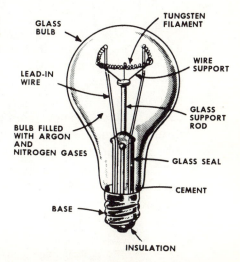

Fig. 264. Diagram showing parts of an incandescent light bulb. Light is produced when current causes the tungsten filament to become white hot.

GLASS BULB

TUNGSTEN FILAMENT

WIRE SUPPORT

LEAD-IN WIRE

GLASS SUPPORT ROD

BULB FILLED WITH ARGON AND NITROGEN GASES

GLASS SEAL

CEMENT

BASE

INSULATION

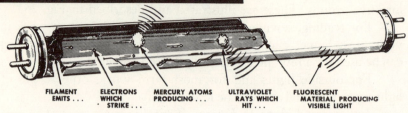

How the Fluorescent Tube Works . . .

FILAMENT   ELECTRONS   MERCURY ATOMS   ULTRAVIOLET   FLUORESCENT
EMITS . . .   WHICH   PRODUCING . . .   RAYS WHICH   MATERIAL, PRODUCING
                STRIKE . . .   HIT . . .   VISIBLE LIGHT

Fig. 265. Diagram of a fluorescent tube.

TABLE 28

Comparison of Incandescent and Fluorescent Light Sources

Fluorescent Does This	*Incandescent Does This*
Produces a line of light	Produces a spot of light
Casts little or no shadow	Casts shadows and produces glare if open to view
Different wattages not interchangeable	Different wattages are interchangeable in standard sockets
Slightly more expensive	Most economical in first cost
Lasts about 2,500 hours	May last from 700 to 1,000 hours
Older models are slow to start, but newer ones start instantly	Starts instantly
Gives off very little heat	Gets hot while in use
Special fixture containing ballast is necessary	Requires no ballast
Produces 2½ to 3 times more light than incandescent	

reading, writing, sewing, or other close work. This type of light is produced by a different principle than is the incandescent bulb.

Upon examining the diagram in Fig. 265, you will see that there is no filament or wire through the tube. The space inside the tube becomes filled with mercury vapor when an electric current begins to flow. The current "arcs" across the space inside the tube through the aid of these mercury particles. The inside walls of the tube are coated with a substance called phosphor. The bombardment of the current on the mercury particles produces ultraviolet light. This, in turn, acts on the phosphor coating to produce fluorescent light.

By varying the phosphor coating, different shades of white light can be produced. Tubes can be bought in seven or more different shades of "white" light. The most popular shade for the farm home is the de luxe warm white. The standard cool white is recommended for the laundry.

How Fluorescent Lighting Compares with Incandescent. Fluorescent lighting equipment is somewhat more expensive than incandescent. However, the life of flourescent tubes and Circlines is three to five times greater than incandescents; fluorescent tubes, watt for watt, produce about three times more usable light than incandescents.

The most important features of both types are compared in Table 28.

Other Light Sources. Several light sources for special uses on the farm include heat lamps, germicidal lamps, and black-light insect traps. Illustrations of some of these can be found near the end of this chapter.

How Can You Provide Good Light in Your Farm Home?

You will be concerned with two systems of lighting for your farm home: (1) good *general* light for each room or other area, and (2) good *local* light for all close work.

How to Provide Good General Light. For your living room, bedrooms, and hallways, you will need from 5 to 10 foot-candles of general light; for your kitchen, 10 foot-candles. This is neces-

Fig. 266. The background (general) light from two ceiling fixtures keeps the table lamps from making bright spots in the room.

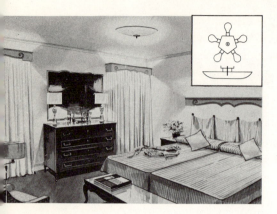

Fig. 267. A five-lamp ceiling fixture and two valance lights provide adequate general lighting for a bedroom.

sary for fill-in lighting so that there will not be bright and dark spots in a room.

Type and Placement of Fixtures for General Lighting. Incandescent ceiling fixtures are the kind that are most often used for general lighting. A recessed type of fixture, shown in Fig. 266, is used less often than surface-mounted or suspended fixtures but is becoming popular at the present time. The fixtures shown in this scene come prewired for easy and correct installation. Each fixture in the illustration carries two 75w bulbs.

Without general light in this living room, there would be dark areas around the bright spots of each portable lamp.

Close-to-Ceiling Fixtures. The ceiling fixture in the bedroom in Fig. 267 is a more common type. It carries five 40w bulbs and has a 17-inch shield or diffuser.

Fig. 268. A large fluorescent center fixture in the kitchen gives good general light and also supplements local light.

Fig. 269. A lighting arrangement for den, playroom, and breakfast room includes valance lights, a drop fixture, and reading lamps.

Cornice Lights. Notice also the two cornice lights over the windows. These furnish general light, but, in addition, they supplement the local light at the dressing table.

Fluorescent Ceiling Fixtures. A modern trend in kitchen lighting is illustrated in Fig. 268. The fluorescent ceiling fixture shown carries two 40w tubes. In the same scene you will notice a recessed fluorescent fixture over the sink. Although this is local light, it also supplements the general light in the kitchen.

Combination Fixtures. The scene in Fig. 269 illustrates the use of a combination of fixtures and lamps for general and local light. Notice the long runs of cornice lights around two walls. A three-unit suspended fixture is located over the breakfast table. Portable lamps complete the lighting system for this large room. The light here is good light for viewing television.

Methods of Wall Lighting. The diagram in Fig. 270 shows details of three methods of wall lighting. Fluorescent tubes and brackets, which can be bought at any good appliance store, are installed on the wall. A board is mounted in front of the tube to break the direct light rays. The result is a very fine quality light.

Porch and Step Lights. The scene in Fig. 271 shows how general light for the front porch and steps is provided by the recessed fixture installed directly overhead. If this fixture were located on the porch wall, the light would have a "blinding" effect on anyone approaching the building. Notice the attractive fixtures

Fig. 270. Three arrangements of wall lighting using fluorescent tubes and brackets. Build these yourself.

Cornice   Valance   Wall- Bracket

recessed into the steps. Perhaps you could do this wiring job as a project.

A word of caution about fixtures. A high priced fixture may not produce the best light. In highly decorated lamps, you pay for the decorations and finish. *Be sure you get your money's worth in good light first.* Decoration and finish should come second, if at all.

How to Provide Good Local Light for Close Work. The amount of light required for close work ranges up to 150 foot-candles for sewing dark-colored fabrics. However, you will be concerned not only with providing a sufficient amount of light for the many special needs in your home; you will also want to provide good quality light.

Fig. 271. Built-in step lights and a recessed porch fixture.

PORTABLE LAMPS

DIFFUSERS SPREAD AND SOFTEN THE LIGHT

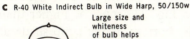

A CLM GLASS DIFFUSER (Certified Lamp Makers)

B BOWL-SHAPED GLASS DIFFUSER (Various Designs)

8" top dia. 50/150w,
or 30/230w;
or 10" top dia.
100/300w (mogul)
Design shields bulb
from top viewing

White glass preferable
8" top dia. 50/150w,
or 30/230w;
or 10" top dia.
100/300w (mogul)

C R-40 White Indirect Bulb in Wide Harp, 50/150w

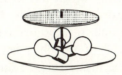

D PLASTIC DIFFUSING DISC (Multiple Socket)

Large size and
whiteness
of bulb helps
diffuse
the light

Total 180w — 3-step
switch desirable

Disc about 1" above
shade bottom, louvered
or slightly curved

Also shield at top if upper
edge less than 58"
above floor

Fig. 272. Four types of portable lamps.

Things to Look for in Choosing Lamps or Fixtures for Local Lighting. The four most common types of portable lamps are shown in Fig. 272. All of the types shown can be bought in either table or floor models. All four styles produce indirect lighting. Check on the following points in buying or arranging lamps.

1. *A large diffuser* is perhaps the most important single feature to look for in a portable lamp. If you cannot afford a lamp with a diffuser, the white indirect bulb in Fig. 272-C should be chosen for close work, in preference to ordinary inside frosted bulbs. Though all four lamps shown will give indirect lighting, some cost more than others. You will be wise to study a good catalog of lighting fixtures before buying.

2. Another important feature of a lamp is a *three-lite* arrangement. Sizes usually range as follows: 30-70-100w, 50-100-150w, and 100-200-300w. The latter size has a large base called a *mogul* base. The advantage of a three-lite lamp is that three levels of light can be had from one lamp.

3. Choose lamp shades that are wide enough at the bottom to throw light across the work area and wide enough at the top to allow good upward projection.

Fig. 273. Correct placement of table lamps. The bottom of the lamp shade should be level with eye height.

4. The lower edge of the lamp shade should be level with the eye. Observe that the table at left in Fig. 273 must be higher than the one at right in order to have the bottom of the lamp shade at eye height. This is due to the shorter base of the lamp on the left.

5. The material of which a lamp shade is made should be light in color, or the inside surface should be white. Dark colored shades absorb and waste light. Lamp shades should be dense enough to prevent light from shining through them.

6. The depth of a lamp shade should be sufficient to conceal the bulb from the bottom or top view, whether you are sitting or standing.

7. Convert your one-lite table lamps to three-lite by installing a converter switch which can be bought at most appliance stores for $1.50; a white indirect bulb will cost another $1.25.

How to Provide Good Light for Reading. The correct position of a three-lite, 100-200-300w, senior floor lamp is shown in Fig. 274. Study the placement dimensions of the lamp in relation

Fig. 274. Senior floor lamp correctly placed for reading.

Fig. 275. (A) Table lamp and (B) pull-down lamp correctly placed for reading. Note the dimensions.

to the reader. The bottom edge of the shade is 47 inches from the floor. Observe that the table lamp in Fig. 275-A is lower than the senior floor lamp (Fig. 274). This is due to the lower wattage and smaller shade of the table lamp, which is a three-lite, 50-100-150w size.

Fig. 275 shows (A) table lamp and (B) pull-down lamp correctly placed for reading. Note the dimensions shown in the diagrams.

There are many other possible arrangements for good reading. The ones shown here, however, are the most common ones.

How to Provide Good Light for Studying and Writing. If you are to make the best possible progress in school work, you must have good light for studying at home. Fig. 276-A and B shows two arrangements, either of which will provide the 40 foot-candles needed for this important task.

In Fig. 276-A, two pin-to-wall lamps are mounted 30 inches apart, 15 inches above the desk top, and 17 inches from the front of the desk. Each lamp is equipped with a 6-inch plastic bowl and carries a 100w inside frosted bulb. Lamp shades are light-colored and have a wide bottom. Two lamps placed as shown in Fig. 276-A will eliminate almost all shadows.

Fig. 276. (A) Two pin-to-wall lamps provide shadowless light for studying. (B) A fluorescent study lamp that can be built at home.

The fixture shown in Fig. 276-B carries a 33-inch, 25w, de luxe warm white tube. You can purchase the tube and the channel at any good appliance store for about $6 each. The height of the desk bracket after mounting is 15 to 18 inches above the desk top.

How to Provide Good Light for Sewing and Reading Music. According to Table 26, hand sewing requires more light than any

Fig. 277. (A) A senior swing-arm floor lamp furnishes ideal light for sewing. (B) The same lamp used for reading music. Note the proper placement for both activities.

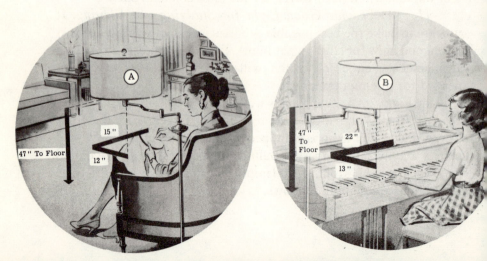

other task done in the home. The senior swing-arm floor lamp in Fig. 277-B will provide the 100 to 150 foot-candles needed for this difficult visual activity. This lamp carries a three-lite, 100-200-300w bulb and a 10-inch white bowl diffuser. An even better arrangement would be the same style lamp equipped with a 12-inch diameter, 32w, de luxe warm white Circline tube. The bottom of the lamp shade is 47 inches above the floor.

In homes where one or more members of the family play the piano or read other music; the same senior swing-arm floor lamp can be used to provide the 40 foot-candles of light called for in Table 26. Fig. 277-B shows the correct placement dimensions for the lamp at a piano. Note that the bottom of the lamp shade is 47 inches from the floor.

How to Provide Good Light for Shaving. Table 26 shows that 40 foot-candles are needed from three sides for easy shaving. The ideal setup for this is shown in Fig. 278-A. Two 24-inch, 20w, shielded fluorescent lamps are centered 60 inches above the floor, one on each side of the mirror; these lamps are spaced 30 inches apart. One 18-inch, 15w, fluorescent fixture is mounted over the mirror, about 15 inches above head height and 12 to 18 inches out from the wall. De luxe warm white tubes are best for this bathroom arrangement.

An incandescent fixture combination can be used instead of the fluorescents. The globe diffusers for these fixtures should be of

Fig. 278. (A) The proper set-up for shaving requires light from three sides. (B) Two dresser lamps properly placed for grooming. Note the placement of the fixtures in both scenes.

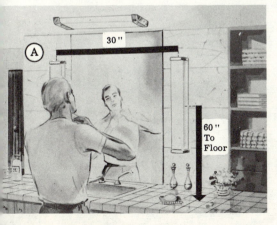

opal or ceramic-enameled glassware. At least one 60w bulb should be carried in each wall and ceiling unit.

How to Provide Good Light for Grooming. In the bedroom, 20 foot-candles of special light are needed at a dresser. Fig. 278-B shows a good arrangement of dresser lamps for make-up. The two lamps shown are centered 36 inches apart, with the shades 22 inches above the dressing table. This is the correct height for a standing position.

Dresser lamps do not have a diffuser but rather have an ivory or translucent shade (9-inch diameter), which produces a strong light from two sides. The bulb may be either a three-lite, 30-70-100w, or a 100w white bulb.

How to Provide Good Light for Work in the Kitchen. The family's health demands that plenty of good local light be provided in the kitchen where food is prepared and utensils are washed. Table 26 shows that from 30 to 40 foot-candles should be pro-

Fig. 279. (A) Fluorescent tubes and bracket mounted over a kitchen sink and behind a face board. (B) A fluorescent tube and bracket mounted underneath a cabinet over a food preparation area. Build these yourself.

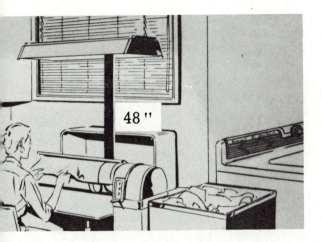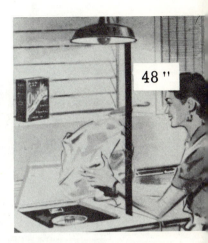

Fig. 280. Either the fluorescent fixture at left or the reflector lamp at right is suitable for the laundry. Note the dimensions for placement.

vided. The light source should be de luxe warm white fluorescent tubes or Circlines, if possible.

Notice the excellent lighting setup at the sink in Fig. 279-A. This fluorescent fixture carries two 33-inch, 25w tubes mounted behind a faceboard. You can purchase standard tubes and channel at any good lighting appliance store and build the wood bracket as a project.

A lighting arrangement for the food preparation counter in the kitchen is shown in Fig. 279-B. In this setup, a fluorescent tube and channel is mounted underneath a cabinet less than 52 inches high. If the cabinet is more than 52 inches high, the fixture should be mounted on the wall underneath. Similar fixtures and arrangements can be placed over the range.

How to Provide Good Light for the Laundry. Approximately 20 foot-candles are needed for ironing, washing, and other laundry work. Fig. 280 (left) shows an ideal setup for ironing. A rectangular fluorescent fixture is mounted 48 inches above the work. It carries two 33-inch, 25w, standard cool white tubes.

Another good arrangement is shown in Fig. 280 (right). This arrangement uses a standard dome reflector equipped with a 150w

Fig. 281. One yardpole and a battery of PAR 38 flood bulbs may provide enough light for the entire farmstead.

silver-bowl bulb. In both scenes, the reflector is mounted 48 inches above the work. Recessed fixtures are especially adapted to use in the laundry, where head room is often scarce.

How Can You Provide Good Light for Your Farm Grounds?

A dark farmstead is dangerous. An investment of a few dollars in a yard light may pay for itself many times over by preventing accidents and increasing chore time. A good rule of thumb is to have at least 2 or 3 foot-candles of light on all major chore paths on the farmstead. Barnyards and building entrances should be lighted separately if the farmstead buildings are scattered. It may be possible to get adequate light with one yardpole equipped with a battery of PAR 38 lamps as shown in Fig. 281. The PAR 38 bulb

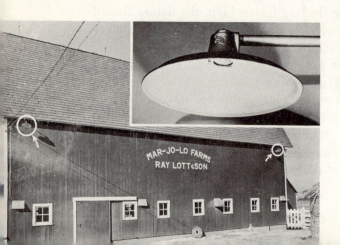

Fig. 282. Two reflector lamps placed near the corners of a barn produce light for the barnyard at both ends and at the side of the barn. At upper right is a weatherproof reflector for outdoor use.

is a weatherproof type that has sealed-beam features similar to an automobile headlight.

Lighting Equipment Needed for the Farm Grounds. The barnyard in Fig. 282 is lighted by two reflector lamps mounted at opposite corners of the barn. Reflectors used outdoors must be of the weatherproof type as shown in Fig. 282 (upper right), and must always be equipped with porcelain sockets. Metal sockets will corrode if used outdoors for any length of time.

How Can You Provide Good Light for Your Farm Service Buildings?

Good light in your farm service buildings is essential to farm production, convenience, and sanitation. The figures in Table 26 call for as much as 50 foot-candles (in the milk house) of the right kind of light. Special lighting equipment is required to provide this much light.

Special Equipment Needed for Lighting Farm Buildings. The high walls and dark-colored interiors usually found in farm buildings do not reflect light very well. Therefore, ordinary household lighting equipment does not provide good light. Generally, good light for farm service buildings can be provided by special equipment as shown in Fig. 283. These are described in the following:

Reflectors. Fig. 283-A shows a standard dome reflector which is widely used for inside lighting. Interior reflectors also come in the shallow dome style.

Reflector Bulbs. Reflector bulbs come in several types. The flood lamp shown in Fig. 283-B is for either outside or inside use. A reflector-type bulb has a silvered inner surface which directs the light onto the desired area. Reflector bulbs are not as efficient as reflectors, but the result is satisfactory for most inside uses. The smoke-box light patterns in Fig. 261-B illustrate the effectiveness of reflector bulbs.

Bulb Protectors. The fruit jar fixture shown in Fig. 283-C is for protection against breakage and excessive dust. The jar can be wiped clean every day or two as needed and will prevent dust from getting into the socket.

Fluorescent Fixtures. The fluorescent fixture shown in Fig. 283-D carries two 40w tubes. The 40 to 50 foot-candles of light needed for close work in the shop or in the milk room can be

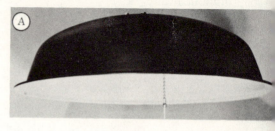

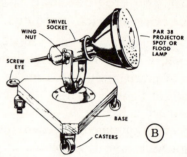

Fig. 283. Special equipment needed for the inside lighting of farm buildings.

provided by a fixture of this type. In fact, there is a trend toward the use of fluorescent tubes in many types of farm work.

Special Lamps. A battery of heat lamps is shown in use at a washing vat in Fig. 284. Heat lamps are moderate in cost, are easy to install, and have a wide range of uses. For information on cost and operation of heat lamps, refer to page 353.

Summary

Good light consists of the right kind and the right amount at the right place. Good vision and healthy eyes are dependent upon

Fig. 284. A battery of hard-glass heat lamps keeps the operator warm while working in a milk house.

good light. The foot-candle is the standard measure of amount of light. The right amount for the farmstead ranges from 2 or 3 foot-candles for general lighting on the farm grounds to 150 foot-candles of local light for sewing dark fabrics. The amount of light for a given need can be varied by increasing the wattage of light bulbs, by increasing the number of bulbs, by selecting the proper color combinations for interiors, and by placement of the lamps or fixtures.

Good quality light can be had by choosing the correct type of bulbs or tubes and by using the best type of lighting for a given need. Either fluorescent or incandescent fixtures can be purchased in five types of lighting according to the direction of light. These are (1) indirect, (2) semi-indirect, (3) general diffuse, (4) semi-direct, and (5) direct.

For the farm home, indirect or semi-indirect fixtures and lamps should be used. A large diffuser or globe usually provides better quality light than a small one. If indirect fixtures or lamps are not available, a good substitute is to use white indirect light bulbs. Another possible improvement of farm home lighting is to convert ordinary table lamps to three-lite styles. This can be done by installing a special three-lite converter switch and a three-lite bulb.

The right places for light are (1) proper locations for general light in the farm home, on the farm grounds, and in the farm service buildings; (2) local light for special tasks in the farm home and in the farm service buildings.

General light for the farm home is usually supplied by ceiling fixtures and wall brackets, either fluorescent or incandescent types. Among these are dozens of different styles, sizes, and finishes, which can be selected to suit the individual taste and match the furnishings of the home.

Fluorescent fixtures, although superior for most lighting needs, are more expensive than incandescent bulbs. But fluorescent tubes last longer and use less electricity per watt of output than do incandescents. The life of incandescent bulbs is considerably shorter than fluorescents. For use in the kitchen and milk house and for grading fruits and vegetables, fluorescent lighting is well worth the extra cost.

Local light for the farm home is usually provided by one or more portable or wall lamps. Portable styles include a wide variety of both table and floor models. A well-placed table lamp, of good design and proper size, can be used with as good effect as a more expensive floor lamp. Correct placement and proper design is more important in getting good light for close work than is having costly floor models that may be highly decorated. The color and placement of lamp shades also influences the kind of light provided.

Lighting requirements for farm grounds are not great, but a little light is essential in the interests of safety and convenience in doing after-dark chores. One yard light may take care of the farm grounds except at barnyards and entrances to buildings, providing the farmstead is not scattered. This one yard light may be a battery of PAR 38 lamps. Additional lighting may be needed around certain buildings. For this, reflector units or spot bulbs may be installed at the gable ends of buildings, or more poles can be used.

Generally, good lighting inside farm buildings requires reflector units, reflector bulbs, or spot bulbs. Ordinary light bulbs are not satisfactory in farm buildings because of the large, open interiors. The walls and ceilings, moreover, do not reflect much light in most farm buildings.

Local light for farm buildings and special tasks is usually provided by reflector units mounted at proper places, by spot and reflector bulbs.

Special lamps used on the farm include germicidal, infrared heat lamps, insect killers, and burglar repellers.

Questions

1. What is meant by the right amount of light? Is it possible to have too much light for a given task?

2. Why is fluorescent light considered better for reading than incandescent light?
3. How can improper lighting cause permanent damage to the eyes?
4. What happens to the 95 per cent of light that is not reflected in a room painted dark blue?
5. How can lighting be used to increase farm income?
6. Why are reflectors or reflector-type bulbs required in lighting farm buildings that have high ceilings or large, open spaces?

Additional Readings

Beveridge, Elizabeth, and Krewatch, Albert V., *Electric Light for the Farmstead*. Farmers Bulletin No. 1838. Washington, D.C., U.S. Department of Agriculture, 1951.

General Electric Corporation, *See Your Home in a New Light*. Cleveland, Ohio (no date).

Illuminating Engineering Society, *Recommended Practice for Residence Lighting*. New York, 1953.

Sylvania Electric Products, Inc., *Better Lighting for Your Farm*. Salem, Massachusetts (no date).

Westinghouse Electric Corporation, *Lamps: How to Choose Them*. Pittsburgh, Pennsylvania, 1954.

Suggested Projects for Problem-Unit Five

1. Concrete Watering Tank. By writing to the nearest Portland Cement Association office you can obtain blueprints for the concrete watering tank shown in Fig. 285. Ask your local agriculture teacher or club agent for the address. To prevent freeze-ups, the tank should be equipped with an electric water warmer.

Fig. 285. Concrete watering tank.

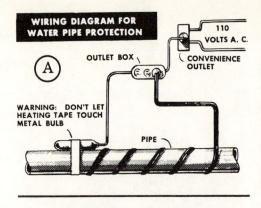

WIRING DIAGRAM FOR
WATER PIPE PROTECTION

A

110
VOLTS A. C.

OUTLET BOX

CONVENIENCE
OUTLET

WARNING: DON'T LET
HEATING TAPE TOUCH
METAL BULB

PIPE

B

SPIRAL LIKE THIS
ALLOW AT LEAST ½" BETWEEN SPIRALS

NEVER ALLOW TAPE TO
CROSS ITSELF LIKE THIS

Fig. 286. (A) Method of connecting a heating cable to a circuit. *(B)* Method of applying a cable to a water pipe.

2. **Protect Water Pipes With Antifreeze Heating Tape.** Fig. 286-A shows how to connect heating tape to water pipes. In Fig. 286-B, correct and incorrect methods of applying tape to pipes are illustrated.

3. **Portable Heat Lamp.** In Fig. 287-A, note the layout of parts for constructing a heat lamp project. The assembled project is shown in Fig. 287-B. A flood bulb can be substituted for the heat lamp to give emergency light. The clip at lower left holds the lamp in place.

Fig. 287. Parts for a portable heat lamp.

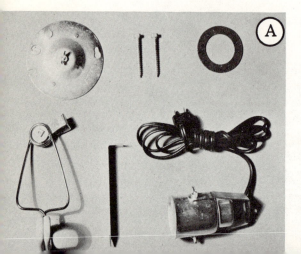

A

B

4. Portable Emergency Light. Obtain a swivel socket, a PAR 38 bulb, 50 feet of rubber cord, and a plug-in at a hardware store. Other parts can be made from junk material. Have on hand a 6-foot length of 1-inch iron pipe, one floor flange, and material for the base (either 2 x 4 inch lumber or iron pipe). Construct as shown in Fig. 288. Note the swivel base at lower left.

Fig. 288. Homemade portable emergency lamp.

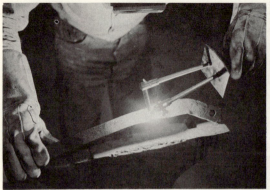

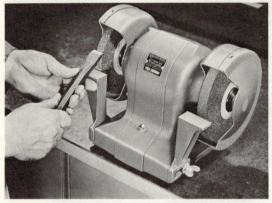

PROBLEM-UNIT **VI**

How to Select and Care for Other Electric Farming Equipment

Previous sections of this book have stressed opportunities for using electricity to improve the farm. The remaining chapters deal with the selection and care of electric equipment needed in taking advantage of some of these opportunities. Since electricity is used in more than four hundred ways on the farm, however, it has been necessary to include only those uses that are rather common to the country as a whole. If you need information on equipment not included in this book, you should check with professional agricultural workers and reliable equipment dealers in your locality.

Five sections on electric equipment are included in these latter chapters: (1) equipment for dairy farming, (2) equipment for poultry farming, (3) equipment for feed handling, (4) equipment for crop drying, and (5) power tools for the farm shop.

The problem of equipping a modern farm raises several questions on economics that should be studied before going into the selection of a given machine. A brief discussion follows.

What Management Problems Should Be Considered in Equipping the Farm?

A book on electricity cannot go very deeply into economics. However, it is a fact that the wrong decision on equipping a farm —whether the equipment be electric or otherwise—can result in financial disaster. This is equally true of buying equipment that can not be justified economically or not buying equipment that is badly needed on the farm. By giving careful study to your situation before equipping your farm, you can avoid either or both of these mistakes. No doubt you will find it helpful to refer to Chapter 1 and review the section on farm-management problems involved in equipping the farm. Give very careful attention to the following points: (1) the need for better equipment to increase farm production; (2) the need for equipment that will reduce human labor requirements on the farm; (3) the need to keep up with market trends, especially those that may change future demands for certain products; (4) the need for improved storage facilities, especially those that improve the quality of products and reduce the risk of loss in storage; and (5) the need to keep your farm up to par in overall efficiency.

Consider All Factors Involved in Cost. As has been pointed out before, an electric machine may pay for itself in several forms: through increased production, better market prices, reduced risk, and so on. Some economists say that a good rule of thumb is that a machine or an electric system is a sound investment if it will pay for itself in three to five years. The point to remember here is that total cost involves more than one factor. Make certain that you consider all of these items before investing in a machine. The following outline of fixed and operational costs should give accurate enough figures.

Fixed Costs. The fixed costs for electric equipment include: (1) annual depreciation at one-twelfth the original purchase price (deduct salvage value before dividing by 12); (2) annual cost of housing at 1 per cent of the original purchase price; (3) annual interest at 6 to 8 per cent on the average investment; (4) annual charge for taxes and insurance at 1 per cent of the original purchase price; (5) installation (wiring, etc.) at one-tenth the original cost of wiring and other installation expenses.

Cost of Operation. The major costs of operation of electric equipment include the cost of electricity and the cost of repairs and maintenance of equipment. The method of estimating the annual cost of electricity has been discussed in previous sections. In brief, the steps required are (1) obtain the amperage rating of motors, (2) convert this to wattage, (3) determine the approximate number of hours used during a year, (4) convert to kwh, and (5) apply the average price of electricity to find the annual cost. For more complete information on estimating costs of electricity, refer to Chapter 2.

The cost of repairs and maintenance on electric equipment generally runs about 5 per cent annually, figured on the original purchase price of a machine.

Things to Consider After Deciding to Purchase a New Appliance. Other very important considerations in purchasing a new appliance are:

1. The dealer should be located within 100 miles of your farm in order to provide emergency services.

2. The appliance should be a standard brand for which you know you can obtain parts without difficulty.

3. The dealer should have a reputation for fair play and prompt service.

*H*ow to Select and Care for Electric Equipment for Dairy, Poultry, and Livestock Farming

Each year a larger share of the labor required in dairy-poultry-livestock farming is being taken over by electric equipment. Indeed, many of the appliances being used in modern farming are not only electric but are automatic as well. This trend is almost certain to continue, and the resulting competition is likely to force all farmers to electrify every operation on the farm, wherever it is at all economical to do so.

Fig. 289. Cutaway view of a milking parlor and milk room equipped with combine (pipe line) milker, in-place cleaning system, and bulk-milk cooler. Note the ¾-hp motor and in-place cleaning pump underneath the wash vat; a 2-hp milker unit is at far right.

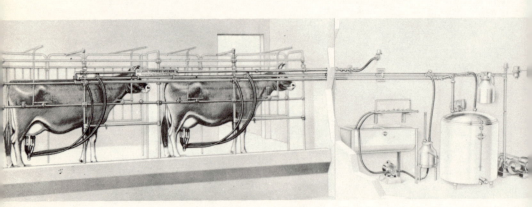

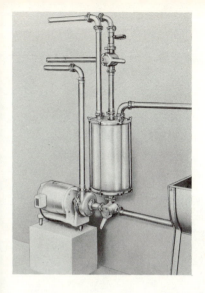

Fig. 290. Close-up view of an in-place cleaning unit. A ¾-hp motor and pump circulate cleaning fluids through the milking equipment.

What Major Electric Appliances Should You Have for Your Dairy?

Since 1930, the electrification of the dairy has brought about a 50 per cent reduction in labor requirements per cow. A fully electrified dairy that saves so much labor probably is equipped with a combine (pipe-line) milker, bulk-tank cooler, water heater, gutter cleaner (in stanchion barns), silo unloader and other mechanical feeding devices, as well as automatic watering equipment. Other appliances probably include ventilators, a milk house heater, clippers, and cow trainers (in stanchion barns).

Things to Consider in Selecting a Milker. In addition to the points already considered, the selection of a milker should be based on herd size, barn arrangement, and amount of time available for milking.

Fig. 289 shows a modern arrangement of a *combine* milker equipped with an in-place cleaning system. The milk flows through the stainless steel (or glass) pipes directly into a bulk-tank cooler. This milker consists of a vacuum pump, a ½-hp electric motor, a ¾-hp electric motor, suction lines and pulsators, teat cups, stainless steel milk lines, and in-place cleaning equipment.

The setup shown in Fig. 291 is a conventional milker. It differs from the combine type in not having milk lines and in-place cleaning equipment. With this type of milker, it is necessary to empty the milk into cans or bulk tanks by hand. This may require walking back and forth to the milk room, and therefore requires a longer milking period. The type of vacuum pump and motor for a two-

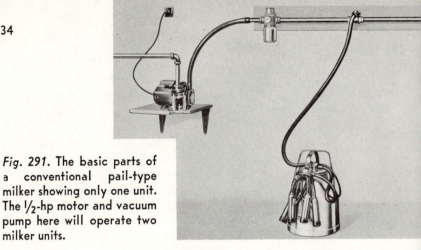

Fig. 291. The basic parts of a conventional pail-type milker showing only one unit. The $1/2$-hp motor and vacuum pump here will operate two milker units.

unit conventional milker is about the same as that used with the combine milker except that it is smaller.

Fig. 292 shows an inexpensive milker, often called the *cow-to-can* type. With this equipment you should be able to milk from 8 to 10 cows per hour with one unit or 16 to 20 cows per hour with two units. (NOTE: A unit is the pail and milking equipment

Fig. 292. (*A*) A "Cow-to-Can" milker in a two-place milking parlor is suitable for herds up to 15 head. (*B*) A one-place arrangement is suitable for 8 to 10 head. (*C*) Filter arrangement.

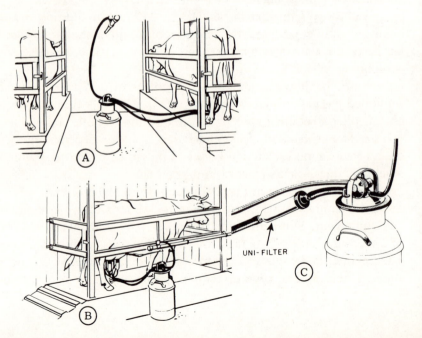

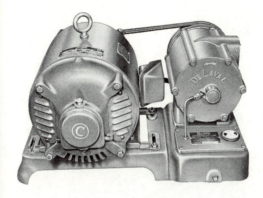

Fig. 293. Close-up view of a motor and vacuum pump. Keep the belt properly adjusted and follow the operator's manual in servicing the motor and pump.

used to milk one cow; thus, with two units, you could milk two at a time.)

The cow-to-can milker differs from the conventional milker in Fig. 291 in that the milker pails are eliminated; that is, the milk goes directly into the can. The milk lines contain filters that strain the milk as it flows to the cans. If no expansion is planned, the cow-to-can milker is the least expensive system you can own for herds up to 12 or 15 cows.

How to Care for Milker and Motor. Pulsators and drains should be removed and wiped dry with a clean cloth once a week. The motor and all milker parts should be lubricated according to instructions in the operator's manual. Motor belts should be tight and properly aligned at all times. It is a good practice to keep extra belts on hand. If your lights dim when the cooler or milker comes on, check your voltage and wire size.

Summary of Comparison of Milkers. A two-unit, combine milker will handle about 30 cows per hour (one operator) in a four-place, walk-through milking parlor; or 24 cows per hour in a three-place, tandem-style milking parlor (three-units); or 20 cows per hour in a stall barn. The purchase price and installation costs range from $1,600 to $2,000. The combine milker is most efficient when used in a milking parlor.

A conventional, two-unit milker will handle from 18 to 20 cows per hour, whereas a single-unit outfit will handle about 10 cows per hour. The cost of a two-unit milker installed is around $500.

A one-unit cow-to-can milker, costing about $300 installed, will handle from 8 to 10 cows per hour.

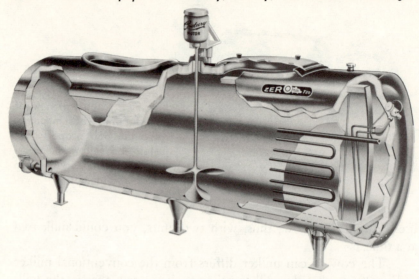

Fig. 294. Cutaway view of a direct-expansion bulk cooler. Note the refrigerating coils at right. Note also the propeller type agitator which makes the tank self-cleaning. The vacuum feature allows the milk lines to empty directly into the tank without vacuum releases.

Important Things to Consider in Selecting a Milk Cooler. Among the advantages claimed for the bulk-tank cooler over the wet type are easier handling of the dairy chores, less labor required, no milk cans to handle, and greater sanitation along with lower bacteria counts.

The main disadvantage of the bulk-tank system is the higher initial cost of the tank; also, the larger sizes require extra wiring. A 10-can, wet-type cooler can be purchased for $700 or so, whereas a 300-gallon bulk tank costs from $2,000 to $2,500. A well-built 400-gallon bulk tank costs around $3,000 and should last from 20 to 30 years.

It is claimed by manufacturers and dairy specialists that savings on hauling, elimination of cans, and so on, will normally pay for a 300-gallon tank in about 4 years when production averages 700 to 800 pounds or more daily. The tank should be large enough to hold two days' production, since hauling is usually done every other day. Of course you can buy bulk tanks in smaller sizes and cheaper models. A "cheap" tank should last from 10 to 15 years in comparison to 20 to 30 years for a better model.

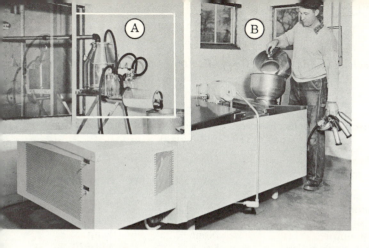

Fig. 295. (A) A vacuum release is necessary where a combine milker and an open (non-vacuum) bulk tank is used. (B) A dairyman pours milk from a milker pail into a bulk-tank cooler by hand.

Types of Bulk Tanks. According to the method of cooling used, the two types of bulk tanks are classified as direct-expansion and ice-bank. In the direct-expansion tank, the refrigerant is in direct contact with the walls of the tank. The ice-bank type, as the name indicates, makes use of a bank of ice that forms around the refrigeration coils. Cold water from this ice bank is pumped against the walls of the tank.

Dairy specialists say that the overall cost of the direct-expansion tank is about the same as the ice-bank type when pro-rated over a 12 to 15 year period. The ice-bank tank costs less to purchase but uses more electricity than does the direct-expansion tank. These two factors balance over a period of time.

Either type of tank is designed to cool the milk to 50 degrees F. or below in one hour.

Fig. 296. A direct-expansion bulk cooler with counterbalanced lid makes opening and closing easy.

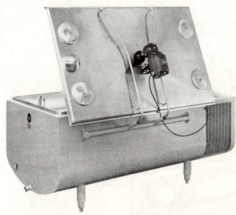

TABLE 29

Comparison of Selected Features of Direct-Expansion and Ice-Bank Tanks (300-Gallon Size)

Feature	*Direct-Expansion*	*Ice-Bank*
Original cost	Somewhat higher	Somewhat lower
Compressor-unit motor	2 or 3 hp	1 or 1½ hp
Agitator motor	¼, ½ hp*	⅛ hp
Condenser-fan motor	⅙ hp	⅙ hp
Water-pump motor	None	¼ hp
Hours of operation per day	5 to 6	15 to 20
Amount of electricity to cool 100 lbs. milk (every other day pickup)	.8 to 1.1 kwh	1.2 to 1.6 kwh

* Some manufacturers use up to 1-hp motors on the agitator of the direct-expansion tank. They claim faster cooling with better circulation of milk inside the tank.

Another type of tank is referred to as a vacuum tank (Fig. 294) because it operates under vacuum. Milk lines lead from the cows directly into the tank. No vacuum releaser is necessary. A releaser is required to release milk from pipe lines into an open (non-vacuum) tank.

For obtaining production records of each cow, you need a meter or weigh jar installed in the milk lines of a pipe-line system.

Wet-Type Coolers. A 10-can immersion cooler costs around $700. The compressor for this size cooler is equipped with a 1- to 2-hp motor. About 5 kwh of electric energy are required to cool ten 10-gallon cans of milk to 50 degrees F. The motor operates

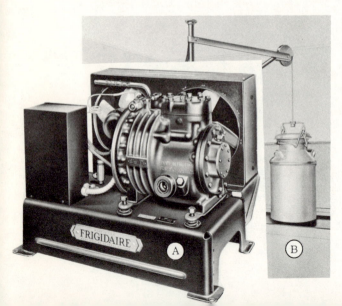

Fig. 297. A wet-type cooler (*B*) requires that the cans be lifted over the side. The electric hoist relieves the backache of the dairyman. The compressor unit (*A*) should be installed where it can get adequate ventilation.

from 2 to 4 hours per day, depending upon the outside temperature and the motor size.

Another wet-type cooler operates by having cold water sprayed onto the milk cans. The principle advantage of this type is that the cans may be placed into the cooler from the side, thus eliminating most of the lifting. The main difference between the spray-type and immersion coolers is that a small (⅙- to ¼-hp) motor is required to operate the pump. The consumption of electricity is about the same for both types, but the first cost of the spray type is somewhat greater.

What Care Should You Give Your Cooler? As has been stressed throughout this book, the first and most important rule on caring for an appliance is to follow the operator's manual. Your main concerns will be to keep the tank clean and to make certain that the cooler is properly installed so that the compressor gets plenty of circulation. Also make certain that the wiring is adequate.

Things to Consider in Selecting a Water Heater. Most water heaters used in dairies are of the pressure type. The non-pressure type is less expensive and may be plugged into a convenience outlet without additional wiring. Wattage usually ranges from 300w to 1,500w. About 15 gallons of hot water per day is the maximum amount you can get from the non-pressure heater. Water must be poured into this type of tank since it is not connected to the water system. Of course, you can run a water line to the tank and install a faucet to empty directly into it. A non-pressure water heater is suitable only where a few head of cows are kept.

In the pressure-type water heater, the water lines are connected to the tank and fresh water enters as hot water is drained.

This type of heater ranges from 30 to 150 gallons in size. An 80- to 100-gallon heater is considered adequate for a 25- to 30-cow dairy equipped with a pipe-line milker and in-place cleaning.

Fig. 298 shows a cutaway section of a double-element water heater of 2,500w to 4,000w. This heater is capable of rapid heating or "recovery."

A single-element heater is less expensive but recovers hot water more slowly. Wattage may range as low as 1,500w for a 20-gallon tank or 2,400w for a 60-gallon size.

A 60-gallon, double-element water heater costs in the neighborhood of $100 installed. This heater uses about 1 kwh of electricity in heating 4 gallons of water to 160 degrees F.

340

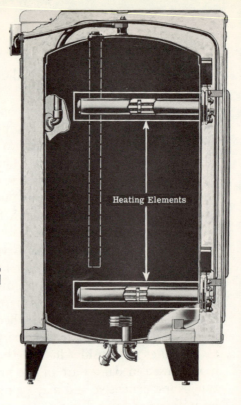

Fig. 298. Double element, 80-gallon water heater rated at 4,000w.

If you live in a section of the country where you can get off-peak rates for heating water, your electric bill will be much less. Also, some water heaters are equipped with a house-heating attachment that may be used on the off-peak cycle. This allows the milk house to be heated in the early morning hours while the off-peak rate is still in effect. A well insulated house will stay warm for several hours, usually through the milking chore. Fig. 299 shows a combination water/house heater.

How to Care for a Water Heater. A modern water heater is fully automatic and requires very little attention. Leaky faucets are expensive and should be repaired. If your water is hard, you should use a water softener to keep lime deposits from forming in the tank.

Things to Look for in a Gutter Cleaner. During the six to eight months of the year (in the northern sections of the country) that a herd of 30 cows are kept inside, you handle 100 to 150 tons of manure. If you do this job by hand (hand scoop and conveyor) you handle this tonnage twice.

Types of Gutter Cleaners. One of the first types of barn cleaners to be used extensively was a scoop fastened to a cable that

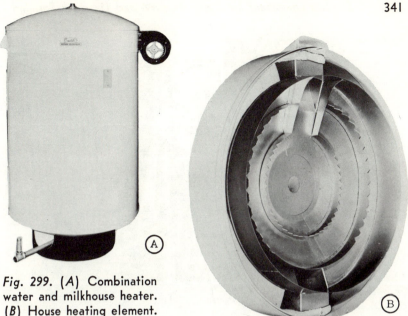

Fig. 299. (A) Combination
water and milkhouse heater.
(B) House heating element.

wound up on a drum located at the outer end of the run. Since
the scoop is made to fit the gutter, it cleans the gutter as it picks
up a load of manure on the trip out. A motor (or manual operation) pulls the scoop back to the starting point again. Also, an
overhead track and conveyor has been used extensively in cleaning
dairy barns.

One of the newer "shuttle stroke," paddle-type, barn cleaners
is shown in Fig. 301. On the forward stroke, the paddle stands out
at a right angle to the gutter, thereby pushing the manure forward
the length of the stroke. On the backward stroke the paddle folds

Fig. 300. Scoop-type gutter
cleaner in operation.

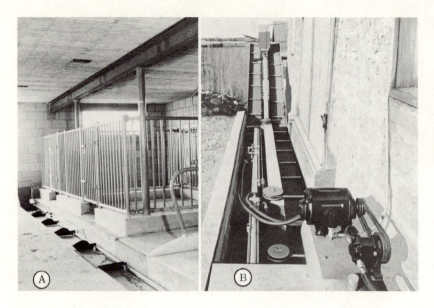

Fig. 301. Shuttle-stroke gutter cleaner: (A) inside installation; (B) elevator unit to the dumping pit.

back against the side of the gutter in a dragging position. The effect of this shuttle action is to move the manure in the gutter a certain distance at each stroke; within a few minutes it reaches the dumping pit. It is better to arrange your equipment to unload the manure directly onto a spreader.

The installation shown is a hydraulic unit consisting of continuous bars, chains, and paddles that deliver the manure to an elevator. The corner construction of the chain allows for turns of

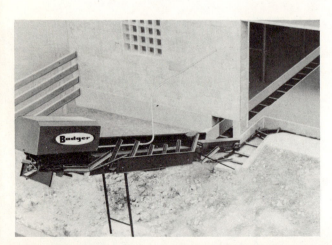

Fig. 302. Endless-chain gutter cleaner installation.

Fig. 303. The corner installation in *A* shows how to turn 90° corners with an endless-chain gutter cleaner. The chain link (*B*) is easy to install.

90 degrees or more. The elevator is independent of the gutter mechanism and is equipped with a 1½-hp, single-phase motor.

A 2-, 3-, or 5-hp, single-phase motor is used to operate the gutter unit, according to the size of the barn.

The cost of an installation of the type shown in Fig. 301 varies, depending upon the size of the barn. Also, you may save considerable money if your barnyard has sufficient slope so that unloading can be done without the elevator. Total investment ranges from $900 to $1,600, the latter sum including the elevator.

Records show that ½ to 1 kwh per cow per month is used in operating a barn cleaner.

Care of Barn Cleaners. If your barn cleaner is properly installed, it should operate for many years with very little attention. A link in the chain may have to be replaced occasionally, and parts must be lubricated according to the instructions in your manual. Improper installation leads to rapid wear of parts and expensive breakdowns.

Clean and lubricate motors as instructed by the operator's manual. Be sure that your motors are properly wired and fused.

Miscellaneous Equipment. See your local appliance dealers and your electric power representative for information on ventilation systems, cow trainers, clippers, automatic fountains, and other equipment.

What Equipment Is Needed for Feeding Livestock or Dairy Cattle?

Several large manufacturers are now marketing mechanical feed handling systems. Some of them operate automatically.

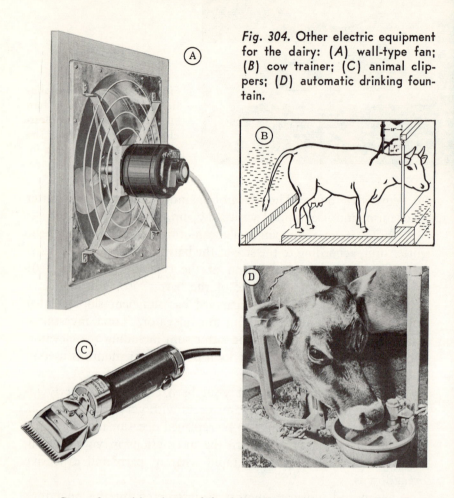

Fig. 304. Other electric equipment for the dairy: (*A*) wall-type fan; (*B*) cow trainer; (*C*) animal clippers; (*D*) automatic drinking fountain.

Several combinations of feed handling units are used in these systems. The basic parts of such systems include a combination of the following: (1) holding bins or tanks, which are often located overhead so as to operate by gravity; (2) elevators or screw conveyors for moving feed from a wagon to a holding bin or from one bin to another; (3) a feed grinder or a crimper; (4) a mixer; (5) feed distributors; and (6) controls for the system.

How to Arrange a Feed Handling System Using a Crimper Mill. In the feed handling system shown in Fig. 305, several types of grain, from overhead bins, are metered into the crimper mill, which is operated by a 5-hp, single-phase motor. The crimped feed passes into a mixer at the left end of the unit. The mixed feedstuff

Fig. 305. These parts of a feed-handling installation include a metering unit, a crimper mill, a mixer, and an elevator.

is then elevated back to overhead holding bins. The elevator shaft can be seen in the background near a ceiling light fixture. The feed can then be handled in several ways. For example, it can be dumped by gravity into a self-unloading truck, or it can be distributed directly into feed bunkers by gravity, by conveyors, or by other types of feed distributors.

How to Arrange a Feed Handling System Using Hammer Mill and Dial Controls. One manufacturer is marketing a unit often referred to as a "dial feed mill." At the upper left in Fig. 307 is

Fig. 306. (A) The feed rollers in a typical crimper mill, with the housing removed. (B) The shaft and agitator unit of the system in Fig. 305. A 5-hp motor operates the mill, mixer, and elevator.

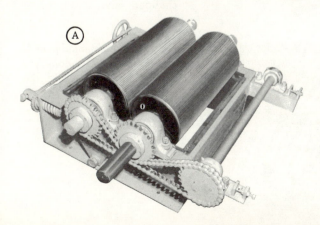

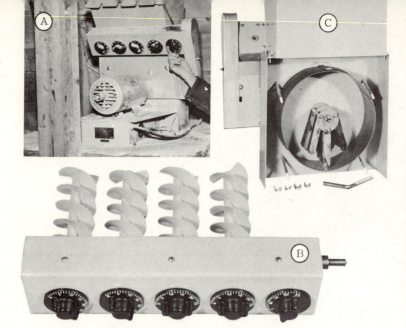

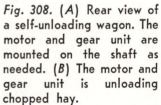

Fig. 307. (A) "Dial" mix-mill ready for operation: the operator sets the time switch for I hour of operation. (B) Mixer unit of the same installation. (C) Inside view of a hammer mill.

Fig. 308. (A) Rear view of a self-unloading wagon. The motor and gear unit are mounted on the shaft as needed. (B) The motor and gear unit is unloading chopped hay.

Fig. 309. Homemade endless-chain elevator-conveyor moving baled hay into the barn.

Fig. 310. Portable screw-type elevator transferring grain from a pickup truck to a large wagon.

shown the mill unit and the dials for setting the proportion of each ingredient to be included in the ration. A 2-hp, single-phase motor powers the mill. Grains and supplements are fed by gravity from overhead holding bins into this mill. The mill is of the hammer type, as shown at upper right. A close-up view of dials and control augers is shown at the lower part of Fig. 307. Notice the timer switch, which is the extreme right hand dial. The mill grinds and mixes 1,200 pounds of feed per hour and shuts itself off at the proper time. This unit is popular with poultry producers since it works well with automatic feed dispensers and reduces man labor for the feeding chore to almost nothing.

Equipment for Handling Hay. Chopped hay is easily handled by a self-unloading wagon as shown in Fig. 308. In this scene, chopped green hay is going into a silo. The hay can be blown into the mow or may be unloaded onto an elevator and conveyed into the storage.

In the large mow in Fig. 309, baled hay is easily handled by a homemade conveyor of the endless-chain type. A ¾-hp motor takes the backache out of hay handling for this farmer. The cost of this unit was under $300.

Other Equipment for Handling Grain. In Fig. 310 you see a portable, screw-type elevator. This is one of the most useful elevators you can have. In this scene, the farmer is transferring grain from one truck to another. He can use the elevator to unload

Fig. 311. Surface-type silage unloader: a 3- to 5-hp motor is required, depending upon the type of silage to be handled.

grain from the large truck into an overhead bin. Many other jobs are also possible with this equipment.

Equipment for Handling Silage. A silo unloader eliminates the climbing and most of the hard labor in handling silage. The two general types are the surface unloader (Fig. 311), and the bottom unloader (Fig. 312).

The first cost of silo unloaders ranges from $1,000 to $1,500 for the surface type and from $1,500 to $2,000 for the bottom type. Prorated over a period of 12 years useful life, an Ohio study showed that the per-ton cost for surface unloading ranged from 56 cents to $1.55.* The range was due to variation in the kind and total amount of silage handled during a season. In the same study, the cost of electricity accounted for 5 to 9 cents a ton.

* *Silo Unloaders on Ohio Farms,* Ohio State University Bulletin 360 (April, 1957), pp. 6-7.

Fig. 312. "Lazy Susan" bottom-type silage unloader.

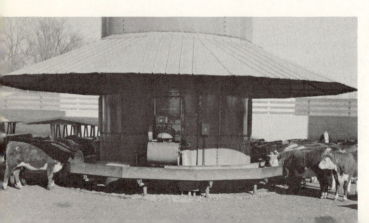

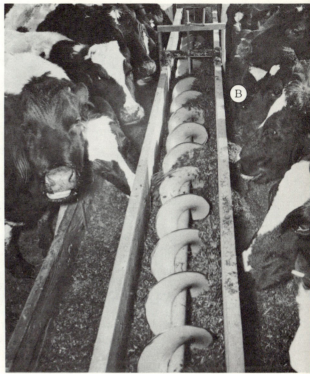

Fig. 313. (*A*) Complete silage feeding system, using a surface-type unloader and a screw-type conveyor. (*B*) Close-up of the screw-type conveyor in operation.

The total cost for bottom-type unloading, as reported in the same study, ranged from 50 cents to $1.76 per ton. Naturally, the larger operations (500 tons per season) gave the lower costs. The 100-ton operations resulted in the highest cost per ton.

In both surface and bottom unloaders, a 3- to 5-hp motor is required. If tough grass silage is handled, the 5-hp size is needed, but corn or sorghum silage can be handled by a 3-hp size. A silo unloader seems to be justified for a 30-cow herd. It is questionable, however, to use a silo unloader for herd sizes of less than twenty.

Fig. 314. Shuttle-stroke silage conveyor: (*A*) cows eating from a homemade bunker; (*B*) paddles in closed position during the back stroke; (*C*) paddles in open position on the forward stroke—same as the shuttle-stroke gutter cleaner.

The silage conveyor shown in Fig. 314 operates on the shuttle-stroke principle similar to the barn cleaner described on page 340. This arrangement can be used in feeding systems for both dairy and beef cattle, of course, and will handle chopped green hay or silage equally well. Feed bunkers are constructed of concrete and are fitted with side rails. To provide adequate drainage, bunkers should have at least 3 inches fall per 100 feet. For further information on this type of equipment, see the discussion on barn cleaners.

What Appliances Should You Have
for Your Poultry Farm?

It is possible for you to produce broilers with less than one minute of man labor per bird—if your operation is properly equipped and is large enough. An individual farmer can handle up to 12,000 laying hens without hired help.

Things to Consider in Selecting Poultry Equipment. The major items of electric equipment used in poultry houses are electric brooders, electric feeders, automatic waterers, litter cleaners, egg handling machines, egg storage coolers, and ventilators. Some specialized equipment is also required for on-the-farm slaughtering.

*Methods of Brooding.** Until recent years, hover brooding with oil heat was the most widely used method of raising chicks; while this method is still widely used, electricity is becoming one of the most popular ways of heating hover brooders. Other methods of electric brooding are being used more and more each year.

Not only is electric heat economical, but it is less likely to start fires than other fuels and does not use up oxygen that is needed by the chicks.

1. Hover Brooding. Provide 7 to 9 square inches of hover space for each chick or 12 to 14 inches for each turkey poult. For example, a round hover 76 inches in diameter would cover about 4,500 square inches of floor space, enough for 500 to 600 chicks or 350 turkey poults.

Wattage must be sufficient to meet the temperature demands, which are different from one section of the country to another. If

* Information on brooding has been drawn largely from the personal notes of Mr. R. C. Jaska, Department of Agricultural Engineering, The Agricultural and Mechanical College of Texas, College Station, Texas.

Fig. 315. A hover-type brooder, 76 inches across, takes care of 350 turkey poults; this size brooder would handle 500 to 600 chicks.

your brooder house is properly constructed, a 1,000w heater for a 76-inch hover with side curtains should take care of any normal temperature situation. In the South, a 750w heating element is adequate for this size hover.

Your investment in hover brooding equipment will average about $50 for each 500-chick outfit or $75 for each 1,000-chick outfit. The average cost of wiring will increase this to $75 and $100 respectively.

Care and Operation of Hover Brooders. Turn your brooders on and observe their operation for 24 hours before putting chicks in the brooder house. During the first week, maintain the temperature at 90 to 95 degrees F; thereafter drop 5 degrees per week until the temperature is down to 72 degrees.

If thermostats fail to cut off, check the voltage and wiring of your brooder circuit. Check your house ventilators also.

2. Infrared Lamp Brooding. Infrared lamps are becoming popular for brooding chicks as well as other young farm animals. Bulbs come in three standard sizes—125w, 250w, and 375w. The life of an infrared bulb is rated at 5,000 hours. In designing a home-made brooder, or in selecting a ready-made one, see that the lamps are spaced about 20 inches apart. Also, have a total of 4 watts of heating capacity per chick in sections of the country where the house temperature may drop to 20 degrees F. or lower. (See Table 30 for additional information.)

The regular type of infrared bulbs cost from $1 to $1.25 each, while the hard-glass type costs $3.75. At least one manufacturer is putting out a bulb for seventy-five cents. The total investment for

TABLE 30

Thermostat Control Temperatures and Number, Size, and Location of Heat Lamps for Brooding Chicks*

| Minimum Room Temperature Degrees F | Lamps | | |
	No.	Size in Watts	Height in Inches
50	6	125	16
40	8	125	16
30	6	250	18
30	12	125	16
20	8	250	18

* First week, 500 chicks.

Fig. 316. Each four-lamp infrared brooding lamp, as shown, takes care of 100 to 150 chicks. The cardboard guards will be removed after the first few days and automatic feeders will be substituted for hand feeding.

Fig. 317. A workman laying heating cable for underheat brooding. The cable will be covered with a layer of concrete.

brooding 500 chicks by infrared heat will average $30; for 1,000 chicks, $60.

Care and Use of Infrared Lamps. Locate 250w lamps 18 inches above the floor, 125w lamps 16 inches above the floor. Thermostats for infrared brooding must be set to operate at room temperature. Infrared heat cannot be measured directly by a thermometer; therefore, the thermostat should be mounted at some point on the wall, not under the lamps.

3. Underheat Brooding. The most recent trend in brooding is to bury heater elements or soil-heating cable in concrete or black-top (asphalt) floors. If a power failure occurs, the heated floor will provide warmth for about seven hours after the failure began.

At 2 cents per kwh, the cost of electricity for underheat brooding averages about .3 cents per chick, or one-fourth the cost of infrared brooding. Your total investment in this setup would be about $60 for 1,000 chicks. For each chick, allow 1.6w of heater cable. Bury this in sand and plaster over with concrete or black-top material.

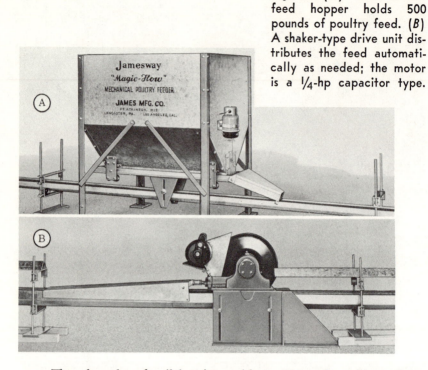

Fig. 318. (*A*) This automatic feed hopper holds 500 pounds of poultry feed. (*B*) A shaker-type drive unit distributes the feed automatically as needed; the motor is a 1/4-hp capacitor type.

Two lengths of soil-heating cable at 230 volts will produce the 1,600w needed for 1,000 chicks. This method of brooding is becoming popular because of the ease of controlling heat and the low investment in wire and equipment. Also, power failures do not mean immediate danger because heat is retained in the floor for six to eight hours.

Fig. 319. A cut-off device automatically stops the shaker unit when the feeders are full.

Things to Consider in Choosing Electric Feeding and Watering Equipment. The feeding installation shown in Fig. 318 operates by means of a reciprocating motion of the feed troughs. This shaking back and forth in ¾-inch strokes causes the feed to move from the 500-pound hopper along the entire length of the feed trough. Feed travels at the rate of 10 to 12 feet a minute. In this setup, no moving parts operate inside the troughs. Other makes, as well as many of the homemade feeders found on farms, use some type of endless chain to drag the feed along the length of the trough.

One ¼-hp capacitor motor will keep two lines of feeders equally full. This system can be made fully automatic and continuous by providing a bulk-feed supply overhead. The device shown in Fig. 319 cuts off the motor when the feed troughs are full. This feeding system, as well as many other mechanical makes and styles, can be adapted to broiler, egg, and turkey production. During the first few days, baby chicks are fed by hand methods. But after the first week you can put your automatic feeder to work. Feed troughs for turkeys must be somewhat larger, but the basic system described here works equally well.

The feeding system shown in Fig. 318 will cost from $300 to $600 installed, depending upon the size of the system. Only 3 to 4 kwh of electricity are used in each 24-hour period. The length of feeder lines and the amount of feed handled determines this. Mechanical feeders have been built by farmers and farm boys throughout the country. Perhaps you too can build your own.

Waterers. Tests in various parts of the country have shown that automatic watering systems for laying hens pay large returns. For example, a 300-hen flock watered by automatic waterers produced 5,100 more eggs in one year than a similar flock watered by hand. Fig. 320 shows two types that are widely used. No doubt you will prefer a waterer that can be installed in the water line, thus completely eliminating the handling of water.

The cost of an 8-foot automatic waterer, as shown in Fig. 320-A, is $20. A good electrification project is a homemade watering trough for your poultry enterprise.

Operation and Care of Feeders and Waterers. There is little skill but considerable care required in handling poultry feeders and waterers that have been properly installed. Keep motors and moving parts lubricated in accordance with the operator's manual and

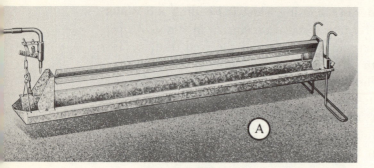

Fig. 320. Automatic waterers relieve the poultryman of this chore and also increase egg production: (*A*) trough-type waterer; (*B*) pail-type waterer.

keep the water container clean. Protect your waterers against frost by using heating cable.

Poultry House Ventilation. Electric ventilator fans and other modern equipment have made it possible to put more laying hens into a given size house. For example a 20- by 40-foot house equipped with cages or multiple roosts will accommodate 500 layers. This averages just a little over 1½ square feet per hen in comparison with four square feet formerly required.

Forced-air ventilation helps to regulate temperature and humidity as well as reduce odors. Also, good ventilation will aid in preventing diseases that can occur as a result of damp conditions.

Conditions from one part of the country to another vary so much that it is not practicable to give detailed instructions for ventilation in this book. Check your ventilation problems with the local farm serviceman.

Egg Handling Equipment for Modern Poultry Farming. If you now have or plan to have a large flock of layers, no doubt you will be interested in some of the newer egg handling machines. Among these are egg cleaners, egg graders, candlers, and refrigerated storage units.

Egg Cleaner-Candler. The farmer shown in Fig. 322 is using a combination cleaner-candler that will handle 1,000 eggs per hour.

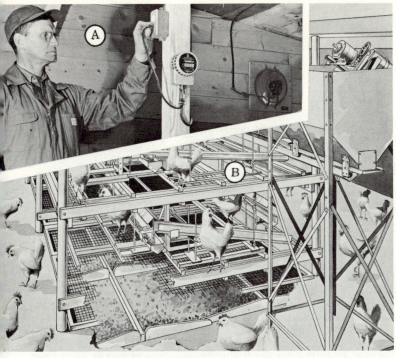

Fig. 321. (A) This poultryman is plugging in the thermostat which controls the ventilator fan in his modern laying house. (B) Note the multiple roosts, which have the effect of increasing floor area.

This "dry" cleaner cleans the eggs as they pass underneath an abrasive belt. The eggs are returned to the operator after being run through the machine.

The cost of this ¼-hp cleaner is approximately $200. It will clean a case of eggs while using about 1 kwh of electricity. The

Fig. 322. (A) Poultryman cleaning and candling eggs at the rate of 1,000 per hour. (B) This grader-candler uses about 1 kwh per case of eggs.

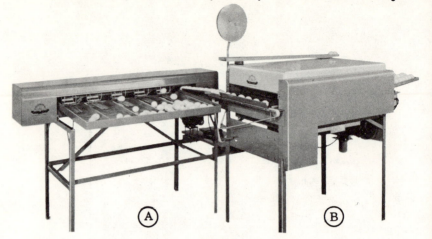

Fig. 323. This egg cleaner-candler-grader handles 1,800 eggs per hour.

major service required to keep this cleaner operating is to adjust and replace cleaning belts. Some minor adjustments of parts may be needed occasionally. Also, the motor may require lubrication. See the operator's manual for instructions.

Washer-type cleaners are also available. The better ones wash the eggs in hot water and dry them in one operation.

A washer or dry-egg cleaner can be set up to operate in conjunction with an egg grader as well as with a candler. It is thus possible to clean and grade 1,000 eggs per hour with these two moderately-priced machines. Note that egg washers usually cost slightly more than dry-egg cleaners of the same capacity. Also, the washer requires a supply of hot water. You can make your own egg candler for a few dollars worth of materials.

Egg Graders. As mentioned in the preceding topic, an egg grader can be operated in conjunction with a cleaner. In the model shown in Fig. 323, a $\frac{1}{20}$-hp motor operates the mechanism that separates eggs into five grades. The capacity is 1,800 eggs per hour.

The price of egg graders of the type illustrated ranges from $200 to $400. The more expensive models will grade up to 3,600 eggs per hour. Ball bearings in this machine should give it long life. Only 1 kwh is required to grade 100 cases of eggs.

Egg Storage. Gone are the days of storing eggs for several days on the pantry shelf "until the next trip into town." Since eggs begin to deteriorate the minute they are laid, a refrigerated storage is necessary to meet the market demands for good quality eggs.

You can purchase a commercial egg cooler, or you can build your own. Homemade coolers, which use room air conditioners as the source of refrigeration, are proving to be satisfactory. The cabinet can be built with an ordinary set of carpenter's tools.

The Oklahoma State University reported satisfactory results from a ¼-ton refrigeration unit installed in a well-insulated cabinet.* The size was sufficient to accommodate six egg cases and two half-case egg baskets (for cooling). This was deemed adequate for a 300- to 400-hen laying flock. For construction details order the leaflet listed in the footnote. By building this cooler at home you can save about $200 in comparison with the cost of a commercial cooler of equal capacity.

Care and Operation. Eggs should be stored in 50 to 60 degree temperature and in 80 to 85 per cent humidity. Eggs should be gathered frequently and cooled in wire baskets (not in boxes or

---

* *A 7-Case Egg Cooling Cabinet.* Oklahoma State University Leaflet L-22, Stillwater, Oklahoma (no date).

Fig. 324. Refrigerated egg storage can be constructed by the farmer. Note the compressor unit on top of the cabinet. A room air-conditioning unit can be used for cooling.

pails) where faster cooling will take place. The cooling unit should be placed so that the sun does not shine directly on it.

The price of egg coolers varies greatly depending upon type and size. Check with your local appliance dealer for quotations. A ¼-ton unit powered by a ½-hp motor, operating 8 hours in 24, would use about 4 kwh of electricity.

Litter Cleaning Equipment for a Laying House. Fig. 325 shows an installation of a shuttle-stroke litter cleaner that operates on the same principle as the dairy barn cleaner previously described. The droppings and litter can be pushed into the gutter where the push-pull action of the paddles carries it out to the end of the conveyor. There it is loaded directly onto a manure spreader.

A second and third-floor arrangement can be fitted into this system by installing chutes to empty from those floors into the first-floor gutter. The motor size required depends on the size of the cleaning system; however a 1- to 2-hp, single-phase motor is usually large enough. The cost of electricity for cleaning a multiple-story laying house is only a few dollars a year. The equipment should last at least 10 to 12 years.

Fig. 325. In *A* and *B*, the shuttle stroke of the paddle moves the litter about 24 inches with each stroke; (C) the drive shaft and header installation connects with the paddle unit for operating the paddle mechanism.

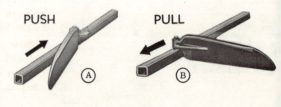

Fig. 326. A poultryman on the second floor of a laying house pushing litter into a chute leading to the gutter cleaner on the first floor.

Summary

Important points to consider in equipping the farm include: (1) expanding farm production, (2) dependable markets, (3) the farm labor situation, (4) trends in consumer demands, (5) improvement in the quality of farm products, and (6) reduction of risk in storage. Consider also the reliability of the dealer in maintaining vital equipment. Remember to include both fixed and operating costs in determining the total annual cost of an appliance.

Major electric appliances for a modern dairy include the following items: (1) milker—conventional one- or two-pail types, cow-to-can type, or combine type, depending upon the size of the herd and the labor situation; (2) milk cooler—wet type or bulk-tank cooler, depending upon the volume of milk and the market demands; (3) water heater—50- to 100-gallon pressure type preferred for a modern dairy (also consider the type equipped with house heating elements); (4) gutter cleaner—either the endless-chain type or the shuttle-stroke paddle type is satisfactory.

Automatic electric feed handling systems now on the market can save up to 70 per cent or more of the human labor required in feeding livestock or dairy cattle. Some of these systems do every operation involved in handling feedstuff from the time it leaves the field until it is dispensed into the feed trough.

The basic units that go into an automatic feed handling system include self-unloading wagons, cup-type or screw-type elevators, overhead holding bins, metering devices, grinders, mixers, and dispensers.

A complete feed handling unit consists of a combination of several of these individual units geared to operate with little or no human labor. Many livestock and dairy farmers build some parts of their feed handling equipment themselves.

Other electric feed handling equipment includes elevators of the screw, endless-chain, and cup types. One of these will handle almost every type of feedstuff on the farm. Either vertical or horizontal elevators-conveyors can be built in the home farm shop or in the school shop and have proven to be one of the most useful projects in farm electrification.

A silo unloader, in conjunction with distributing machinery, can relieve the farmer of much hard labor. And, if the herd is sufficiently large, the equipment will be economical. The addition of a time switch will allow you to go about other work while the silage feeding chore is being done. Several well-known makes of silo unloaders are available. These include both surface and bottom-type unloaders.

In all poultry producing areas, the poultry industry is being electrified on a rapid and widespread scale. This development has resulted in larger flocks. Electric equipment needed to handle these large operations includes: (1) brooders of the hover type, infrared heat lamps, and underheat brooding; (2) automatic feeding systems for all types of poultry production; (3) automatic watering system; (4) egg cleaner-candler machines; (5) egg graders; (6) combination egg cleaner-candler-grader machines; (7) egg coolers; and (8) litter cleaning equipment.

The proper combination of electric equipment will enable you to handle 12,000 or more head of laying hens or up to 35,000 broilers (per turn) without outside help.

Questions

1. Why should trends in market demands be considered in selecting new electric equipment?
2. What should you know about a dealer before buying a major electric appliance from him?
3. What are the advantages of a combine milker? A bulk-tank cooler?
4. What are the basic parts in an automatic feed handling system?
5. What size herd of dairy or beef cattle is needed to justify an electric silage feeding system?

6. What are the advantages of underheat brooding? Infrared brooding?
7. What major pieces of electric equipment are needed to establish a one-man, 12,000-laying-hen operation?

Additional Readings

Edison Electric Institute, *Farm Electrical Equipment Handbook.* New York, 1950.

———, *Farm Electrification Manual.* New York, 1953.

Schaenzer, J. P., *Rural Electrification,* 5th rev. ed. Milwaukee, Wisconsin, Bruce Publishing Co., 1955.

Successful Farming, *Materials Handling,* 2nd ed. Des Moines, Iowa, Meredith Publishing Co., 1956.

CHAPTER 14

*H*ow *to Select and Care for*
Electric Equipment for Crop Drying
and for the Farm Shop

The savings from the use of a crop dryer can run as high as 100 per cent, when, for example, weather conditions could result in a total loss of the crop in the field. Of course, such high savings should not be expected every year. You may, however, expect to save from 5 to 15 per cent more grain in harvesting and up to 25 per cent more nutritional value of hay when crop dryers are used. These savings are the result of a better choice of harvesting period and of better storage. The net result is better prices for the product and a reduction of risk while the crop is in storage.

Since crop drying is a rather technical problem, you should seek the advice of a competent person in this field if you are planning a dryer system. Of course, you can obtain thorough technical information on this subject by writing to the nearest land grant

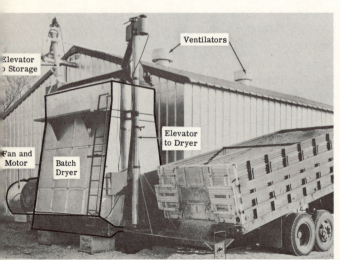

Fig. 327. A batch dryer and electric handling machinery, plus proper storage, not only reduce man labor but also take the guesswork out of harvesting, drying, and storing grain.

364

college or to the USDA. The information presented in this chapter is of a practical nature, dealing with basic principles rather than going very deeply into the technical phases of crop drying. Emphasis is placed on the selection and care of crop drying equipment.

The last section in this chapter presents information needed in selecting basic power tools for the farm shop. The upkeep of the equipment on a modern farm, together with the need for constructing other farm equipment, demands a few basic power tools. In fact, it is uneconomical for most farms to be without these few basic power units.

What Electric Equipment Is Needed for Drying Farm Crops?

Grain, hay, seed, and other crops can be dried on the farm by using either heated or unheated air. The procedures and equipment required for the two methods are quite different, however. Although both methods are discussed in later topics, it should be mentioned here that the use of unheated air is more common to the average farm where crops are dried.

Things Involved in a Crop Drying Problem. The drying of any crop with unheated air involves several factors that vary from one situation to another. In getting ready for drying hay, grain, or seed, you must consider the following things: (1) the type, size, and cost of storage structure required; (2) the type, size, and cost of drying equipment required; (3) the wiring required; (4) the kind and amount of product to be dried, its moisture content at the beginning of storage and the final moisture content desired; (5) local weather conditions during the drying period; and (6) drying procedure.

How Resistance to Air Flow Affects Size of Fan Required. A fan that will move 30,000 cfm (cubic feet of air per minute) in open air will move only 20,000 cfm through a 5-foot layer of shelled corn. The reason for this is that the corn offers resistance to the movement of the air. For example, resistance would be almost 100 per cent in a one-foot layer of sand. A five-foot layer of hay has much less resistance in it than does a five-foot layer of corn. The resistance to air flow is called *static pressure* and is sometimes expressed as "inches of water." The average resistance in grain and seed is from ¾ to 2½ inches and in hay from ½ to 1½ inches.

Since resistance greatly influences the fan size required for a given drying situation, it must always be taken into account. Three things can increase resistance to air flow: (1) denser, closer-lying materials, (2) greater depth in storage, and (3) faster flow of the drying air. Several of the references listed at the end of this chapter include resistance or static-pressure tables for different crops, depths, and so on.

Equipment for Drying Hay With Unheated Air. Why must hay drying fans have such a large capacity? The answer is that 1 ton of dry hay (15 per cent moisture) weighs 2,700 pounds *before drying* (at 35 per cent moisture). Therefore, in drying 60 tons of hay from 35 per cent moisture to about 15 per cent, around 40,000 pounds of water must be removed. Adequate ventilators for the escape of moist air must be provided.

In order to do this job in 1 to 3 weeks, a 25,000 cfm fan is required, and it must work against a resistance determined by the kind of hay and its depth in storage. A 7½- to 10-hp motor is needed to operate a fan this size. This example is based on two general rules of thumb: (1) provide 350 cfm per ton of "dry" hay, or (2) provide 15 to 20 cfm per square-foot of floor area in the hay mow.

The temperature and humidity of the outside air, together with the moisture content of the crop to be dried, determines the amount of time required to dry hay, provided, of course, that the drying structure, equipment, and procedure are proper. A fan does

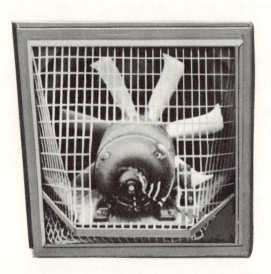

Fig. 328. A crop dryer fan must have adequate capacity and power for moving large quantities of air, since moisture is removed from the crops in this manner. The fan shown has a 25,000-cfm capacity and is operated by a 5-hp single-phase motor.

Fig. 329. Homemade A-frame, main duct, hay dryer installation. Note the slatted sides that allow air to circulate through the hay.

little or no good when the outside temperature is below 50 degrees or the humidity is above 70 per cent.

Hay Drying Systems. Hay drying systems are classified according to the method of air circulation. The three most popular systems are (1) a main (or central) duct, (2) a main duct with side laterals, and (3) a tiered duct arrangement.

Main Duct System. For hay mows from 20 to 30 feet in width, the least expensive and simplest system is a central A-frame. Fig. 329 shows an installation of this type filled with chopped hay. Many farmers make their own A-frames.

Fig. 330. An oval main duct system is suitable for hay mows 30 to 36 feet in width. Note also the metal tie rods that help the walls withstand the lateral pressure of the hay.

Fig. 331. Oval main duct with laterals A and B. It is used in hay mows wider than 36 feet.

For mows from 30 to 36 feet in width, a rectangular or oval-shaped frame should be used. Fig. 330 illustrates this type of installation.

Main Duct with Side Laterals. For mows wider than 36 feet, lateral ducts are used in addition to a main duct. This arrangement provides better distribution of air. The installation in Fig. 331 has a main duct in the center of the mow with laterals to each side. Another arrangement is to have a main duct at one side of the mow

Fig. 332. Tiered duct system of hay drying. Note the vertical arrangement of the fans and ducts in A and B. The workman is laying an expanded-metal type lateral (D) in proper position with main duct (C).

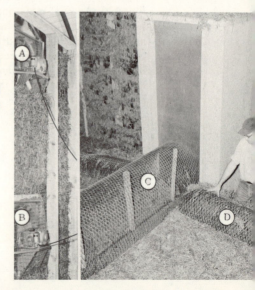

Fig. 333. A farmer discussing a fan and motor installation with a technician. This 25,000-cfm fan and 7½-hp single-phase motor were selected to take care of a 70-ton mow.

with laterals leading across the building. Ducts should end about 10 feet from the ends and sides of the mow.

Tiered Duct System. A recent development in hay drying is to install portable ducts as the depth of hay is increased in the mow. This arrangement makes it possible to dry hay to any depth. Fig. 332 shows an installation of this type. Ducts are made of expanded metal or strong wire on lumber framing.

Hay Drying Fans and Motors. The six-blade, propeller-type fan in Fig. 333 is rated at 25,000 cfm at 1 inch static pressure. This fan is adequate for a 36 x 55 foot mow (or equivalent) containing up to 75 tons of hay. Tables giving information on fan capacity can be found in USDA bulletins and other publications.

Fig. 334. The centrifugal-type fan shown is rated at 25,000 cfm; the motor is a 7½-hp single-phase type. Note the magnetic starter-protector near the top of the fan housing.

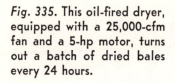

Fig. 335. This oil-fired dryer, equipped with a 25,000-cfm fan and a 5-hp motor, turns out a batch of dried bales every 24 hours.

Fig. 334 shows a centrifugal fan, which is also a popular type for crop drying. Again, the capacity of a centrifugal fan is rated in cubic feet per minute. Usually, the motor is designed for a fan of given type and size.

The single-phase motor in Fig. 334 is rated at 7½ hp. A magnetic switch protects it from overloads and low voltage as well.

A quick rule of thumb on motor size is to allow 1 hp for each 9 or 10 tons of dry hay. For example, a 75-ton mow requires a 7½-hp motor ($75 \div 10 = 7\frac{1}{2}$).

Equipment for Drying Hay with Heated Air. The oil-fired dryer shown in Fig. 335 is powered by a 5-hp, single-phase motor, which provides air movement. The fan is a 36-inch, propeller type, rated at 25,000 cfm.

The advantages of this dryer over the unheated air types are wider choice of harvesting period despite unfavorable weather and quicker, more thorough drying.

Baled hay, at 35 per cent moisture, is stacked on a slatted floor connected to the header duct at the left end. The dryer is connected to the header in such a way that air must circulate through the floor and through the bales of hay.

A tarpaulin protects the hay against rain while the drying is taking place. Notice that the sides of the stack are left open, thus providing an escape for moist air.

The batch shown in Fig. 335 will be dry and ready to place in storage within 24 hours after the hot air begins to circulate. Another batch from the field will replace this one.

Cost of Drying Hay. The cost of an A-frame installation for a 75-ton mow, using a 25,000 cfm fan equipped with a 7½-hp, single-phase motor, ranges from $1,000 to $1,200. This includes the lumber as well as the labor needed for construction of the A-frames.

The same size fan and motor with a main and lateral system for a 75-ton mow runs from $1,250 to $1,600.

The cost of electricity for drying hay with unheated air averages about $1.50 per ton, at 2½ cents per kwh.

The total cost of drying hay with unheated air, including depreciation of equipment, ranges from approximately $3.25 to $4.00 per ton. The total investment for this type of drying ranges from about $15 to $20 a ton of mow capacity.

Data on the cost of drying crops with heated air are not available; however, it appears that the per-ton cost of fuel or energy is somewhat greater with heated-air equipment.

How to Operate and Care for Hay Dryers. Once the dryer is started, keep it running until the top layer of hay is dry (feels dry to your cheek or crackles in your hand). The exception to this is when the temperature gets below 50 degrees F. and/or humidity gets above 70 per cent.

Check for thin areas of hay or open holes around posts. Add hay to these spots and pack firmly until no excess air movement can be felt.

In adding green hay to the mow, limit the amount to 6 feet of chopped hay, 8 feet of long hay, or 3 tiers of bales. Allow each layer to dry before adding another. Limit the total depth over a duct to 15 feet of long hay, 12 feet of chopped hay, or 8 layers of bales.

For unheated-air drying, figure 1 to 3 weeks for drying a mow full of hay; for heated air drying, figure 3 to 24 hours per mow or per batch of bales. The system should be shut off when the very top layer of hay is dry.

Fig. 336. Popular type of 2,000-bushel metal grain bin, equipped with a perforated metal floor and the proper size fan for this size bin. Note the ventilator at the top.

Fig. 337. Quonset-type granary for large grain farms. Note the metal tie rods to support the side walls. Note also the expanded metal ducts on the floor. A fan and motor for each duct is installed outside the building.

Keep the fan and motor lubricated in accordance with the operator's manual. Clean the motor once each season; do not blow it out with an air hose since this forces dust into bearings and windings. Disassemble the motor and clean as directed by the manual. You can use the dryer motor for other farm operations during the fall, winter, and spring.

Grain Drying Structures and Equipment. There is a trend throughout the country toward the use of metal bins and quonset huts for drying and storing grain. Fig. 336 shows a cutaway view of a grain storage bin with a perforated floor. Forced air circulates through the floor openings. The metal walls prevent the air from escaping at the sides and thus forces it through the grain. For large farming operations, the use of quonset metal buildings and multiple fans is becoming popular.

In comparison with hay, the volume of grain is less for equal weight. Therefore, on the average farm, the amount of air required for drying grain is somewhat less than that required for drying hay. However, the higher resistance of grain offsets this insofar as horsepower is concerned.

Many farmers are converting existing buildings into grain-drying structures. The principle precaution to take is to build extra supports underneath floors which might otherwise give way because of the excess weight of grain. Also, install metal tie rods to prevent the walls from bulging (see Fig. 337). Line the inside of old buildings with one or two layers of 30-pound asphalt paper to make them airtight. Inverted V-shaped troughs with perforations may be installed on the floor for ventilators. Take care to provide openings for the escape of moist air. Your fan motor should be located outside the building where good ventilation is possible.

How to Determine Amount of Air and Fan Size Needed. The rule of thumb for amount of air for drying grain is 2½ to 5 cfm per bushel, depending upon the size of the grain or seed to be dried. For example, a storage containing 1,000 bushels of corn or beans would require 5,000 cfm of unheated air; 1,000 bushels of grain sorghum would require 2,500 cfm. The fans have to move the air against a certain resistance, however, so the fan size, in both examples, must have greater capacity than the figures indicated so as to offset this resistance. You can easily read and interpret static pressure tables, which can be found in grain drying publications issued by the USDA and by land grant colleges.

Heated Air Dryers. There is practically no difference between a heated-air dryer for grain and one for hay. Refer to page 370 for information on this type.

Fig. 338. Shelled corn being dried on wagons by a batch drier. The same dryer can be used for drying hay. At lower right, early settlers harvesting and threshing grain by hand.

Fig. 339. Electric moisture tester for grain.

How to Operate and Care for Grain Dryers. Once the dryer is started, operate it continuously until the top layer of grain is dry (use a moisture tester). The exception is when the temperature is below 50 degrees F. or when the humidity is above 70 per cent. Check the air movement on top of the grain; fill thin spots to make the air flow evenly. Clean and lubricate fans and motors as directed in the operator's manual.

Fig. 340. A bench-type tool grinder equipped with a 6-inch wheel and a 1/4-hp motor. This machine is one of the most useful for the farm shop.

Fig. 341. The heavy-duty grinder shown here is valuable for doing heavy farm grinding. This type grinder should be mounted on a pedestal or oil drum filled with concrete. Note the adjustable eye shields.

What Power Tools Are Needed
for the Farm Shop?

There is almost no limit to the possibilities for farm improvement through a well-equipped shop. A good shop should be more than a repair center. It should be an improvement center as well.

The power tools described in the remaining section have been recommended by a well-known authority on farm shops. The descriptive material has been drawn largely from an article written by him.*

Grinders. A grinder is one of the most useful power tools for the shop and should be one of the first pieces of equipment to be purchased. The three types generally found in farm shops are bench, pedestal, and portable grinders.

Bench Grinder. A good farm grinder should meet the following specifications: motor (½-hp, 3,600 rpm, 115-230v, sealed ball bearings), grinder wheel (7 x 1 inch), ⅝-inch arbor, guard, tool rests, and lighted shield. (NOTE: A lighted shield provides both protection and good vision.)

Pedestal Grinder. Heavy veeing, grinding plow shares for hardfacing, and other difficult grinding jobs can be done best with a large grinder with plenty of power. A 1,750 rpm, 1- to 2-hp motor should be large enough for most grinding jobs on the farm. The grinding wheel should be at least 1¼ x 10 inches, and should have sealed ball bearings. This grinder should have an illuminated shield.

If a large grinder is available, a ⅓-hp, bench grinder should be available for tool grinding.

Portable Grinder. A portable grinder is valuable for doing in-place grinding. The preparation of metal for welding will alone justify the cost of this tool on the average mechanized farm. And a portable grinder will buff, wire brush, dress welds, grind bolts, dress rivets, and do other useful jobs. Specifications for a good portable grinder are: wheel size, 5 x ¾ inches with ½-inch arbor; free speed, 4,500 rpm; sealed bearings; adjustable guard. The weight should be about 15 pounds.

Drills. The three types of drills that are common to the farm shop are two sizes of portable types and a drill press.

* V. J. Morford, "Hired Hands with No Demands," *Proceedings of the Seminar "Power Farming: A Better Way of Life."* (Huntley, Illinois, Thor Research Center for Better Living, 1956), pp. 33-35.

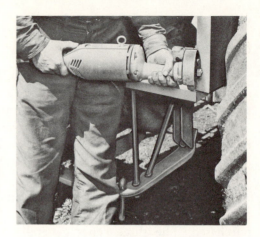

Fig. 342. A portable grinder being used to vee out space for welding. This type of grinder makes it possible to do many grinding jobs in place.

One-half Inch Portable Drill. This is one of the most useful tools on the farm. The following are suggested specifications: ⅓-hp universal motor; 400 to 500 rpm at free speed; ½-inch, three-jaw key chuck; grease-sealed bearings. Both metal and wood can be worked with a portable ½-inch drill. Some well-known makes can be mounted in a bench stand and used as a drill press. Weight will average about 10 pounds.

Fig. 343. The ½-inch portable drill at left is easily mounted in the light-weight frame at right for use as a drill press.

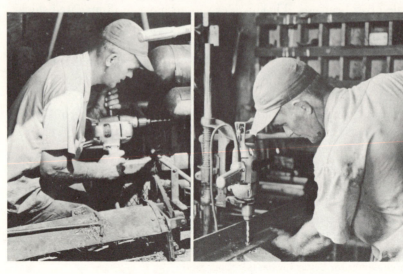

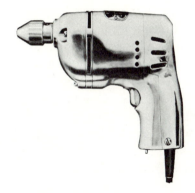

Fig. 344. This light-weight ¼-inch drill is valuable for working metal and wood and will operate numerous attachments for doing other shop jobs.

One-quarter Inch Portable Drill. For light work in metal or wood, you will need a ¼-inch portable drill with the following specifications: universal motor, 2,000 rpm; ¼-inch, three-jaw key chuck; capacity up to ¼-inch drill bits and up to 1-inch wood-working bits; grease-sealed bearings. (NOTE: Use special power wood-working bits in wood.)

Drill Press. For heavy and accurate drilling, you need a bench or floor-type drill press. The drill press should have a capacity from 12 to 17 inches with 14 inches suggested as a good choice (this

Fig. 345. A bench-type 14-inch drill press is needed in the farm shop for accurate heavy-duty drilling. Note the four-speed hookup, depth gauge, adjustable drill table, lamp, slots for drill vise, vertical head lock, and other features.

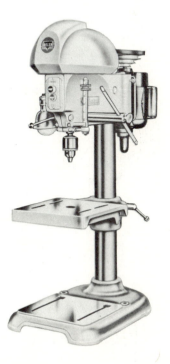

measure refers to the largest diameter circle in which a hole can be drilled in the center). Most drill presses are equipped with ½-inch, three-jaw chucks. If heavier than ½-inch drilling is to be done, you can fit your drill with a No. 2 Morse taper-shank chuck which will handle up to 1-inch drill bits. The use of ⅝- to 1-inch drill bits requires a slow-speed attachment that will operate at 200 rpm.

Other specifications for a good drill press are: 4-inch spindle travel, with spring return and depth gauge; sealed ball bearings; six splines in spindle and sleeve; ½-hp capacitor motor. Floor models should have foot feed, and both floor and bench models should be equipped with a drill vise.

Arc Welder. The farm-type a-c welder is fast becoming one of the essential pieces of equipment for the mechanized farm. Fig. 346 shows a diagram of how this welder converts 37.5 amperes at 230 volts into 180 amperes at 25 to 40 volts. The principle involved here is that a transformer in the welder "induces" the high-amperage, low-voltage current that will produce an arc hot enough to weld metal.

The farm-type welder can be purchased for approximately $200, including regular accessories and a carbon-arc torch. Besides doing many types of welding, you can also use this carbon arc torch to braze, heat, and do other work that requires a hot flame. Fig. 347 shows one of the popular makes of 180-ampere, limited-input welders.

Welders that operate on 115 volts have not proved very successful for farm use. Before purchasing a welder, you should check

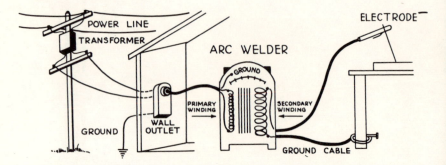

Fig. 346. A farm arc welder takes 37.5 amperes at 230 volts from the transformer at the power line and steps it down to about 25-40 volts. The amperage is stepped up to a maximum of 180 amperes.

Fig. 347. The farm-type arc welder at left will do most of the welding jobs required on the farm and will operate on rural lines. The workman at right is using a farm welder to build up a worn axle shaft.

with your power supplier to make certain that you will be permitted to connect it to a power source. Be prepared to tell the power supplier what kind of welder you will have.

D-c welders are well adapted to the farm but the cost is two to four times greater than that of the a-c welder.

Refer to any good welding instruction manual for information on the use of arc welders. You may wish to enter one of the

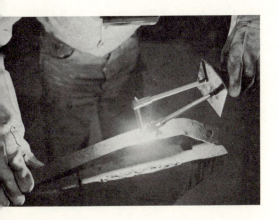

Fig. 348. A farmer using a carbon arc torch to heat steel for bending. This torch operates off the farm welder and provides an open flame for many heating jobs on the farm.

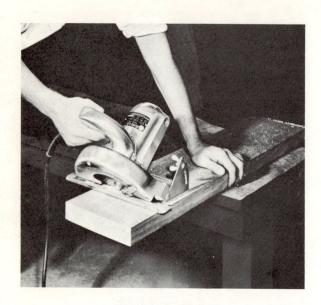

Fig. 349. A portable electric saw operating at a 45° angle. This 6-inch saw will cut through 1 13/16-inch lumber at this angle.

welding contests sponsored by various organizations. See your teacher of agriculture or your club agent for further information.

Electric Saws. You may wish to purchase a portable saw for general carpentry work, and a table saw for cabinet work and for ripping lumber.

Portable Saw. The blade of a portable saw should cut through at least 1⅞ inches at 45 degrees and preferably 2¼ inches at 45 degrees. The motor should be of the universal type with 5,500-rpm free speed. An automatic, telescopic guard should be provided. The saw should weigh 10 to 12 pounds.

Table Saw. A table saw that is to serve any very useful purpose on the farm must have at least a 10-inch blade and preferably a 12-inch one; the motor should be 1 to 2 hp and should have sealed ball bearings. The saw arbor should also be equipped with sealed ball bearings and should tilt to 45 degrees; maximum depth, 3¼ inches at 90 degrees.

Air Compressor. Modern farming with its tractors, trucks, and other needs for compressed air requires an air compressor. Many farmers and farm boys have built their own compressors from old, discarded refrigeration compressors, water tanks, and other materials. If you undertake the job of building a homemade air compressor, make certain to observe all safety precautions in its

Fig. 350. This combination table saw and jointer are powered by the same 1-hp motor.

construction. Improperly constructed compressors have been known to explode and cause serious injuries and death.

Your compressor should be portable (mounted on skids or wheels) so that paint spraying and other jobs can be done in place. Other specifications include: A ⅓- to ½-hp capacitor-start or

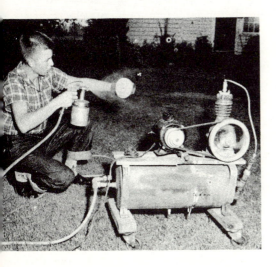

Fig. 351. A farm boy operating a paint gun with a home-made air compressor.

repulsion-induction motor; a single-stage compressor; a pressure gauge; a 20- to 30-gallon tank; a displacement of 2 feet per minute; a cutout that operates at 150 pounds per square-inch; a total weight of 150 to 175 pounds.

Summary

The risk of losing hay, grain, and seed in storage can be eliminated or greatly reduced by a drying system for the farm. In the field, savings of 5 to 15 per cent on hay, grain, or seed are possible. Up to 25 per cent more food value can be retained in hay by curing it in the barn.

Hay-curing structures include the central duct with laterals, the A-frame, and the tiered duct method. Motor and fan size for all types of structures are determined on the basis of the tonnage to be dried, the depth of the hay in storage, and the type of hay (chopped or long). Also, the amount of moisture to be removed affects the requirements for air volume. Chopped hay offers greater resistance to air flow than does long hay.

A fan large enough to provide 350 cfm per ton of hay (dry) or 15 to 20 cfm per square-foot of floor area is required. For a 75-ton mow, a 25,000-cfm fan, powered by a 7½-hp motor, is required. In good haying weather, this fan will cure the 75 tons of hay in 3 weeks. About 6 feet of chopped hay at a time can be added to the dried hay in the mow. The cost of electricity averages about $1 to $1.50 per ton, while the total costs run from $3 to $4 per ton.

Stored grain offers greater resistance to air flow than does hay; therefore, fans for drying grain must be rated to operate at a higher "static pressure" or resistance.

Structures for drying grain must be practically airtight at the sides and bottom, except for the air inlets. Air entering from the bottom is forced upward through the grain. Moist air outlets must be provided.

From 2½ to 5 cfm of unheated air is needed per bushel of grain or seed. A movement of 5,000-cfm is sufficient to take care of 1,000 bushels of shelled corn. Grain sorghum requires less air—2,500 cfm for 1,000 bushels.

Heated air dries grain and seed much faster than does unheated air. A batch dryer requires only a few hours to dry a wagon load of shelled corn or wheat in any kind of weather. Heated air is used also to dry hay, especially baled hay. Usually, heat is supplied by an oil or gas burner, while an electric fan provides the air movement.

A well-equipped farm shop pays off in keeping vital equipment in production. It also results in the improvement of the farm through the construction of labor-saving equipment.

The basic power machines for the farm shop include a bench grinder, a pedestal grinder, a portable drill, a drill press, a bench saw, a portable saw, an arc welder, and an air compressor. Additional power tools may be justified, depending on the size of the farm.

"Cheap," lightweight power tools should be avoided. A good standard machine will usually last a lifetime if given proper care. One of the best features to look for in a power tool is sealed ball bearings. A good grade of extension cord with an adapter for polarizing the plug-in with the circuit wires is another excellent feature to have for operating portable power tools.

Questions

1. Why does the depth of the grain or seed increase the requirements for volume of air flow needed in drying?
2. In what kind of weather is it best to cut off the drying fan?
3. Why are sealed ball bearings generally recommended for power tools in the farm shop?

Additional Readings

Schaenzer, J. P., *Rural Electrification*, 5th rev. ed. Milwaukee, Wisconsin, Bruce Publishing Co., 1955.

Successful Farming, *Materials Handling*, 2nd ed. Des Moines, Iowa, Meredith Publishing Co., 1956.

U.S. Department of Agriculture, *Drying Ear Corn with Heated Air*. Leaflet No. 333. Washington, D.C., 1952.

Suggested Projects for Problem-Unit Six

Many of the items discussed throughout Chapters 13 and 14 are suitable for project work, both in the school shop and on the farm. For example, the homemade compressor in Fig. 351 was made as a club project by a farm boy in Alabama. He used old,

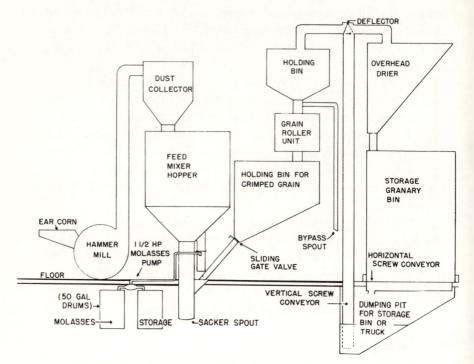

Fig. 352. Diagram of a complete feed-handling system, including a molasses dispenser. In this system, the feed is not touched by human hands at any time.

discarded parts in putting this machine together. Also, the home-made elevator discussed in Chapter 1 is easy to build and makes a valuable addition to the feed handling equipment for the farm. Study the illustrations throughout Chapters 13 and 14 with a view to using some of them for project work in farm electrification.

Electric Feed Handling. There are hundreds of possible variations in feed handling systems. One basic arrangement is shown in Fig. 352. By studying this layout you may find several ideas that will help you to improve your own feeding system. As for individual projects in feed handling, refer back through Chapters 13 and 14.

Additional Projects for Electrifying the Farm Shop. 1. *Convert Old Post Drill to Electric Power*. The drill in Fig. 353 was made from a discarded hand post drill. It is anchored to a piece of 6-inch

Fig. 353. An old post drill converted to electric power. The depth feeding mechanism operates at variable speeds. Variable speed pulleys also make the rpm of the drill variable.

channel steel set in an oil drum filled with ballast and 12 inches of concrete. Variable speed pulleys with a ⅓-hp motor (1,725 rpm) provide a speed range of 125 to 400 rpm. The drill and motor will handle drill bits up to 1¼ inch.

2. *Homemade Hacksaw.* The hacksaw in Fig. 354 was a prize-winning entry in one of the national farm electrification awards programs. It was made from a discarded milking machine and a ½-hp motor. The saw frame was built of welded steel.

Fig. 354. A prize-winning hacksaw made from a discarded milking machine, powered with a ½-hp motor.

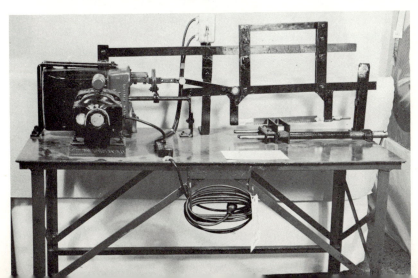

Illustration Credits

The author wishes to thank the following for permission to reproduce illustrations: Aerovent Fan & Equipment Inc., 329, 333, 338, 339 · Agricultural Education Department, Mississippi State College, 230, 353 · Alabama Power Co., 23, 351 · Allis-Chalmers Manufacturing Company, 80, 93, 207, 212, 215 · Anaconda Wire & Cable Company, 54, 55, 132, 133, 138 · Paul M. Anderson, 332 · Cletus Armacost, 343 · Babson Bros. Co., 13, 105 · Badger Northland Inc., 201, 300, 302, 303, 313 · Drawing by Zeno Bailey, 41, 43 · Baldor Electric Company, 200 · Barnes Manufacturing Co., 8 · Belle City Engineering Company, 19, 307 · The Black & Decker Mfg. Co., 46, 60, 340, 343, 344, 349 · The Brown-Brockmeyer Company, 210, 214, 341 · Browning Manufacturing Company, 217, 218, 223, 234 · The Bryant Electric Company, 53, 60, 113, 114, 115, 142 · David Bush, 92 · Bussmann Mfg. Co., 98 · Butler Manufacturing Company, 2, 327, 328, 336 · Carlon Products Corporation, 254 · Century Electric Company, 203, 208 · Cherry-Burrell Corporation, 295 · Chicago Flexible Shaft Co., 304 · Clay Equipment Corp., 3, 17, 20, 313, 330, 331, 334 · Commonwealth Edison Company, 11, 15, 85, 92 · Consumers Power Company, 21 · *County Agent & Vo-Ag Teacher*, 24 · H. C. Davis Sons' Mill Machinery Co., 305, 306 · DeLaval Separator Company, 12, 13, 289, 291, 292, 293, 296, 297 · Delco-Remy, 42 · Delta Power Tool Division, Rockwell Mfg. Co., 345, 350 · The Deming Company, 245, 246, 248 · The Detroit Edison Company, 85, 130, 259, 282, 283 · East Texas State College Photo Laboratory, 45, 50 · Thomas Alva Edison Foundation, Inc., 4, 5, 40, 258 · Robert Eifert, 329 · *Electricity on the Farm*, 27, 37, 69, 79, 256, 266, 317, 342, 352, 354 · A. E. Evans and Robert Bradley, 199 · Fairbanks, Morse & Co., 45, 50, 240, 243, 247 · Farm Electrification Bureau, 151, 152, 153, 165 · Farm Equipment Institute, 1, 2, 9, 12, 15, 255, 338 ·

Index

Directions for doing electrical work are indexed under "How to."